THE KEY

STUDENT STUDY GUIDE

athematics 20-2

THE KEY student study guide is designed to help students achieve success in school. The content in each study guide is 100% curriculum aligned and serves as an excellent source of material for review and practice. To create this book, teachers, curriculum specialists, and assessment experts have worked closely to develop the instructional pieces that explain each of the key concepts for the course. The practice questions and sample tests have detailed solutions that show problem-solving methods, highlight concepts that are likely to be tested, and point out potential sources of errors. **THE KEY** is a complete guide to be used by students throughout the school year for reviewing and understanding course content, and to prepare for assessments.

Rao, Gautam, 1961 –
THE KEY STUDY GUIDE – Mathematics 20-2 Alberta
ISBN: 978-1-77044-678-6

   1. Science – Juvenile Literature. I. Title

Publisher
Gautam Rao

Published by
Castle Rock Research Corporation
2000 First & Jasper
10065 Jasper Avenue
Edmonton, AB T5J 3B1

   10 9 8 7 6 5 4 3 2 1

Dedicated to the memory of Dr. V. S. Rao

THE KEY

THE KEY consists of the following sections:

KEY Tips for Being Successful at School gives examples of study and review strategies. It includes information about learning styles, study schedules, and note taking for test preparation.

Class Focus includes a unit on each area of the curriculum. Units are divided into sections, each focusing on one of the specific expectations, or main ideas, that students must learn about in that unit. Examples, definitions, and visuals help to explain each main idea. Practice questions on the main ideas are also included. At the end of each unit is a test on the important ideas covered. The practice questions and unit tests help students identify areas they know and those they need to study more. They can also be used as preparation for tests and quizzes. Most questions are of average difficulty, though some are easy and some are hard—the harder questions are called *Challenger Questions*. Each unit is prefaced by a **Table of Correlations**, which correlates questions in the unit to the specific curriculum expectations. Answers and solutions are found at the end of each unit.

KEY Strategies for Success on Tests helps students get ready for tests. It shows students different types of questions they might see, word clues to look for when reading them, and hints for answering them.

Practice Tests includes one to three tests based on the entire course. They are very similar to the format and level of difficulty that students may encounter on final tests. In some regions, these tests may be reprinted versions of official tests, or reflect the same difficulty levels and formats as official versions. This gives students the chance to practice using real-world examples. Answers and complete solutions are provided at the end of the section.

For the complete curriculum document (including specific expectations along with examples and sample problems), visit https://education.alberta.ca/programs-of-study.

THE KEY Study Guides are available for many courses. Check www.castlerockresearch.com for a complete listing of books available for your area.

For information about any of our resources or services, please call Castle Rock Research at 1.800.840.6224 or visit our website at http://www.castlerockresearch.com.

At Castle Rock Research, we strive to produce an error-free resource. If you should find an error, please contact us so that future editions can be corrected.

CONTENTS

KEY Tips for being Successful at School

KEY TIPS FOR BEING SUCCESSFUL AT SCHOOL

KEY FACTORS CONTRIBUTING TO SCHOOL SUCCESS

In addition to learning the content of your courses, there are some other things that you can do to help you do your best at school. You can try some of the following strategies:

- **Keep a positive attitude**: Always reflect on what you can already do and what you already know.

- **Be prepared to learn**: Have the necessary pencils, pens, notebooks, and other required materials for participating in class ready.

- **Complete all of your assignments**: Do your best to finish all of your assignments. Even if you know the material well, practice will reinforce your knowledge. If an assignment or question is difficult for you, work through it as far as you can so that your teacher can see exactly where you are having difficulty.

- **Set small goals for yourself when you are learning new material**: For example, when learning the parts of speech, do not try to learn everything in one night. Work on only one part or section each study session. When you have memorized one particular part of speech and understand it, move on to another one. Continue this process until you have memorized and learned all the parts of speech.

- **Review your classroom work regularly at home**: Review to make sure you understand the material you learned in class.

- **Ask your teacher for help**: Your teacher will help you if you do not understand something or if you are having a difficult time completing your assignments.

- **Get plenty of rest and exercise**: Concentrating in class is hard work. It is important to be well-rested and have time to relax and socialize with your friends. This helps you keep a positive attitude about your schoolwork.

- **Eat healthy meals**: A balanced diet keeps you healthy and gives you the energy you need for studying at school and at home.

HOW TO FIND YOUR LEARNING STYLE

Every student learns differently. The manner in which you learn best is called your learning style. By knowing your learning style, you can increase your success at school. Most students use a combination of learning styles. Do you know what type of learner you are? Read the following descriptions. Which of these common learning styles do you use most often?

- **Linguistic Learner:** You may learn best by saying, hearing, and seeing words. You are probably really good at memorizing things such as dates, places, names, and facts. You may need to write down the steps in a process, a formula, or the actions that lead up to a significant event, and then say them out loud.

- **Spatial Learner:** You may learn best by looking at and working with pictures. You are probably really good at puzzles, imagining things, and reading maps and charts. You may need to use strategies like mind mapping and webbing to organize your information and study notes.

- **Kinesthetic Learner:** You may learn best by touching, moving, and figuring things out using manipulatives. You are probably really good at physical activities and learning through movement. You may need to draw your finger over a diagram to remember it, tap out the steps needed to solve a problem, or feel yourself writing or typing a formula.

SCHEDULING STUDY TIME

You should review your class notes regularly to ensure that you have a clear understanding of all the new material you learned. Reviewing your lessons on a regular basis helps you to learn and remember ideas and concepts. It also reduces the quantity of material that you need to study prior to a test. Establishing a study schedule will help you to make the best use of your time.

Regardless of the type of study schedule you use, you may want to consider the following suggestions to maximize your study time and effort:

- Organize your work so that you begin with the most challenging material first.

- Divide the subject's content into small, manageable chunks.

- Alternate regularly between your different subjects and types of study activities in order to maintain your interest and motivation.

- Make a daily list with headings like "Must Do," "Should Do," and "Could Do."

- Begin each study session by quickly reviewing what you studied the day before.

- Maintain your usual routine of eating, sleeping, and exercising to help you concentrate better for extended periods of time.

CREATING STUDY NOTES

MIND-MAPPING OR WEBBING

Use the key words, ideas, or concepts from your reading or class notes to create a mind map or web (a diagram or visual representation of the given information). A mind map or web is sometimes referred to as a knowledge map. Use the following steps to create a mind map or web:

1. Write the key word, concept, theory, or formula in the centre of your page.

2. Write down related facts, ideas, events, and information, and link them to the central concept with lines.

3. Use coloured markers, underlining, or symbols to emphasize things such as relationships, timelines, and important information.

The following examples of a Frayer Model illustrate how this technique can be used to study scientific vocabulary.

Definition	Notes
• Perimeter is the distance around the outside of a polygon.	• Perimeter is measured in linear units (e.g., metres, centimetres, and so on).

Perimeter

Examples	Non-Examples
• The length of a fence around a yard	• The area of grass covering a lawn
• The distance around a circle (circumference)	• The size of a rug lying on a floor

Definition	Notes
• A cube is a solid 3-D object with six faces.	• A cube is different from other shapes because it has six equally-sized square faces, eight vertices, and twelve equal edges.

Cube

Examples	Non-Examples
	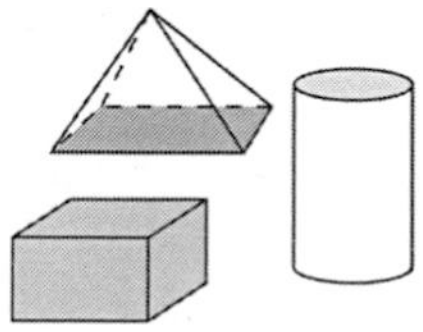

INDEX CARDS

To use index cards while studying, follow these steps:

1. Write a key word or question on one side of an index card.

2. On the reverse side, write the definition of the word, answer to the question, or any other important information that you want to remember.

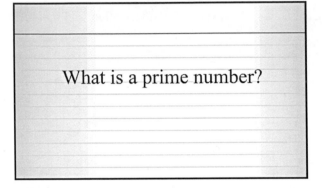

SYMBOLS AND STICKY NOTES—IDENTIFYING IMPORTANT INFORMATION

Use symbols to mark your class notes. For example, an exclamation mark (!) might be used to point out something that must be learned well because it is a very important idea. A question mark (?) may highlight something you are not certain about, and a diamond (◊) or asterisk (*) could highlight interesting information that you want to remember. Sticky notes are useful in the following situations:

• Use sticky notes when you are not allowed to put marks in books.

• Use sticky notes to mark a page in a book that contains an important diagram, formula, explanation, or other information.

• Use sticky notes to mark important facts in research books.

MEMORIZATION TECHNIQUES

- **Association** relates new learning to something you already know. For example, to remember the spelling difference between dessert and desert, recall that the word *sand* has only one *s*. So, because there is sand in a desert, the word *desert* has only one *s*.

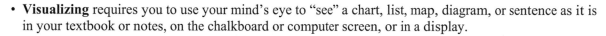

- **Mnemonic** devices are sentences that you create to remember a list or group of items. For example, the first letter of each word in the phrase "Every Good Boy Deserves Fudge" helps you to remember the names of the lines on the treble-clef staff (E, G, B, D, and F) in music.

- **Acronyms** are words that are formed from the first letters or parts of the words in a group.
  For example, RADAR is actually an acronym for Radio Detecting and Ranging, and MASH is an acronym for Mobile Army Surgical Hospital. HOMES helps you to remember the names of the five Great Lakes (Huron, Ontario, Michigan, Erie, and Superior).

- **Visualizing** requires you to use your mind's eye to "see" a chart, list, map, diagram, or sentence as it is in your textbook or notes, on the chalkboard or computer screen, or in a display.

- **Initialisms** are abbreviations that are formed from the first letters or parts of the words in a group. Unlike acronyms, an initialism cannot be pronounced as a word itself. For example, BEDMAS is an initialism for the order of operations in math (Brackets, Exponents, Divide, Multiply, Add, Subtract).

KEY STRATEGIES FOR REVIEWING

Reviewing textbook material, class notes, and handouts should be an ongoing activity. Spending time reviewing becomes more critical when you are preparing for a test. You may find some of the following review strategies useful when studying during your scheduled study time:

- Before reading a selection, preview it by noting the headings, charts, graphs, and chapter questions.

- Before reviewing a unit, note the headings, charts, graphs, and chapter questions.

- Highlight key concepts, vocabulary, definitions, and formulas.

- Skim the paragraph, and note the key words, phrases, and information.

- Carefully read over each step in a procedure.

- Draw a picture or diagram to help make the concept clearer.

KEY STRATEGIES FOR SUCCESS: A CHECKLIST

Reviewing is a huge part of doing well at school and preparing for tests. Here is a checklist for you to keep track of how many suggested strategies for success you are using. Read each question, and put a check mark (✓) in the correct column. Look at the questions where you have checked the "No" column. Think about how you might try using some of these strategies to help you do your best at school.

KEY Strategies for Success	Yes	No
Do you attend school regularly?		
Do you know your personal learning style—how you learn best?		
Do you spend 15 to 30 minutes a day reviewing your notes?		
Do you study in a quiet place at home?		
Do you clearly mark the most important ideas in your study notes?		
Do you use sticky notes to mark texts and research books?		
Do you practise answering multiple-choice and written-response questions?		
Do you ask your teacher for help when you need it?		
Are you maintaining a healthy diet and sleep routine?		
Are you participating in regular physical activity?		

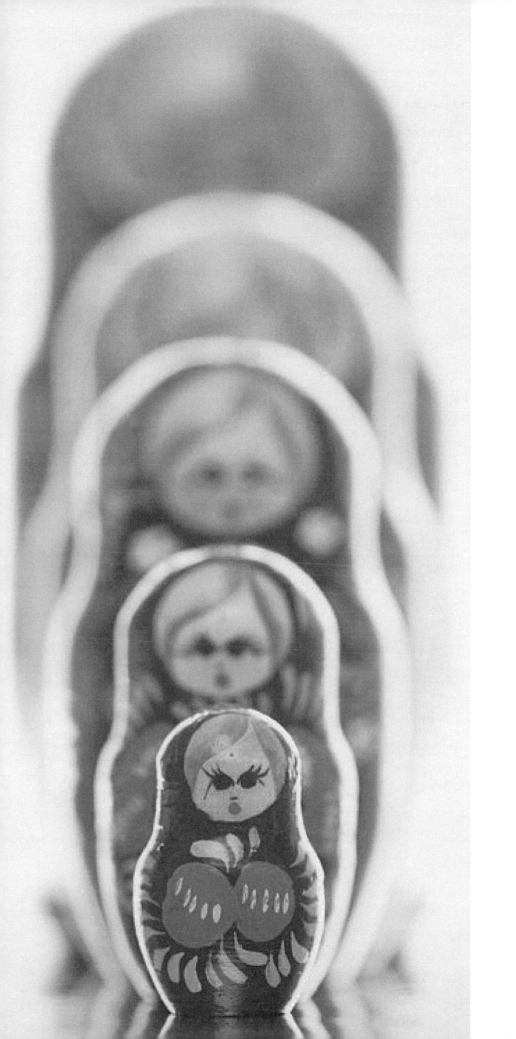

MEASUREMENT

Table of Correlations

Outcome		Practice Questions	Unit Test Questions	Practice Test
20M	Measurement			
20M.1	*Solve problems that involve the application of rates.*	1, 2, 3, 4, 5	1, 2, 3, 4, 5	14, 15, 16
20M.2	*Solve problems that involve scale diagrams, using proportional reasoning.*	6, 7	6, 7	17, 18, 19
20M.3	*Demonstrate and understanding of the relationships among scale factors, areas, surface areas and volumes of similar 2-D shapes and 3-D objects.*	8	8, 9	20, 21, 22

20M.1 Solve problems that involve the application of rates.

CALCULATING UNIT RATES

Total cost per number of units can also be described as **unit rate**.

Rate is a comparison of two items that are measured in different units. As one of the items change, it causes a change in the second item. The relationship between the two items can be used to solve problems.

Rate comparisons often involve money. A unit rate is a rate in which the second measure is 1.
For example, if 5 kg of potatoes cost $10.00, then 1 kg of potatoes costs $2.00.

To change a **rate** into a **unit rate**:

1. Divide the first term by the second term.
2. Write the units of measurement beside the result. The units should go after the unit rate, except for units in dollars.

Example

Allison charged $30.00 for babysitting for 5 h.

How much does she make per hour?

Solution

Step 1
Write the rate.

The rate is $\dfrac{\$30.00}{5\ h}$.

Step 2
Calculate the unit rate. The unit rate is Allison's hourly wage.

Divide the first term ($30.00) by the second term (5 h).

$30 \div 5 = 6$

Rates are written symbolically or in word form.

Symbolically, $\dfrac{\$30.00}{5\ h} = \dfrac{\$6.00}{h}$ or $6.00/h

In words, this rate can be written as "six dollars per hour."

The value of the denominator, 1, does not need to be written.

Allison makes $6.00 per hour.

Example

In a candy store, a sign says that chocolate fudge costs $2 per 100 g.

What is the cost of the chocolate fudge per gram?

Solution

Since 100 grams of fudge cost $2, divide $2 by 100 to get the cost of 1 gram.
$2.00 \div 100 = \$0.02$

A quick way to divide by 100 is to move the decimal point 2 places to the left. For this problem, you need to add a zero before the 2 to have 2 places.

$2.00 \rightarrow 0.02$

The cost of 1 g of chocolate fudge is $0.02.

20M.1 Solve problems that involve the application of rates.

COMPARING RATES

A **rate** is a comparison of two items that are measured in different units. A **unit rate** compares two items, but the second item must have a unit of 1. The rate someone charges per hour is a common unit rate. The cost of fruit per kilogram is another common unit rate.

When comparing the cost of merchandise, a unit rate must be calculated before determining the better value. To calculate the better value, follow these steps:

1. From the given rate, calculate the unit rate of each item.
2. Compare the unit rates.

Example

In a local grocery store, tuna is sold in packs of 6 or in cases of 24. The pack of 6 costs $7.68 before tax. The case of 24 costs $26.88 before tax.

Which is the better value?

Solution

Step 1

From the given rate, calculate the unit rate of each item.

Divide the numerator by the denominator.

Rate	Unit Rate
$7.68 / 6 cans	7.68 ÷ 6 = $1.28 / can
$26.88 / 24 cans	26.88 ÷ 24 = $1.12 / can

Step 2

Compare the unit rates.

Since $1.28 per can is more than $1.12 per can, buying the tuna by the case is the better value.

_____

20M.1 Solve problems that involve the application of rates.

UNDERSTANDING THE RATE OF CHANGE FOR A FUNCTION

Many real-world scenarios involve a rate of change.

The speed of an object is an example of a rate of change. **Speed** is defined as the rate of change of distance with respect to time.

Example

If an object travels at a constant speed of 5 m/s, this means that the distance changes by 5 m for every 1 s change in time. If v represents the speed, then the speed of the object can be written as $v = 5$ m/s.

The graph of speed versus time for this constant speed of 5 m/s is a horizontal line since the speed is not changing. In this case, the rate of change of speed, or the **acceleration**, is zero.

Whenever the rate of change of a quantity is zero, the corresponding graph is a horizontal line.

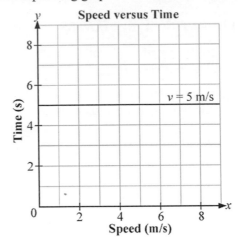

The graph of distance versus time for a constant speed of 5 m/s is an oblique line with a slope of 5 m/s, which is equal to the speed. Whenever the rate of change of a quantity is constant, or uniform, the graph will be an oblique line.

If d represents the distance, and t the amount of time passed, then the equation $d = 5t$ represents the situation algebraically.

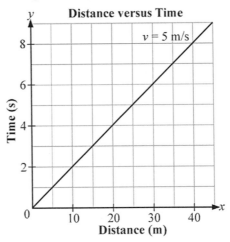

For functions of the form $y = f(x)$, the average rate of change of $f(x)$ with respect to x, between two values x_1 and x_2, is given by $\dfrac{f(x_2) - f(x_1)}{x_2 - x_1}$.

This ratio also represents the slope of the line joining these points on the graph of $y = f(x)$.

Example

A balloon is being inflated mechanically in such a way that the volume is increasing at a constant rate of 15 cm^3/s. If the volume of the balloon was originally 30 cm^3.

Compare the average rate of change of the volume of the balloon with respect to the radius of the balloon, to the nearest centimetre cubed per centimetre, between 0 s and 10 s, and between 10 s and 20 s.

Solution

It is given that the rate of change of volume with respect to time is a constant 15 cm^3/s. For every 10 s, the volume will increase by 10 s × 15 cm^3/s = 150 cm^3.

After 10 s, the volume would be 30 cm^3 + 150 cm^3 = 180 cm^3, and after 20 s it would be 180 cm^3 + 150 cm^3 = 330 cm^3.

Next, determine the radius at 0 s, 10 s, and 20 s. Using the formula for the volume of a sphere,

$V = \dfrac{4}{3}\pi r^3$, solve for r, which gives $r = \sqrt[3]{\dfrac{3V}{4\pi}}$.

Substituting the three values for V, gives a radius of approximately 1.93 cm initially, 3.50 cm after 10 s, and 4.29 cm after 20 s.

The average rate of change of volume with respect to radius is calculated by $\dfrac{V_2 - V_1}{r_2 - r_1}$.

Therefore, between 0 s and 10 s, the average rate of change of volume with respect to radius is $\dfrac{180 - 30}{3.50 - 1.93} \approx 96$ cm^3/cm, and between 10 s and 20 s, it is $\dfrac{330 - 180}{4.29 - 3.50} \approx 190$ cm^3/cm.

These two values illustrate that the rate of change of volume with respect to radius is not constant.

20M.1 Solve problems that involve the application of rates.

GRAPHING A RATE OF CHANGE

A scenario that features a rate of change can be graphed to show the relationship between the two variables. Graphing the rate of change is useful for comparing how one quantity changes with respect to another.

The horizontal axis will have the independent variable, such as time, and the vertical axis will have the dependent variable, such as speed or distance.

Furthermore, the graph may be linear or non-linear, and it may or may not begin at the origin.

Example

Margaret was riding her bicycle at a constant speed on a level road. She came to a hill and decelerated while climbing it. Once she reached the top, the road became flat again, so she accelerated back to her original speed. She then slowed to a stop when she came to another, steeper hill.

Sketch a speed versus time graph of Margaret's bicycle trip.

Solution

Since Margaret is initially travelling at a constant speed, the graph will start from the vertical axis as a horizontal line.

To show her deceleration while climbing the first hill, the graph will curve downward. The graph will then begin to curve upward to show the point when she reached the top of the hill and began to accelerate again. Given that she accelerated back to her original speed, the graph will rise until it reaches the same height (speed) as it originally had. At this point, it will become a horizontal line again.

To show the point when she began to decelerate upon reaching the second hill, the graph will begin to curve downward. The graph will continue downward until it reaches the horizontal axis because her speed became zero when she came to a stop.

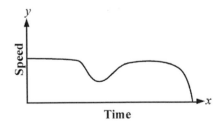

Sketch a distance versus time graph of Margaret's bicycle trip.

Solution

The graph can start from the origin if the distance travelled is measured from the instant the graph starts. Since Margaret is initially travelling at a constant speed, the graph will begin as an oblique line rising to the right from the origin.

The slope of the graph will begin to curve to the right to show her deceleration while climbing the first hill. However, even though the slope of the graph has decreased, the total distance travelled will still continue to increase.

The graph will then begin to curve upward to show her acceleration at the top of the first hill. To show her return to a constant speed, the graph will once again become an oblique line with the same slope as it originally had.

To show Margaret's final deceleration upon reaching the second hill, the graph will curve to the right again, and it will become horizontal at the point when she stopped. From here on, the slope of the graph is horizontal, indicating that she has stopped moving.

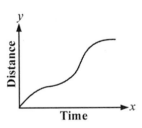

In the given examples, the graphs are approximate representations because the actual speed and distance travelled are not given. If these types of values are available, graph a more accurate representation of the rates of change by labelling the scales on the horizontal axis and the vertical axis.

When specific rates of change are given, it is possible to verify the accuracy of the resulting scaled graphs by using a combination of different technologies. For example, experiments can be conducted that involve the use of motion detectors and concrete materials, while other technologies, such as a graphing calculator or a calculator-based ranger (CBR), can also be used. Using these technologies, the data collected from experiments can be plotted, and the graphs compared, to verify accuracy.

20M.1 Solve problems that involve the application of rates.

Solving Problems with Applications of Rates

A rate compares quantities that have different units. To solve problems involving rates, it is important to calculate the unit rate. For example, the rate of 300 km in 4.0 h is equivalent to a unit rate of $\frac{300 \text{ km}}{4.0 \text{ h}} = 75$ km/h. Then, use the unit rate with other information in the problem to solve it.

Example

A pool attendant began to fill a swimming pool at a rate of 1 800 L in 5 min. After 40 min, he increased the rate so that the pool was completely filled with 80 000 L in a total time of 2 h.

What was the increased filling rate after 40 min?

Solution

Step 1
Calculate the unit rate at the beginning.
$$\frac{1\ 800 \text{ L}}{5 \text{ min}} = 360 \text{ L/min}$$

Step 2
Find the volume of water in the pool after 40 min.
360 L/min × 40 min = 14 400 L

Step 3
Determine the increased filling rate after 40 min. Find the remaining water to be filled at this new rate by subtracting the volume in the pool from the total volume.
80 000 L – 14 400 L = 65 600 L
Find the time by subtracting 40 min from 2 h. Since 2 h = 120 min, the time needed is
120 – 40 = 80 min.
Now, find the unit rate.
$$\frac{65\ 600 \text{ L}}{80 \text{ min}} = 820 \text{ L/min}$$
Therefore, the increased filling rate after 40 min was 820 L/min.

20M.1 Solve problems that involve the application of rates.

Problem Solving with Work Rates

Solving problems with work rates involves problems that relate time to completed work or combined work. The word *work* implies tasks done by one or more people or machines. In order to solve these problems, a general ratio can be used.

$$\text{Work rate} = \frac{\text{work completed}}{\text{time}}$$

The following examples show some general methods of solving work rate problems.

Example

At a grain storage facility, two loaders are used. The largest loader can completely fill a grain silo in 60 min, whereas the smaller loader can fill the same silo in 90 min.

If both loaders are used at the same time, how long will it take to fill the silo?

Solution

Since the larger loader can fill the entire silo in 60 minutes, it fills $\frac{1}{60}$ of the silo in one minute. Similarly, since the smaller loader can fill the entire silo in 90 minutes, it fills $\frac{1}{90}$ of the silo in one minute.

Working together, they can fill $\frac{1}{60} + \frac{1}{90}$ of the silo in one minute. Using a common denominator, it follows that $\frac{2}{180} + \frac{3}{180} = \frac{5}{180}$ of the silo is filled each minute.

Since $\frac{5}{180}$ of the silo is filled in one minute, the total number of minutes to fill the silo is the reciprocal. The reciprocal is the number that is multiplied to an original number to yield a product of 1. The reciprocal of $\frac{5}{180}$ is $\frac{180}{5}$.

Taking the reciprocal, it can be determined that the entire silo will be filled in $\frac{180}{5} = 36$ minutes.

Example

Jake can paint a house in 4 h using a spray gun. Using just a roller, Susan will need 5 h to paint the same house. Ted requires 20 h to paint the same house using only a paint brush.

If they all decide to work together, how long will it take to paint the house?

Solution

Step 1

Find how much of the house each person can paint in 1 h.

The following painting rates of each painter are given:

- Jake: 1 house every 4 h, or $\frac{1}{4}$ of a house in 1 h

- Susan: 1 house every 5 h, or $\frac{1}{5}$ of a house in 1 h

- Ted: 1 house every 20 h, or $\frac{1}{20}$ of a house in 1 h

Step 2

Combine the different painting rates of Jake, Susan, and Ted to find how much of a house they can paint in 1 h.

$$\frac{1}{4} + \frac{1}{5} + \frac{1}{20}$$

Step 3

Simplify the expression using a common denominator of 20.

$$\frac{1}{4} + \frac{1}{5} + \frac{1}{20} = \frac{5}{20} + \frac{4}{20} + \frac{1}{20}$$
$$= \frac{10}{20}$$
$$= \frac{1}{2}$$

It takes the combined team 1 h to paint $\frac{1}{2}$ the house.

To paint a complete house, it will take them 2 h.

Combined work implies total work completed over time.

20M.2 Solve problems that involve scale diagrams, using proportional reasoning.

DRAWING SIMILAR POLYGONS

A **polygon** is any closed plane figure constructed by three or more line segments. Similar polygons have the same shape, though they do not necessarily have the same size.

When drawing similar polygons, it is important to ensure that the corresponding angles are equal in measure and the corresponding sides are proportional in length.

The **scale factor** between the original shape and the new image is a number that indicates how much larger or smaller the shape was made. In other words, the scale factor represents a ratio between the image side length and the original side length.

$$\text{scale factor} = \frac{\text{image length}}{\text{original length}}$$

If the scale factor is greater than one, the image will be an **enlargement** of the original shape. In other words, the new image will be larger than the original figure. If the scale factor is less than one, the image will be a **reduction** of the original shape. In other words, the new image will be smaller than the original figure.

When given a polygon and asked to draw a similar polygon, follow these steps:

1. Select a scale factor.
2. Use the scale factor formula to determine the length of each side in the image diagram.
3. Draw and label the image diagram. If necessary, use the prime symbol (′) to indicate this is the image.
4. Verify that the corresponding angles are equal.

Example

The given polygon is a regular pentagon with interior angles measuring 108°.

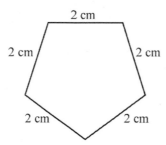

2 cm

2 cm   2 cm

2 cm   2 cm

Draw a similar polygon.

Solution

Step 1
Select a scale factor.
The scale factor will be 2.5.

Step 2
Use the scale factor formula to determine the length of each side in the image diagram.
Each of the sides in the regular pentagon is 2 cm.

$$\text{scale factor} = \frac{\text{image length}}{\text{original length}}$$

$$2.5 = \frac{\text{image length}}{2}$$

$$2(2.5) = 2\left(\frac{\text{image length}}{2}\right)$$

$$5 = \text{image length}$$

The image pentagon will have sides measuring 5 cm.

Step 3
Draw and label the image diagram.

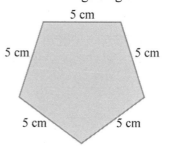

5 cm

5 cm   5 cm

5 cm   5 cm

Step 4
Verify that the corresponding angles are equal.
The new polygon is also a regular pentagon.
As with the original, all angles measure 108°.

20M.2 Solve problems that involve scale diagrams, using proportional reasoning.

DETERMINING THE SCALE FACTOR OF A DIAGRAM

Scale drawings are used when objects are either too large or too small to be drawn on a piece of paper.

The **scale factor** between the original shape and the new image is a number that indicates how much larger or smaller the shape was made. The scale factor can be calculated using the formula

$$\text{scale factor} = \frac{\text{image length}}{\text{original length}}.$$

If the scale factor is less than 1, the image is a **reduction** of the original shape. If the scale factor is greater than 1, the image is an **enlargement** of the original shape.

When given a diagram and its image, determine the scale factor by following these steps:

1. Pick one known length in the image diagram.
2. Find the corresponding length in the original diagram.
3. Use the scale factor formula to determine the scale factor.

Example

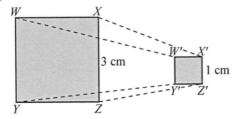

A scale drawing is given.

What is the scale factor of the given diagram?

Solution

Step 1
Pick one known length in the image diagram.
$X'Z' = 1$ cm

Step 2
Find the corresponding length in the original diagram.
$XZ = 3$ cm

Step 3
Use the scale factor formula to determine the scale factor.

$$\text{scale factor} = \frac{\text{image length}}{\text{original length}}$$
$$= \frac{X'Z'}{XZ}$$
$$= \frac{1 \text{ cm}}{3 \text{ cm}}$$
$$= \frac{1}{3}$$

The diagram shows a reduction with a scale factor of $\frac{1}{3}$.

Example

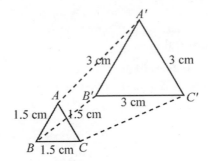

A scale drawing is given.

What is the scale factor of the given diagram?

Solution

Step 1
Pick one known length in the image diagram.
$A'C' = 3$ cm

Step 2
Find the corresponding length in the original diagram.
$AC = 1.5$ cm

Step 3
Use the scale factor formula to determine the scale factor.

$$\text{scale factor} = \frac{\text{image length}}{\text{original length}}$$
$$= \frac{A'C'}{AC}$$
$$= \frac{3 \text{ cm}}{1.5 \text{ cm}}$$
$$= 2$$

The diagram shows an enlargement with a scale factor of 2.

20M.2 Solve problems that involve scale diagrams, using proportional reasoning.

APPLYING SCALE FACTORS TO EXPAND AND CONTRACT THREE-DIMENSIONAL GEOMETRIC SHAPES

An expansion or a contraction of a three-dimensional shape involves taking the shape and making it larger or smaller. This can be done by multiplying the dimensions of the original linear measurements by the scale factor. The scale factor between the original shape and the new image is a number that describes the size difference between the two shapes.

$$\text{scale factor} = \frac{\text{image length}}{\text{original length}}$$

If the scale factor is a number greater than 1, the new image will be an **enlargement** of the original shape. If the scale factor is a number less than 1, the new image will be a **reduction** of the original shape.

To calculate the volume of a scaled image, the scale factor is cubed and multiplied by the volume of the original shape. The formula for the volume of a scaled image is $V_2 = V_1 \times \text{scale factor}^3$, where V_2 represents the volume of the scaled image and V_1 represents the volume of the original shape.

Example

Bob fills two boxes with jellybeans. The volume of the smaller box is 6 cm^3. The larger box is a scaled expansion of the smaller box.

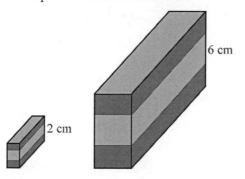

6 cm

2 cm

Find the volume of the larger box.

Solution

Step 1

Determine the scale factor.

The scale factor between the original shape and the new image is given by the formula

$$\text{scale factor} = \frac{\text{image length}}{\text{original length}}.$$

Substitute the given side lengths into the formula.

$$\text{scale factor} = \frac{6}{2}$$
$$= 3$$

Step 3

Calculate the volume of the larger prism.

The formula for the volume of a scaled image is $V_2 = V_1 \times \text{scale factor}^3$, where V_2 represents the volume of the scaled image and V_1 represents the volume of the original shape.

Substitute $V_1 = 6$ and scale factor $= 3$ into the formula, and simplify.

$$V_2 = 6 \times 3^3$$
$$V_2 = 6 \times 27$$
$$V_2 = 162 \text{ cm}^3$$

20M.3 Demonstrate and understanding of the relationships among scale factors, areas, surface areas and volumes of similar 2-D shapes and 3-D objects.

APPLYING SCALE FACTORS OF TWO-DIMENSIONAL GEOMETRIC SHAPES TO PERIMETER AND AREA

If the scale factor is a number greater than 1, the new image is an **enlargement** of the original shape. If the scale factor is a number less than 1, the new image is a **reduction** of the original shape.

To calculate the perimeter of a scaled image, the original perimeter is multiplied by the scale factor.
$$P_2 = P_1 \times \text{scale factor}$$

Example

Two similar rectangles have lengths of 4 cm and 12 cm.

4 cm   12 cm

If the perimeter of the smaller rectangle is 10 cm, it follows that the perimeter of the larger rectangle is _____ cm.

Solution

Step 1

Calculate the scale factor.

$$\text{scale factor} = \frac{12 \text{ cm}}{4 \text{ cm}}$$
$$= 3$$

The length of the smaller rectangle is multiplied by 3 to get the length of the larger rectangle.

Step 2

Apply the scale factor to the original perimeter.

$P_2 = P_1 \times \text{scale factor}$

$P_2 = 10 \times 3$

$P_2 = 30 \text{ cm}$

The perimeter of the larger rectangle is 30 cm.

To calculate the area of a scaled image, the original area is multiplied by the squared scale factor.

$A_2 = A_1 \times \text{scale factor}^2$

Example

Two similar rectangles have lengths of 9 cm and 3 cm.

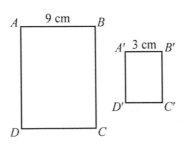

If the area of the larger rectangle is 108 cm², what is the area of the smaller rectangle?

Solution

Step 1

Calculate the scale factor.

$$\text{scale factor} = \frac{\text{image length}}{\text{original length}}$$
$$= \frac{3}{9}$$
$$= \frac{1}{3}$$

The smaller rectangle is $\frac{1}{3}$ the size of the larger rectangle.

Step 2

Apply the scale factor to the area of the larger rectangle.

The scale factor is squared to calculate the area of the new image.

$A_2 = A_1 \times \text{scale factor}^2$

$= 108 \times \left(\frac{1}{3}\right)^2$

$= 12$

The area of the smaller rectangle is 12 cm².

20M.3 Demonstrate and understanding of the relationships among scale factors, areas, surface areas and volumes of similar 2-D shapes and 3-D objects.

EFFECT OF SCALE FACTOR ON SURFACE AREA OF PRISMS

Scale factor is a number which scales or multiplies a given quantity. It is the amount that linear measurements are multiplied by to create a new figure of the same shape but in a larger or smaller size. The new shape is in direct proportion to the original shape.

Each dimension of the original shape or object is multiplied by the scale factor to determine the size of the proportional shape or object. If the scale factor is greater than 1, the proportional shape or object will be larger than the original. If the scale factor is between 0 and 1, the proportional shape or object will be smaller than the original.

TWO-DIMENSIONAL SCALING

The dimensions of a proportional two-dimensional shape can be calculated by multiplying each corresponding dimension of the original shape by the scale factor. If the area of a shape is given, this value can be multiplied by the square of the scale factor to find the area of the proportional shape.

$$A_{\text{proportional shape}} = A_{\text{original shape}} \times \text{scale factor}^2$$

For example, the area of the original rectangle from the given table can be multiplied by the square of the scale factor to find the area of the proportional shape.

scale factor = 4

$$
\begin{aligned}
A_{\text{proportional shape}} &= A_{\text{original shape}} \times \text{scale factor}^2 \\
&= 3 \times 4^2 \\
&= 48 \text{ yd}^2
\end{aligned}
$$

TWO-DIMENSIONAL SCALING APPLIED TO SURFACE AREA OF PRISMS

The dimensions of the surface area of a three-dimensional object, such a prism, can be calculated by multiplying each corresponding dimension of the original shape by the scale factor. Each surface area is calculated, and the total surface area will be the sum of all these values. If the total surface area of an object is given, this value can be multiplied by the square of the scale factor to find the surface area of the proportional object.

$$SA_{\text{proportional object}} = SA_{\text{original object}} \times \text{scale factor}^2$$

For example, the surface area of the prism from the given table can be multiplied by the square of the scale factor to find the surface area of the proportional object.

scale factor = 3

$$
\begin{aligned}
SA_{\text{proportional object}} &= SA_{\text{original object}} \times \text{scale factor}^2 \\
&= 22 \times 3^2 \\
&= 198 \text{ cm}^2
\end{aligned}
$$

Example

Janet makes two similar rectangular prisms for a mathematics exhibition. The height of the first prism is 2 in, and the height of the second prism is 4 in. She covers all the faces of the prisms with coloured paper.

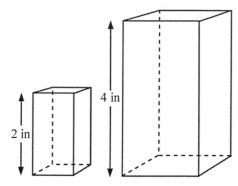

If Janet uses 10 in^2 of coloured paper to cover the smaller prism, how much coloured paper will she require for the larger prism? in^2

Solution

Step 1

Calculate the scale factor.

Divide the height of the larger prism by the height of the smaller prism.

$$\text{scale factor} = \frac{4 \text{ in}}{2 \text{ in}} = 2$$

The height of the small prism is multiplied by 2 to get the height of the larger prism.

Step 2

Apply the scale factor to calculate the area of the larger prism.

The surface area of the smaller prism is 10. Multiply this value by the scale factor.

$$
\begin{aligned}
SA_2 &= SA_1 \times \text{scale factor}^2 \\
&= 10 \times 2^2 \\
&= 10 \times 4 \\
&= 40 \text{ in}^2
\end{aligned}
$$

Janet requires 40 in^2 of coloured paper to cover the larger prism.

Example

The ratio of the radii of the two cylinders shown is 1:4. The larger cylinder has a surface area of 48π cm^2.

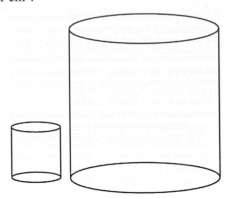

What is the surface area of the smaller cylinder?

Solution

Step 1

Calculate the scale factor.

Since the ratio of the radii is 1:4, the radius of the larger cylinder is multiplied by $\dfrac{1}{4}$ to get the radius of the smaller cylinder.

Step 2

Apply the scale factor to the surface area of the larger cylinder.

Let the surface area of the larger cylinder by SA_1 and the surface area of the smaller cylinder be SA_2.

The surface area of the smaller cylinder is the product of the square of the scale factor and the surface area of the larger cylinder.

$$SA_2 = SA_1 \times \text{scale factor}^2$$
$$= 48\pi \times \left(\frac{1}{4}\right)^2$$
$$= 48\pi \times \frac{1}{16}$$
$$= \frac{48\pi}{16}$$
$$= 3\pi \text{ cm}^2$$

The surface area of the smaller cylinder is 3π cm^2.

20M.3 Demonstrate and understanding of the relationships among scale factors, areas, surface areas and volumes of similar 2-D shapes and 3-D objects.

DETERMINING HOW CHANGES IN DIMENSIONS AFFECT THE VOLUME OF SOLIDS

Changing the dimensions of any three-dimensional geometric shape affects the volume of the shape. There must be a change in dimension to increase or decrease the volume of a shape.

Example

Jude has a fish tank in the shape of a rectangular prism that is 7 cm long, 7 cm wide, and 15 cm high.

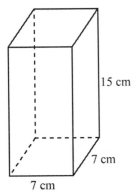

He buys a bigger fish tank with the same shape but 5 cm longer, the same width, and 6 cm higher than the original fish tank.

How much additional water is needed to fill the new fish tank?

Solution

Step 1

Calculate the volume of the first fish tank, V_1.

Substitute $l = 7$, $w = 7$, and $h = 15$ into the volume formula for a rectangular prism and solve.

$$V_1 = l \times w \times h$$
$$= 7 \times 7 \times 15$$
$$= 735 \text{ cm}^3$$

Step 2

Calculate the dimensions of the second fish tank.

$l_2 = 7 + 5$

$\quad = 12$

$w_2 = w_1$

$\quad = 7$

$h_2 = 15 + 6$

$\quad = 21$

Step 3

Calculate the volume of the new fish tank, V_2.

Substitute $l_2 = 12$, $w_2 = 7$, and $h_2 = 21$ into the volume formula for a rectangular prism and solve.

$V_2 = l_2 \times w_2 \times h_2$

$\quad = 12 \times 7 \times 21$

$\quad = 1\ 764\ \text{cm}^3$

Step 4

Calculate the additional amount of water needed to fill the second fish tank.

$V_2 - V_1 = 1\ 764 - 735$

$\qquad\quad = 1\ 029\ \text{cm}^3$

Jude needs $1\ 029\ \text{cm}^3$ of additional water to fill the second fish tank.

Example

For a class project, George is building a model of an Egyptian pyramid. The height of the model square pyramid is 25 in, and each side length of the square base is 16 in. He wants to increase the volume of his model pyramid. To avoid damaging his model, he found that he can either double the height of the square pyramid or add 6 in to each side length of the square base.

What change in dimension should George make to his model in order to increase the volume the most?

Solution

Calculate the volume for each possible change in dimension, and compare.

Step 1

Calculate the volume when the height is doubled.

The height of the new pyramid is $2(25) = 50$ in. Use the volume formula for a pyramid to find the new volume.

$V_1 = \dfrac{A_{\text{base}} \times h}{3}$

$\quad = \dfrac{(16)(16)(50)}{3}$

$\quad = \dfrac{12\ 800}{3}$

$\quad \approx 4\ 266.7\ \text{in}^3$

Step 2

Calculate the volume when 6 in are added to each side length of the square base.

Each new side length of the square base is $16 + 6 = 22$ in.

Use the volume formula for a pyramid to find the new volume.

$V_2 = \dfrac{A_{\text{base}} \times h}{3}$

$\quad = \dfrac{(22)(22)(25)}{3}$

$\quad = \dfrac{12\ 100}{3}$

$\quad \approx 4\ 033.3\ \text{in}^3$

Therefore, George should double the height of his square pyramid to increase its volume the most.

---

1. Which of the following graphs represents the number of daylight hours as a function of calendar date for Ottawa, Ontario?

A.
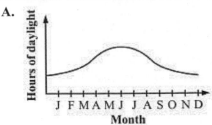

B.
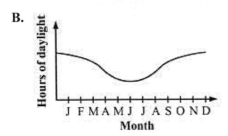

C.
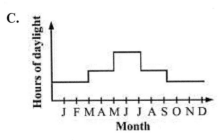

D.
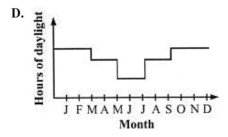

Use the following information to answer the next question.

The table shown gives the population of a city over a 29-year period.

Year	Population
1965	128 445
1970	166 408
1980	219 494
1990	266 406
1994	282 133

2. The average yearly rate of change of the population of the city was **greatest** between
   A. 1965 and 1970 B. 1970 and 1980
   C. 1980 and 1990 D. 1990 and 1994

Use the following information to answer the next question.

Jody, a mountain hiker, climbs a mountain by walking a total of 8 km. During the flatter part of the climb, she hikes at a rate of 50 m / min for 2 h. She rests for 0.5 h and finishes her climb in a total of 4 hr.

3. At what rate does Jody climb the steeper part of the mountain?
   A. 16.7 m / min
   B. 20.0 m / min
   C. 22.2 m / min
   D. 25.0 m / min

Use the following information to answer the next question.

Tom, Diana, Enrique, and Ahmad tested the fuel efficiency of their vehicles. Tom drove 320 km on 40 L of fuel, Diana drove 390 km on 50 L of fuel, Enrique drove 222 km on 30 L of fuel, and Ahmad drove 152 km on 20 L of fuel.

4. Who has the **most fuel-efficient** vehicle?
   A. Tom   B. Diana
   C. Ahmad   D. Enrique

Use the following information to
answer the next question.

Nicki earned $54 babysitting one night for
six hours.

5. What is Nicki's hourly wage?
   A. $7.25   **B.** $8.50
   C. $9.00   **D.** $10.00

Use the following information to
answer the next question.

A particular polygon is as shown.

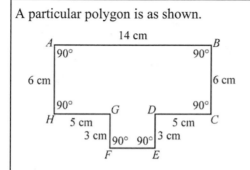

Polygon $A'B'C'D'E'F'G'H'$ is similar to
the given polygon.

6. Which of the following statements about
   the image diagram is **false**?
   A. If a scale factor of 0.8 is used, then the
   length of side $E'F'$ will be 3.2 cm.
   B. If a scale factor of 1.5 is used, then the
   length of side $B'C'$ will be 9 cm.
   C. The sum of the measures of angles
   A' and H' will be 180°.
   D. The measure of each interior angle
   will be 90°.

Use the following information to
answer the next question.

A cylinder is shown.

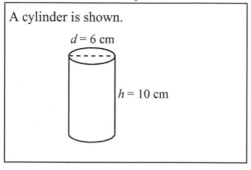

7. Rounded to the nearest centimetre, when
   3.14 is used for the value of π, what is the
   surface area of the cylinder after a scale
   factor of 4.2 is applied?
   A. 2 029 cm^2 **B.** 4 320 cm^2
   C. 11 583 cm^2 **D.** 18 148 cm^2

Use the following information to
answer the next question.

This right triangular prism has a surface
area of 42 m^2.

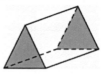

8. If the given prism increases in size by a
   scale factor of 3, then what will the surface
   area of the new prism be?
   A. 378 m^2 **B.** 336 m^2
   C. 252 m^2 **D.** 126 m^2

ANSWERS AND SOLUTIONS
MEASUREMENT

1. A	3. C	5. C	7. B
2. A	4. A	6. D	8. A

1. A

The number of daylight hours as a function of calendar date is typically a sinusoidal function. The graph begins with a curve that increases as each month passes, which corresponds to increasing daylight from winter to spring months. This curve will increase until it reaches the longest day of the year, June 21. At this point, the graph will begin to curve downward as daylight hours begin decreasing during the months from summer to winter.

Therefore, the graph that represents the number of daylight hours as a function of calendar date for Ottawa, Ontario, is graph A.

2. A

Determine the average yearly rate of change of the population for each time interval using the ratio $\dfrac{P_2 - P_1}{t_2 - t_1}$, where P_1 and P_2 are populations and t_1 and t_2 are the years in which those populations occurred.

Step 1
Calculate the average yearly rate of change between 1965 and 1970.

$$\frac{P_2 - P_1}{t_2 - t_1} = \frac{166\ 408 - 128\ 445}{1\ 970 - 1\ 965}$$
$$= \frac{37\ 963}{5}$$
$$= 7\ 592.6$$

Step 2
Calculate the average yearly rate of change between 1970 and 1980.

$$\frac{P_2 - P_1}{t_2 - t_1} = \frac{219\ 494 - 166\ 408}{1\ 980 - 1\ 970}$$
$$= \frac{53\ 086}{10}$$
$$= 5\ 308.6$$

Step 3
Calculate the average yearly rate of change between 1980 and 1990.

$$\frac{P_2 - P_1}{t_2 - t_1} = \frac{266\ 406 - 219\ 494}{1\ 990 - 1\ 980}$$
$$= \frac{46\ 912}{10}$$
$$= 4\ 691.2$$

Step 4
Calculate the average yearly rate of change between 1990 and 1994.

$$\frac{P_2 - P_1}{t_2 - t_1} = \frac{282\ 133 - 266\ 406}{1\ 994 - 1\ 990}$$
$$= \frac{15\ 727}{4}$$
$$= 3\ 931.75$$

The average yearly rate of change of the population was greatest between 1965 and 1970, when the population increased at an average of 7 592.6 people per year.

3. C

Step 1
Find the distance covered over the flatter part.

Distance = Rate × Time
= 50 m / min × 2 h
= 50 m / min × (2 × 60) min
= 6 000 m

Step 2
Find the distance of the steeper part.

Since the total climb is 8 km = 8 000 m, the steeper part of the climb is 8 000 − 6 000 = 2 000 m.

Step 3
Find the time taken to climb the steeper part.

Since the hiker covers the flatter part in 2 h and rests for 0.5 h, the the steeper part is covered in 4 − 2 − 0.5 = 1.5 h.

Step 4
Find the unit rate of hiking the steeper part.

$$\frac{2\ 000\ \text{m}}{1.5\ \text{h}} = \frac{2\ 000\ \text{m}}{(1.5 \times 60)\ \text{min}} \cong 22.2\ \text{m} / \text{min}$$

Jody climbs the steeper part of the mountain at a rate of about 22.2 m / min.

4. A

Step 1

Calculate the unit rate for each vehicle.

- Tom's fuel efficiency is $\dfrac{320 \text{ km}}{40 \text{ L}} = 8$ km/L.

- Diana's fuel efficiency is $\dfrac{390 \text{ km}}{50 \text{ L}} = 7.8$ km/L.

- Enrique's fuel efficiency is $\dfrac{222 \text{ km}}{30 \text{ L}} = 7.4$ km/L.

- Ahmad's fuel efficiency is $\dfrac{152 \text{ km}}{20 \text{ L}} = 7.6$ km/L.

Step 2

Compare the unit rates.

Since Tom can travel 8 km on 1 L of fuel, his vehicle is the most fuel efficient.

5. C

Step 1

Write the rate.

The rate is $\dfrac{\$54}{6 \text{ h}}$.

Step 2

Calculate the unit rate. The unit rate is Nicki's hourly wage.

Divide the first term, which is $54, by the second term, which is 6 h.

$54 \div 6 = 9$

Step 3

Rates are written symbolically or in word form.

Symbolically, the rate is $\dfrac{\$54}{6 \text{ h}} = \dfrac{\$9}{\text{h}}$, or $9.00/h.

In words, this rate can be written as nine dollars per hour.

6. D

Step 1

Determine the length of side $E'F'$ in the image diagram if the scale factor is 0.8.

The length of side EF in the given polygon is $14 \text{ cm} - (5 \text{ cm} + 5 \text{ cm}) = 4$ cm.

Using a scale factor of 0.8, substitute the known values to determine the length of side $E'F'$.

$$\text{scale factor} = \frac{\text{image length}}{\text{original length}}$$
$$0.8 = \frac{\text{image length}}{4}$$
$$0.8 \times 4 = \text{image length}$$
$$3.2 = \text{image length}$$

If the scale factor is 0.8, the length of side $E'F'$ in the image diagram will be 3.2 cm.

Step 2

Determine the length of side $B'C'$ in the image diagram if the scale factor is 1.5.

The length of side BC is 6 cm.

Using a scale factor of 1.5, substitute the known values to determine the length of side $B'C'$.

$$\text{scale factor} = \frac{\text{image length}}{\text{original length}}$$
$$1.5 = \frac{\text{image length}}{6}$$
$$1.5 \times 6 = \text{image length}$$
$$9 = \text{image length}$$

If the scale factor is 1.5, the length of side $B'C'$ in the image diagram will be 9 cm.

Step 3

Determine the sum of the measure of angles A' and H' in the image diagram.

Corresponding angles in similar polygons must be equal in measure. Therefore, the measures of angles A' and H' in the image diagram must each be 90°.

The sum of the measures of angles A' and H' in the image diagram is $90° + 90° = 180°$.

Step 4

Determine the measure of each interior angle in the image diagram.

Corresponding angles in similar polygons must be equal in measure, so the measures of angles A', B', C', E', F', and G' in the image diagram must each be 90°. However, the measure of exterior angle HGF in the given polygon is 90°, which implies that the measure of interior angle HGF is $360° - 90° = 270°$. Similarly, the measure of interior angle CDE in the given polygon is also 270°. Thus, in the image diagram, the angle that corresponds to interior angle HGF in the given polygon must be 270°, and the angle that corresponds to the interior angle CDE in the given polygon must have a measure of 270°. It then follows that the measure of each interior angle in the image diagram will not be 90°.

7. B

Step 1

Determine the radius of the cylinder.

$$r = \frac{d}{2}$$
$$r = \frac{6}{2}$$
$$r = 3 \text{ cm}$$

Step 2

Calculate the area of the two circular bases and the rectangle.

First, calculate the area of one of the circular bases.

$A_{circle} = \pi \times r^2$

$A_{circle} \approx 3.14 \times 3^2$

$A_{circle} \approx 3.14 \times 9$

$A_{circle} \approx 28.26 \text{ cm}^2$

Multiply the area of the circular base by 2 because the measures of the circular bases are the same.

$A_{circles} \approx 2 \times 28.26$

$A_{circles} \approx 56.52 \text{ cm}^2$

To calculate the area of the rectangle, use the length and height. Let the length (l) equal the height (h) of the rectangular part of the cylinder, which is 10 cm. Since the length of the rectangle is equal to the circumference of the circle, calculate the circumference of the circle.

$C \approx \pi d$

$C \approx 3.14 \times 6$

$C \approx 18.84 \text{ cm}^2$

Now that the length (height) and width of the rectangular part are known, calculate the area of the rectangle.

$A_{rectangle} = h \times l$

$A_{rectangle} \approx 10 \times 18.84$

$A_{rectangle} \approx 188.4 \text{ cm}^2$

Step 3

Calculate the surface area of the cylinder.

$SA_{cylinder} = A_{circles} + A_{rectangle}$

$SA_{cylinder} \approx 56.52 + 188.4$

$SA_{cylinder} \approx 244.92 \text{ cm}^2$

Step 4

Apply the scale factor.

The scale factor is being applied to the surface area of the cylinder, so the formula

$SA_2 = SA_{cylinder} \times$ scale factor^2 is used. Substitute 244.92 for $SA_{cylinder}$ and 4.2 for the scale factor.

$SA_2 = SA_{cylinder} \times$ scale factor^2

$SA_2 \approx 244.92 \times (4.2)^2$

$SA_2 \approx 244.92 \times 17.64$

$SA_2 \approx 4\ 320.3888$

$SA_2 \approx 4\ 320 \text{ cm}^2$

8. **A**

Step 1

Determine the scale factor.

The scale factor is given as 3.

Step 2

Apply the scale factor to determine the surface area of the new prism.

Since the surface area of the original object is given as 42 m^2 and the scale factor is 3, the surface area of the new prism can be calculated using the formula

$SA_{proportional\ object} = SA_{original\ object} \times$ scale factor^2.

In other words, $SA_2 = SA_1 \times$ scale factor^2.

$SA_2 = SA_1 \times$ scale factor^2

$SA_2 = 42 \times (3)^2$

$SA_2 = 42 \times 9$

$SA_2 = 378 \text{ m}^2$

Therefore, the surface area of the new prism will be 378 m^2.

UNIT TEST — MEASUREMENT

Use the following information to answer the next question.

While the cars of a train are being loaded, the train moves forward quickly, then backs up slowly just a little, and finally rolls forward to a stop.

1. Which of the following "total distance travelled vs. time" graphs best illustrates the situation described?

A.   B.

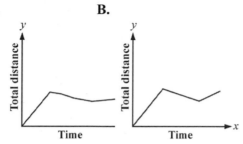

C.   D.

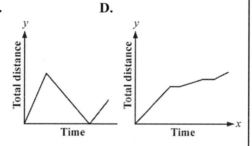

Use the following information to answer the next question.

The speed of sound at 0°C is 331 m/s. For every increase of 10°C, the speed of sound increases 11 m/s.

2. If Tom stands on a hill 1 000 m away from Bob and hears Bob's yell after 2.8 s, what is the air temperature?

A. 20°C   B. 22°C

C. 24°C   D. 26°C

Use the following information to answer the next question.

Amanda is baking bread and needs to buy flour. She checks four grocery stores to see which offers the best price.

Grocery Store	Store Prices
I	10 kg for $10.00
II	15 kg for $15.15
III	20 kg for $19.00
IV	25 kg for $24.50

3. Which grocery store offers the **best** price for flour?

A. Store *I*   B. Store *II*

C. Store *III*   D. Store *IV*

Use the following information to answer the next question.

Jackson spends $300 to purchase 15 cans of paint to finish painting the interior of his house.

4. What is the price for each can of paint?

A. $10   B. $17

C. $20   D. $23

Use the following information to answer the next question.

A tank can be filled with liquid in 5 h and emptied in 7 h.

5. If the tank's inlet and outlet are opened at the same time when the tank is empty, how long will it take to fill the tank?

A. 5 h   B. $7\frac{1}{2}$ h

C. 12 h   D. $17\frac{1}{2}$ h

*Use the following information to
answer the next question.*

Lorina is asked to draw a similar polygon
to this one.

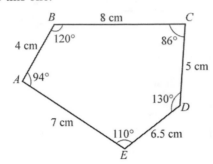

She decides to use a scale factor of 0.6.
If Lorina draws her pentagon correctly,
then the side in her pentagon that
corresponds to side *DE* in the given
pentagon will have a length of
____*i*____ cm, and the angle that corresponds
to angle *B* in the given pentagon will have
a measure of _____*ii*_____°.

6. The given statement is completed by
   information in which of the
   following tables?

   A.

i	ii
3.9	72

   B.

i	ii
3.9	120

   C.

i	ii
10.8$\overline{3}$	72

   D.

i	ii
10.8$\overline{3}$	120

*Use the following information to
answer the next question.*

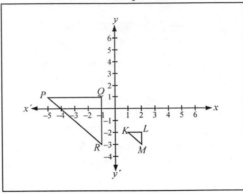

7. By what scale factor is triangle *PQR* larger
   than triangle *KLM*?

   A. 2   **B.** 3

   C. 4   **D.** 5

*Use the following information to
answer the next question.*

A five-pin bowling ball has a diameter of
approximately 12.6 cm, and a ten-pin
bowling ball has a diameter that is
approximately 9.2 cm more than that of a
five-pin bowling ball. Given these
dimensions, prior to drilling the finger
holes in a ten-pin bowling ball, its volume,
using $\pi = 3.14$, is x cm^3 more than the
volume of a five-pin bowling ball.

Numerical Response

8. To the nearest hundred, the value of x is
   _____.

Use the following information to answer the next question.

A rectangular prism is shown.

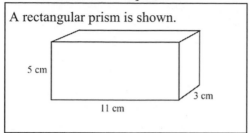

5 cm

3 cm

11 cm

9. Rounded to the nearest tenth of a cubic centimetre, what is the volume of the given rectangular prism when a scale factor of 0.7 is applied to it?

   A. 56.6 cm^3 **B.** 59.3 cm^3

   C. 62.8 cm^3 **D.** 65.1 cm^3

ANSWERS AND SOLUTIONS — UNIT TEST

1. D	4. C	7. C
2. C	5. D	8. 4400
3. C	6. B	9. A

1. D

The graph starts at the origin because the distance travelled is measured from the instant the graph begins. Since the train is initially travelling at a constant speed, the graph would begin as an oblique line rising to the right from the origin. Since the train was moving forward, it must stop in order to move backward. This is indicated by a short horizontal line.

Then, the train moves at a slower constant rate, which would be shown by an oblique line with a slight slope rising to the right from the horizontal line. The line is rising because the total distance covered increases despite the train's change in direction.

After moving backward, the train must stop again in order to roll forward. The stop is indicted by another short horizontal line.

As the train rolls forward, the graph will once again become an oblique line with a slight slope rising to the right from the previous horizontal line.

The explanation is illustrated in the following graph.

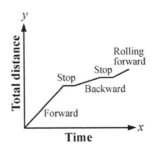

2. C

Step 1
Find the speed of sound (rate) for Bob's yell.

$$\text{speed} = \frac{\text{distance}}{\text{time}}$$
$$= \frac{1\ 000\ m}{2.8\ s}$$
$$\cong 357.14$$

Step 2
Find the increase in the speed of sound by subtracting 331 m/s from the calculated speed.
$357.14 - 331 = 26.14\ m/s$

Step 3
State the unit rate of temperature increase per increase in the speed of sound.

$$\frac{10°C}{11\ m/s} \cong 0.909°C \Big/ m \Big/ s$$

Step 3
Multiply the increase in the speed of sound by the unit rate.
$26.14\ m/s \times 0.909°C/m/s \cong 23.76°C$

Therefore, the air temperature when Tom heard Bob's yell was about 24°C.

3. C

Step 1
Calculate the unit rate for each rate.

I. 10 kg for $10.00
$$\frac{\$10.00}{10kg} = \$1.00/kg$$

II. 15 kg for $15.15
$$\frac{\$15.15}{15kg} = \$1.01/kg$$

III. 20 kg for $19.00
$$\frac{\$19.00}{20kg} = \$0.95/kg$$

IV. 25 kg for $24.50
$$\frac{\$24.50}{25kg} = \$0.98/kg$$

Step 2
Compare the unit rates.
Store *III* has the lowest unit rate where flour costs $0.95/kg.

4. C

Step 1
Write the rate.

The rate is $\dfrac{\$300}{15\ cans}$.

Step 2
Calculate the unit rate for the price of one paint can. Divide the first term ($300) by the second term (15 cans).
$300 \div 15 = 20$

Step 3

Write the rate symbolically or in word form.

Symbolically, $\dfrac{\$300}{15 \text{ cans}} = \dfrac{\$20}{\text{can}}$, or $20 per can.

Each can of paint costs $20.

5. D

The portion of the tank that is filled in one hour is $\dfrac{1}{5}$.

The portion of the tank that is emptied in one hour is $\dfrac{1}{7}$.

Take into account the filling and emptying of the tank at the same time, and calculate the net filling in one hour.

$$\dfrac{1}{5} - \dfrac{1}{7} = \dfrac{7-5}{35}$$
$$= \dfrac{2}{35}$$

Since the total number of hours to fill the tank is the reciprocal of $\dfrac{2}{35}$, the time it will take to fill the tank is $\dfrac{35}{2} = 17\dfrac{1}{2}$ h.

Therefore, it will take $17\dfrac{1}{2}$ hours to fill the tank.

6. B

Step 1

Determine the length of the side in Lorina's polygon that corresponds to side DE in the given polygon.

Since the scale factor that Lorina used is 0.6 and the length of side DE in the given polygon is 6.5 cm, the length of the side that corresponds to side DE in Lorina's polygon can be determined by applying the scale factor formula.

$$\text{scale factor} = \dfrac{\text{image length}}{\text{original length}}$$

Substitute 0.6 for the scale factor and 6.5 for the original length, and then solve for the image length.

$$0.6 = \dfrac{\text{image length}}{6.5}$$
$$0.6 \times 6.5 = \text{image length}$$
$$3.9 = \text{image length}$$

In Lorina's polygon, the side that corresponds to side DE in the given polygon will have a length of 3.9 cm.

Step 2

Determine the measure of the angle in Lorina's polygon that corresponds to angle B in the given polygon.

In similar polygons, corresponding angles are equal in measure. Therefore, since the measure of angle B in the given polygon is 120°, it follows that the measure of the angle in Lorina's polygon that corresponds to angle B will also have a measure of 120°.

Therefore, the length of the side in Lorina's polygon that corresponds to side DE in the given polygon must be 3.9 cm, and the measure of the angle in Lorina's polygon that corresponds to angle B in the given polygon must be 120°.

7. C

Step 1

Find the lengths of the legs of the triangles.
Find the lengths of PQ, QR, KL, and LM.
The length of $PQ = 4$ units.
The length of $QR = 4$ units.
The length of $KL = 1$ unit.
The length of $LM = 1$ unit.

Step 2

Find the ratio of corresponding legs of the triangle to find the scale factor.
$$\dfrac{PQ}{KL} = \dfrac{QR}{LM}$$
$$\dfrac{4}{1} = \dfrac{4}{1}$$
$$4 = 4$$

The scale factor is 4.

8. 4400

Step 1

Determine the volume of a five-pin bowling ball, V_1, by applying the formula for the volume of a sphere.

The diameter of a five-pin bowling ball is 12.6 cm, so its radius is $12.6 \div 2 = 6.3$ cm.

Substitute 3.14 for π and 6.3 for r_1 in the formula $V = \dfrac{4}{3}\pi r^3$, and then solve for V_1.

$$V_1 = \dfrac{4}{3}\pi r_1^3$$
$$\approx \dfrac{4}{3} \times 3.14 \times 6.3^3$$
$$\approx \dfrac{4 \times 3.14 \times 250.047}{3}$$
$$\approx 1\ 046.86 \text{ cm}^3$$

Step 2

Determine the radius of a ten-pin bowling ball.
Since the diameter of a ten-pin bowling ball is
9.2 cm more than the diameter of a five-pin bowling
ball, it follows that the diameter of a ten-pin bowling
ball is $12.6 + 9.2 = 21.8$ cm. Therefore, the radius
of a ten-pin bowling ball is $21.8 \div 2 = 10.9$ cm.

Step 3

Determine the volume of a ten-pin bowling ball,
V_2, by applying the formula for the volume of
a sphere.
Substitute 3.14 for π and 10.9 for r_2 in the formula
$V = \dfrac{4}{3}\pi r^3$, and then solve for V_2.

$$V_2 = \frac{4}{3}\pi r_2^3$$
$$\approx \frac{4}{3} \times 3.14 \times 10.9^3$$
$$\approx \frac{4 \times 3.14 \times 1\ 295.029}{3}$$
$$\approx 5\ 421.85 \text{ cm}^3$$

Step 4

Determine the value of x.
Since the volume of a five-pin bowling ball is
approximately $1\ 046.86$ cm^3 and the volume of a
ten-pin bowling ball is approximately
$5\ 421.85$ cm^3, it follows that the volume of a ten-pin
bowling ball is approximately
$5\ 421.85$ cm$^3 - 1\ 046.86$ cm$^3 \approx 4\ 374.99$ cm^3
more than the volume of a five-pin bowling ball.
To the nearest hundred, the value of x is $4\ 400$.

9. **A**

Step 1

Calculate the volume of the prism.
$$\begin{aligned} V_{prism} &= A_{base} \times h \\ &= l \times w \times h \\ &= 11 \times 3 \times 5 \\ &= 165 \text{ cm}^3 \end{aligned}$$

Step 2

Apply the scale factor to the volume of the prism.
Substitute 165 for V_{prism} and 0.7 for the scale factor
in the equation $V_2 = V_{prism} \times (\text{scale factor})^3$.

$$\begin{aligned} V_2 &= V_{prism} \times (\text{scale factor})^3 \\ &= 165 \times (0.7)^3 \\ &= 165 \times 0.343 \\ &= 56.595 \\ &\approx 56.6 \text{ cm}^3 \end{aligned}$$

Geometry

GEOMETRY

Table of Correlations			
Outcome	**Practice Questions**	**Unit Test Questions**	**Practice Test**
20G Geometry			
20G.1	*Derive proofs that involve the properties of angles and triangles.*	1, 2, 3	1, 2	23, 24
20G.2	*Solve problems that involve properties of angles and triangles.*	4, 5, 6, 7, 8, 9, 10	3, 4, 5, 6, 7, 8, 9, 10	25, 26, 27
20G.3	*Solve problems that involve the cosine law and the sine law, excluding the ambiguous case.*	11, 12, 13, 14, 15, 16	11, 12, 13, 14, 15, 16	28, 29, 30, 31

20G.1 Derive proofs that involve the properties of angles and triangles.

INVESTIGATING THE ANGLE SUM THEOREM

When you are working with triangles, it is useful to understand the relationships between the interior angles. The angle sum theorem states that the sum of the measures of the interior angles in any triangle is 180°.

Example

Cut a triangle from a piece of paper.

Tear the corners off the triangle, and place them together.

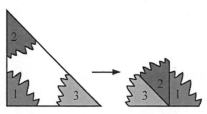

When they are placed together, the angles form a straight line. The measure of a straight line is 180°. Therefore, the combined measures of the interior angles of a triangle must be 180°.

20G.1 Derive proofs that involve the properties of angles and triangles.

INVESTIGATING AND JUSTIFYING THE ISOSCELES TRIANGLE THEOREM

An isosceles triangle is a triangle with two congruent sides and two equal angles.

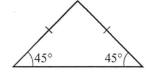

Example

In $\triangle ABC$, side AB is equal in length to side AC.
$AB = AC = 3$ cm

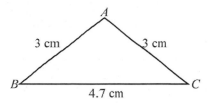

Measure $\angle B$ and $\angle C$ to the nearest degree.

The measure of $\angle B$ is approximately equal to 38°.
The measure of $\angle C$ is approximately equal to 38°.
Therefore, the measure of $\angle B$ is equal to the measure of $\angle C$.

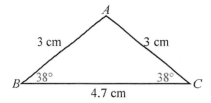

If two sides of a triangle are congruent, then the angles opposite them are equal in measure.

Example

In $\triangle DEF$, $\angle E$ is equal in measure to $\angle F$.
$\angle E = \angle F = 66°$

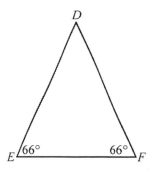

Measure the length of sides *DE* and *DF* to the nearest centimetre.

The length of *DE* is approximately equal to 4 cm. The length of *DF* is approximately equal to 4 cm. Therefore, the length of *DE* is equal to the length of *DF*.

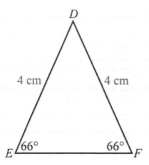

If two angles are of equal measure, the sides opposite them are congruent in length.

These exercises illustrate the following isosceles triangle theorem and its converse:

- The isosceles triangle theorem states that if two sides of a triangle are congruent, then the angles opposite them are congruent.
- The converse of the isosceles triangle theorem states that if two angles in a triangle are congruent, then the sides opposite them are congruent.

The isosceles triangle theorem and its converse can be justified separately by using triangle congruency theorems.

Example
In Δ*RST*, side *RS* is equal in length to side *RT*.

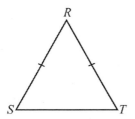

In order to justify the isosceles triangle theorem, the interior angle bisector of ∠*R* must be drawn. The angle bisector *RP* is a line that cuts ∠*R* into two congruent halves; that is, ∠*SRP* = ∠*TRP*.

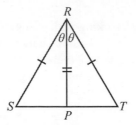

When the angle bisector of ∠*R* is drawn, according to the side-angle-side congruency theorem, two congruent triangles are formed.

$$RS = RT$$
$$\angle SRP = \angle TRP$$
$$RP = RP$$

Therefore, Δ*RSP* is congruent to Δ*RTP*. In other words, all corresponding parts are congruent. Thus, ∠*S* = ∠*T*.

Example
In Δ*PQR*, ∠*R* is equal in measure to ∠*Q*.

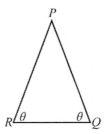

In order to justify the converse of the isosceles triangle theorem, the interior angle bisector of ∠*P* must be drawn. The angle bisector *PS* is a line that cuts ∠*P* into two congruent halves; that is, ∠*RPS* = ∠*QPS*.

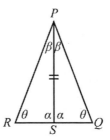

The triangle angle sum theorem states that the interior angles of any given triangle sums 180°; thus, $\angle PSR = \angle PSQ$.

As a result, according to the angle-side-angle congruency theorem, two congruent triangles are formed.

$\angle RPS = \angle QPS$
$PS = PS$
$\angle PSR = \angle PSQ$

Therefore, $\triangle PSR$ is congruent to $\triangle PSQ$. In other words, all corresponding parts are equal in measure. Thus, $PR = PQ$.

20G.1 Derive proofs that involve the properties of angles and triangles.

INVESTIGATING THE EXTERIOR ANGLE THEOREM

The interior angles of a triangle are the inside angles formed by the sides of the triangle. The sum of all the interior angles of a triangle is 180°.

An exterior angle is created by extending one side of a regular polygon, as shown in this diagram.

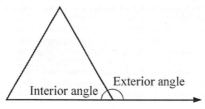

Interior angle   Exterior angle

The relationship between the interior and exterior angles of a triangle is referred to as the **exterior angle theorem**. This theorem states that an exterior angle of a triangle is equal to the sum of the remote (opposite) interior angles. It can be justified by looking at the sum of an exterior angle and its corresponding interior angle and comparing it to the sum of all the interior angles of the triangle.

Example

In the image shown, $\angle a$, $\angle b$, and $\angle c$ are interior angles, and $\angle d$ is an exterior angle.

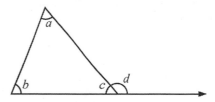

The sum of the exterior angle and its corresponding interior angle is 180° because together they form a straight line.

$\angle d + \angle c = 180°$

The sum of the interior angles of a triangle is 180°.

$\angle a + \angle b + \angle c = 180°$

Since both equations equal 180°, they can be substituted into each other and simplified.

$\angle d + \angle c = \angle a + \angle b + \angle c$
$\angle d = \angle a + \angle b$

Since $\angle a$ and $\angle b$ are remote interior angles to $\angle d$, the exterior angle theorem is proven true.

An exterior angle is always larger than either of the remote interior angles. Each angle within a triangle must have a measure greater than 0°. Since the measure of an exterior angle is the sum of the remote interior angles, each remote interior is smaller than the exterior angle by an amount equal to the other remote interior angle.

20G.1 Derive proofs that involve the properties of angles and triangles.

INVESTIGATING THE RELATIONSHIP BETWEEN THE NUMBER OF SIDES AND THE ANGLES OF REGULAR POLYGONS

When working with regular polygons, it is useful to know the relationships between the angles of these polygons. In a regular polygon, there is a distinct relationship between the measure of any interior angle and the measure of its corresponding exterior angle. You can calculate either of these values if the number of sides in the regular polygon is known.

If a polygon has *n* sides, the sum of its interior angles is $(n - 2) \times 180°$. If the polygon is regular, the sum of the angles can be divided by the number of sides to calculate the measure of each interior angle, $\angle I$.

$$\angle I = \frac{\text{sum of angles}}{n}$$

$$\angle I = \frac{(n - 2) \times 180°}{n}$$

$$\angle I = \frac{n180° - 2(180°)}{n}$$

$$\angle I = \frac{n180° - 360°}{n}$$

$$\angle I = 180° - \frac{360°}{n}$$

Each interior angle of an *n*-sided regular polygon has a measure of $180° - \frac{360°}{n}$.

By extending one side of a regular polygon, an exterior angle is created, as shown in this diagram.

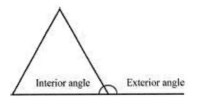

The sum of the interior angle and exterior angle is 180° because together they form a straight line. If a polygon is regular, the measure of each exterior angle, $\angle E$, can be found by subtracting the measure of an interior angle from 180°.

$$\angle E = 180° - \angle I$$

$$\angle E = 180° - \left(180° - \frac{360°}{n}\right)$$

$$\angle E = 180° - 180° + \frac{360°}{n}$$

$$\angle E = \frac{360°}{n}$$

Each exterior angle of an *n*-sided regular polygon has a measure of $\frac{360°}{n}$.

20G.1 Derive proofs that involve the properties of angles and triangles.

INVESTIGATING THEOREMS OF THE SUM OF INTERIOR AND EXTERIOR POLYGON ANGLES

When working with polygons, it is useful to know the relationships among the angles. Two of these relationships are the sum of the interior angles and the sum of the exterior angles. In mathematics, the sum of the angles is often referred to as the sum of the measures of the angles.

SUM OF INTERIOR POLYGON ANGLES

You can calculate the sum of the interior angles by using the number of sides in the polygon.

The sum of the interior angles in a triangle is 180°. This can be demonstrated by drawing any triangle on a piece of paper, tearing the corners off, and placing them together to form a straight line (measure = 180°).

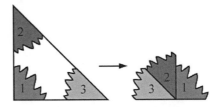

Notice that a square can be split into two triangles. Therefore, the sum of the interior angles in a square is $2 \times 180° = 360°$.

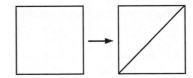

A pentagon can be split into three triangles; therefore, the sum of the interior angles in a pentagon is $3 \times 180° = 540°$.

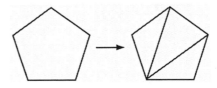

A hexagon can be split into four triangles; therefore, the sum of the interior angles in a hexagon is $4 \times 180° = 720°$.

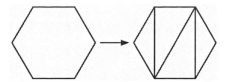

If a polygon has n sides, the sum of its interior angles is $(n - 2) \times 180°$. This formula applies to all polygons, whether they are regular (all sides and angles congruent) or irregular.

SUM OF EXTERIOR POLYGON ANGLES

The sum of the exterior angles does not change, regardless of how many sides the polygon has.

By extending one side of a regular polygon, an exterior angle is created, as shown in this diagram.

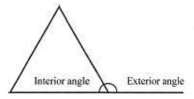

The sum of an interior angle and an exterior angle is 180° because together they form a straight line. The sum of all exterior and interior angles for an n-sided polygon is $n180°$.

It follows that the sum of all the exterior angles is the sum of all the interior and exterior angles, $n180°$, minus the sum of the interior angles, $(n - 2) \times 180°$.

sum of exterior angles
$= n180° - (n - 2)180°$
$= n180° - (n180° - 2(180°))$
$= n180° - n180° + 2(180°)$
$= 2(180°)$
$= 360°$

The sum of all exterior angles in a polygon is 360°.

This rule applies only when each line segment of the polygon is extended in the same direction to ensure there is only one exterior angle per line segment. If there are multiple exterior angles on one line segment, the sum will no longer be 360°.

Example
By extending each side of a hexagon, six exterior angles are created.

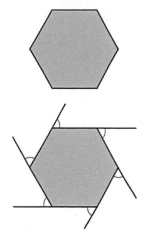

If the hexagon is scaled down to an infinitely small size, you can see that the sum of all the external angles makes up one complete revolution, 360°.

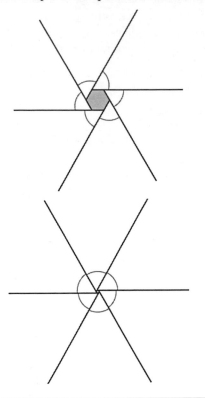

20G.1 Derive proofs that involve the properties of angles and triangles.

PROPERTIES OF VERTICAL ANGLES AND ANGLES FORMED BY A TRANSVERSAL

At the intersection of two lines, the angles opposite each other are called **vertical opposite angles**, or simply **vertical angles**. In the diagram shown, the vertical opposite angles are the angle pairs a and d, and b and c.

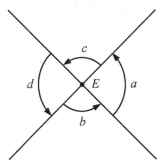

There are two main properties of vertical opposite angles:

1. The **vertical angle theorem** states that vertical opposite angles have equal measures. In the given diagram, angles a and d are equal to each other. Also, angles b and c are equal to each other.
2. Any two adjacent angles formed at the intersection of two lines are called **supplementary**. The sum of supplementary angles is always 180°. For example, the sum of angle a and angle b is equal to 180° The other pairs of supplementary angles include a and c, d and b, and d and c. Each of these pairings produces a straight line or half of a full rotation.

PROPERTIES OF ANGLES FORMED BY A TRANSVERSAL

A **transversal** is a line that crosses two parallel lines, as shown.

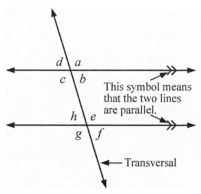

The angles that are formed between the transversal and the two parallel lines are described and named according to their position in the diagram and their position relative to each other.

Corresponding angles are pairs of angles that are in the same position relative to the transversal and each of the parallel lines. For example, one pair of corresponding angles in the diagram is angle *a* and angle *e*.

The property of corresponding angles states that corresponding angles are equal. For example, in the given diagram, angle *c* is equal to angle *g* and angle *b* is equal to angle *f*.

The angles can also be described relative to their position in the diagram.

- **Interior angles** are all angles found inside two parallel lines. In the diagram, angles *b*, *c*, *e*, and *h* are the interior angles.
- **Exterior angles** are on the outside of the two parallel lines. Angles *a*, *d*, *g*, and *f* are the exterior angles.

Angles are described based on their position with respect to the transversal.

- **Same-side angles** are the angles that are on the same side of the transversal.
- **Alternate angles** are the angles that are on opposite sides of the transversal.

Pairs of angles can be identified by a combination of the terms *interior*, *exterior*, *alternate*, and *same side*. Some common descriptions of pairs of angles are as follows:

- Angles *b* and *h* are called alternate interior angles since they are in the interior (space between two parallel lines) and on opposite sides of the transversal.
- Angles *d* and *f* are called alternate exterior angles since they are located on the outside of the space between two parallel lines and on opposite sides of the transversal.
- Angles *b* and *e* are called same-side interior angles since they are in the interior (space between two parallel lines) and on the same side of the transversal.
- Angles *a* and *f* are called same-side exterior angles since they are located on the outside of the space between two parallel lines and on the same side of the transversal.

Each of the types of angles mentioned have equality properties:

- Alternate interior angles are equal.
- Alternate exterior angles are equal.
- Same-side interior angles are supplementary.
- Same-side exterior angles are supplementary.

Since the transversal cuts each of the parallel lines individually and thereby produces an intersection of two lines, there are pairs of vertical angles and pairs of supplementary angles.

Example

The given diagram shows the angles formed when a transversal intersects two parallel lines.

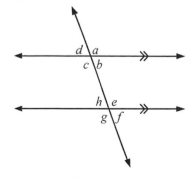

From the given diagram, name the pairs of corresponding angles that are formed.

Solution

Corresponding angles are pairs of angles that occupy the same position relative to the transversal and each parallel line.

The pairs of corresponding angles are *a* and *e*, *d* and *h*, *c* and *g*, and *b* and *f*.

Example

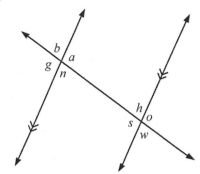

The transversal cuts across two parallel lines.

Name four pairs of opposite angles in the given diagram.

Solution

Step 1

Identify which two lines are parallel and which line is the transversal.

The two parallel lines are the lines angling up to the right. The transversal is the single line angling down to the right.

Step 2

Identify the pairs of opposite angles.

The opposite angles are angles ∠*b* and ∠*n*, ∠*a* and ∠*g*, ∠*s* and ∠*o*, and ∠*h* and ∠*w*.

Example

A diagram is given.

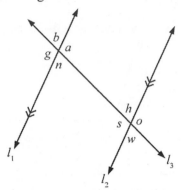

Identify and properly name all the pairs of interior angles in the given diagram.

Solution

Step 1

First, identify which two lines are parallel and which line is the transversal.

Lines l_1 and l_2 are parallel since they contain parallel marker signs and they do not intersect. Line l_3 intersects two parallel lines, so it is the transversal line.

Step 2

Identify all angles in the interior of the diagram.

Angles *a*, *n*, *h*, and *s* are located in the space between two parallel lines. These angles are the interior angles.

Step 3

Name the pairs of interior angles.

There are six pairs of interior angles:

1. Angles *a* and *n* are supplementary interior angles.
2. Angles *a* and *h* are same-side interior angles.
3. Angles *a* and *s* are alternate interior angles.
4. Angles *h* and *n* are alternate interior angles.
5. Angles *s* and *n* are same-side interior angles.
6. Angles *s* and *h* are supplementary interior angles.

20G.1 Derive proofs that involve the properties of angles and triangles.

PROVING PARALLEL-LINE THEOREMS

When two parallel lines are cut by a transversal (another line that is not parallel to the given lines), eight angles are produced. These eight angles have specific names and relationships. The theorems that apply to these angles are called parallel-line theorems. These theorems can be used to solve problems involving parallel lines and transversals.

The given diagram shows the angles that are formed when two parallel lines are cut by a transversal. Refer to this diagram for an illustration of the various angles that are described in this lesson (alternate interior angles, corresponding angles, and interior angles).

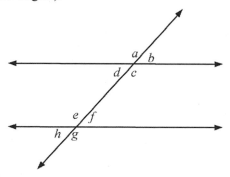

CONGRUENT ALTERNATE INTERIOR ANGLES

Two lines that are intersected by a transversal are parallel if the alternate interior angles are congruent. In the above diagram, ∠c, ∠e and ∠d, ∠f are the pairs of alternate interior angles.

Example

Two parallel lines, N and M, have a transversal intersecting line N at point D and line M at point B.

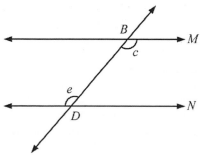

Prove that ∠c = ∠e.

Solution

Draw a perpendicular line to line N that goes through the midpoint of DB.

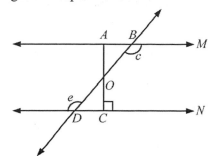

Statement	Reason
∠BAO = ∠DCO	Lines M and N are parallel, so a line perpendicular to one is perpendicular to the other.
DO = BO	Point O is the midpoint of DB.
∠DOC = ∠AOB	Opposite angle theorem
△AOB ≅ △COD	Angle-angle-side congruency
∠CDO = ∠ABO	Since △AOB ≅ △COD
∠e + ∠CDO = 180°	Angles adjacent to each other on a line are supplementary.
∠c + ∠ABO = 180°	Angles adjacent to each other on a line are supplementary.
∠c + ∠ABO = ∠e + ∠CDO ∠c + ∠CDO = ∠e + ∠CDO ∠c = ∠e	By substitution

Therefore, it is proven that ∠c is congruent to ∠e.

_____

CONGRUENT CORRESPONDING ANGLES

Two lines that are intersected by a transversal are parallel if the corresponding angles are congruent. In the given diagram, ∠a and ∠e, ∠b and ∠f, ∠c and ∠g, and ∠d and ∠h are the pairs of corresponding angles.

Example

Two parallel lines that are cut by a transversal produce eight angles, as shown.

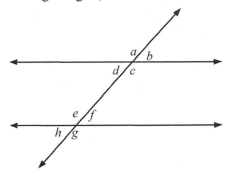

Prove that ∠a = ∠e.

Solution

Create a statement-reason table.

Statement	Reason
∠c = ∠e	Alternate angle theorem
∠c = ∠a	Opposite angle theorem
∠e = ∠a	By substitution

Therefore, it is proven that ∠a is congruent to ∠e.

The proofs that ∠b = ∠f, ∠g = ∠c, and ∠d = ∠h follow the same procedure.

SUPPLEMENTARY INTERIOR ANGLES

Two lines that are intersected by a transversal are parallel if the interior angles on the same side of the transversal are supplementary (add up to 180°). In the given diagram, angles *d* and *e* and angles *c* and *f* are the interior angles on the same side of the transversal.

Example

Two parallel lines cut by a transversal produce eight angles, as shown.

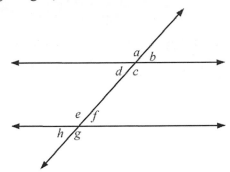

Prove that ∠e + ∠d = 180°.

Solution

Create a statement-reason table.

Statement	Reason
∠d = ∠f	Alternate angle theorem
∠e + ∠f = 180°	Angles adjacent to each other on a line are supplementary.
∠e + ∠d = 180°	By substitution

Therefore, it is proven that ∠e + ∠d = 180°.

The proof that ∠c + ∠f = 180° follows the same procedure.

20G.1 Derive proofs that involve the properties of angles and triangles.

PROBLEM SOLVING WITH CONGRUENT TRIANGLES

One way to identify congruence is to trace one triangle and then slide the tracing over the other triangle to show that it fits exactly over the other.

Another way to identify congruence is to use one of the five triangle relationships:

1. If three sides of one triangle are equal to three sides of another triangle, the triangles are congruent. This is called the side-side-side condition, or **SSS**.

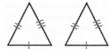

2. If two sides of one triangle and the included angle are equal to two sides of another triangle and the included angle, the triangles are congruent. This is called the side-angle-side condition, or **SAS**.

3. If two angles of one triangle and the side included by them are equal to two angles of another triangle and the side included by them, the triangles are congruent. This is called the angle-side-angle condition, or **ASA**.

4. If two angles of one triangle and a non-included side of one triangle are congruent to two angles and the corresponding non-included side of another triangle, the triangles are congruent. This is called the angle-angle-side condition, or **AAS**.

5. If the hypotenuse and leg of one right triangle are equal to the hypotenuse and leg of the other right triangle, the triangles are congruent. This is called the right angle-hypotenuse-leg condition, or **RHL**.

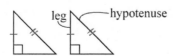

Example

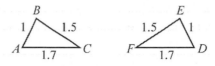

State why $\triangle ABC \cong \triangle DEF$.

Solution

Step 1
Identify which sides or angles are given.
All the sides are given.

Step 2
Identify the condition that will prove congruency.
Side-side-side (SSS) is the condition that proves congruency, since three sides of one triangle are equal to three sides of another triangle.

Step 3
Apply the condition.
Verify that the corresponding sides are equal.
$AB = DE$
$BC = EF$
$AC = DF$

$\triangle ABC \cong \triangle DEF$ satisfies the condition SSS.

Example

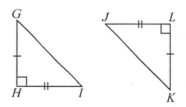

State why $\triangle GHI \cong \triangle KLJ$.

Solution

Step 1
Identify which sides or angles are given.
Two sides and an angle are given.

Step 2
Identify the condition that will prove congruency.
Side-angle-side (SAS) is the condition that proves congruency, since two sides and one included angle are equal to the two sides and one included angle of the other triangle.

Step 3

Apply the condition.

Verify that the corresponding sides and angles are equal.

$GH = KL$

$\angle H = \angle L$

$HI = LJ$

$\triangle GHI \cong \triangle KLJ$ satisfies the condition of SAS.

Example

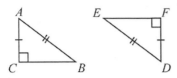

Explain why the triangles are or are not congruent.

Solution

Step 1

Identify which sides or angles are given.
The hypotenuse and leg are given.

Step 2

Identify the condition that will prove congruency.

Right angle-hypotenuse-leg (RHL) is the condition that proves congruency, since the hypotenuse and leg of one triangle are equal to the hypotenuse and leg of the other triangle.

Step 3

Apply the condition.

Verify that the corresponding hypotenuse, leg, and angle measures are equal.

$AB = DE$

$AC = DF$

$\angle C = \angle F$

$\triangle ABC \cong \triangle DEF$ satisfies the condition of RHL.

All pairs of corresponding sides and angles in congruent triangles are equal.

20G.2 Solve problems that involve properties of angles and triangles.

APPLYING THE ANGLE SUM THEOREM FOR TRIANGLES

The sum of the interior angles of any triangle is 180°. This means that the sum of the interior angles of a triangle can be represented as $\angle a + \angle b + \angle c = 180°$.

You can use the angle sum theorem to find missing angles in a triangle by following these steps:

1. Determine which angles are given.
2. Substitute the given values into the angle property for a triangle, and simplify.

Example

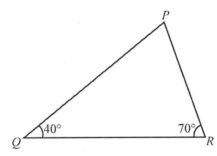

Find the measure of $\angle P$.

Solution

Step 1

Determine which angle measures are given.

$\angle Q = 40°$

$\angle R = 70°$

Step 2

Substitute the given values into the formula for the angle property for a triangle, and simplify.

$\angle P + \angle Q + \angle R = 180°$

$\angle P + 70° + 40° = 180°$

$\angle P + 110° = 180°$

$\angle P = 70°$

The measure of $\angle P$ is 70 °.

Example

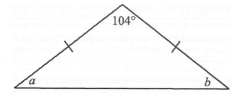

Find the measures of ∠*a* and ∠*b*.

Solution

Step 1

Determine what angle measures are given.
Since this is an isosceles triangle, ∠*a* and ∠*b*
have the same measure: ∠*a* = ∠*b*.
So, the property is modified and becomes

∠*a* + ∠*b* + ∠*c* = 180°
∠*a* + ∠*a* + ∠*c* = 180°.
2∠*a* + ∠*c* = 180°

Step 2

Substitute the given values into the angle
property for a triangle and simplify.

$$2\angle a + (104°) = 180°$$
$$2\angle a + 104° - 104° = 180° - 104°$$
$$\frac{2\angle a}{2} = \frac{76°}{2}$$
$$\angle a = 38°$$

Therefore, ∠*a* and ∠*b* each have a measure of
38°.

---

*20G.2 Solve problems that involve properties of
angles and triangles.*

APPLYING ISOSCELES TRIANGLE THEOREMS

An isosceles triangle is a triangle with two
congruent sides and two equal angles.

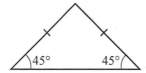

The isosceles triangle theorem states that if two
sides of a triangle are congruent, then the angles
opposite them are congruent. Conversely, if two
angles are congruent, then the sides opposite them
are congruent.

The isosceles triangle theorem and its converse are
useful when solving problems involving isosceles
triangles.

Example

The triangle angle sum theorem states that the
sum of the interior angles of any triangle is
180°. In Δ*DEF*, ∠*D* measures 130°.

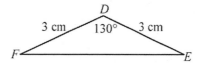

What is the measure of ∠*E*?

Solution

Since *DE* = *DF* = 3 cm, Δ*DEF* is an isosceles
triangle. Thus, the angles' opposite sides, *DE*
and *DF*, are equal in measure. ∠*F* = ∠*E*

Step 1

Label the measure of ∠*F* and ∠*E* as θ.

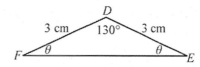

Step 2

Write an equation for the sum of the interior
angles of a triangle.

$$\left(\begin{array}{c}\text{sum of the interior}\\ \text{angles of }\Delta DEF\end{array}\right) = \angle D + \angle E + \angle F$$

Step 3

Substitute all known values into the interior
angle equation.

$$\left(\begin{array}{c}\text{sum of the interior}\\ \text{angles of }\Delta DEF\end{array}\right) = \angle D + \angle E + \angle F$$
$$180° = 130° + \theta + \theta$$

Step 4

Solve for θ.

$180° = 130° + \theta + \theta$
$180° = 130° + 2\theta$
$50° = 2\theta$
$25° = \theta$

The measure of $\angle E$ is equal to θ. Therefore, $\angle E$ measures $25°$.

Example

The perimeter of $\triangle ABC$ is 14.5 cm.

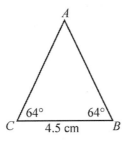

What is the length of side AB?

Solution

Since $\angle B = \angle C = 64°$, $\triangle ABC$ is an isosceles triangle. Thus, the sides opposite $\angle B$ and $\angle C$ are equal in length. $AB = AC$

Step 1

Label sides AB and AC as x.

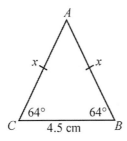

Step 2

Write an equation for the perimeter of $\triangle ABC$.
$P = AB + AC + BC$

Step 3

Substitute all known values into the perimeter equation.

$P = AB + AC + BC$
$14.5 = x + x + 4.5$

Step 4

Solve for x.

$14.5 = x + x + 4.5$
$14.5 = 2x + 4.5$
$10 = 2x$
$5 = x$

The length of side AB is equal to x. Therefore, side AB is 5 cm long.

20G.2 Solve problems that involve properties of angles and triangles.

APPLYING THE EXTERIOR ANGLE THEOREM

The exterior angle theorem states that an exterior angle of a triangle is equal to the sum of the remote (opposite) interior angles.

Example

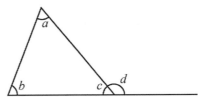

According to the exterior angle theorem, in the given triangle, $\angle d = \angle a + \angle b$.

You can apply the exterior angle theorem to find unknown measures in triangles.

Example

Triangle STU is given.

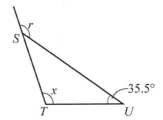

If $\angle r = 143.5°$, determine the measure of $\angle x$.

Solution

The exterior angle theorem states that an exterior angle of a triangle is equal to the sum of the remote (opposite) interior angles. Therefore, $\angle r = \angle x + \angle U$.

Substitute the known measures and solve for $\angle x$.

$$\angle r = \angle x + \angle U$$
$$143.5° = \angle x + 35.5°$$
$$108° = \angle x$$

The measure of $\angle x$ is 108°.

Example

Triangle *MNO* is given with an exterior angle at *M*.

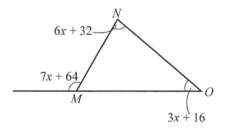

Determine the value of *x* in the given triangle.

Solution

The exterior angle theorem states that an exterior angle of a triangle is equal to the sum of the remote (opposite) interior angles.

Determine the value of *x*.
$$7x + 64 = (6x + 32) + (3x + 16)$$
$$7x + 64 = 9x + 48$$
$$-2x = -16$$
$$x = 8$$

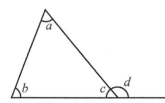

It follows from the equality $\angle d = \angle a + \angle b$ that the exterior angle is greater than both opposite interior angles. Therefore, in the given diagram, $\angle d > \angle a$ and $\angle d > \angle b$.

Example

The triangle *ABC* is given.

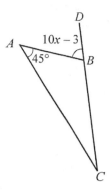

What are the possible values of *x* if $0° < x < 180°$?

Solution

Step 1

Determine the value that *x* must be less than. Since $\angle ABD$ and $\angle ABC$ produce a straight line, $\angle ABD < 180°$ and $\angle ABC < 180°$. Substitute $10x - 3$ for $\angle ABD$, and solve for *x*.
$$\angle ABD < 180°$$
$$10x - 3 < 180°$$
$$10x < 183°$$
$$x < 18.3°$$

Step 2

Determine the angle that *x* must be greater than. The exterior angle theorem states that an exterior angle of a triangle is equal to the sum of the remote (opposite) interior angles, so $\angle ABD = \angle A + \angle C$. From this it is possible to conclude that the exterior angle is greater than both opposite interior angles, so $\angle ABD > \angle A$ and $\angle ABD > \angle C$. In the diagram, $\angle C$ is not given, so use the value of $\angle A$.
$$\angle ABD > \angle A$$
$$10x - 3 > 45°$$
$$10x > 48°$$
$$x > \frac{48°}{10}$$
$$x > 4.8°$$

Therefore, the possible values of *x* are $4.8° < x < 18.3°$.

20G.2 Solve problems that involve properties of angles and triangles.

ANGLES IN A POLYGON

The sum, *S*, of the measures of the interior angles of a polygon is $S = 180(n - 2)°$.

Example

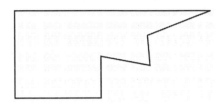

Determine the sum of the measures of all the interior angles for the given polygon.

Solution

Step 1
Determine the number of sides, and identify the appropriate strategy.

The given polygon has 7 sides. One method to determine the sum of all the interior angles is to split the polygon into triangles. Another method to determine the sum of all the interior angles is to apply the formula $180°(n - 2)$, in which *n* is the number of sides.

Step 2
Determine the sum of the measures of the interior angles.
$180°(7 - 2) = 900°$

A polygon is considered a **regular polygon** when all its sides are equal in length and all its interior angles are equal in measure.

The measure of each interior angle of an *n*-sided regular polygon is $\left(180 - \dfrac{360}{n}\right)°$.

Therefore, for a regular polygon, each angle will be $\dfrac{(180n - 360)°}{n} = \left(180 - \dfrac{360}{n}\right)°$, in which *n* is the number of sides.

Example
Determine the measure of an interior angle of a regular hexagon.

Solution

Step 1
Apply the properties of interior angles of regular polygons.
All the interior angles of a regular polygon have the same measure, given by the formula $180° \dfrac{n - 2}{n}$.

Step 2
Determine the measure of each interior angle of a hexagon.
A hexagon contains $n = 6$ sides. Substitute 6 for *n*:

$$\text{Interior angle} = 180° \dfrac{6 - 2}{6}$$
$$= 180° \dfrac{4}{6}$$
$$= 120°$$

Example
Determine the sum of the interior angles of a 24-sided polygon.

Solution

The sum of the interior angles of a polygon is determined by formula $S = 180°(n - 2)$.

Substitute 24 for *n*:
$$S = 180°(24 - 2)$$
$$= 180°(22)$$
$$= 3\ 960°$$

20G.2 Solve problems that involve properties of angles and triangles.

SOLVING PROBLEMS USING THE RELATIONSHIP BETWEEN ANGLES IN POLYGONS

Numerous applications of the relationship between angles in polygons exist in fields such as construction, design, and engineering. To solve problems involving the relationship between angles in polygons, it is important to know the properties of complementary, supplementary, vertical, and exterior angles.

Some problems require a unique approach. The following techniques may be helpful in solving these problems:

- Work with a diagram.
- Identify any given information (interior and exterior angles and side lengths).
- Look for relationships (properties) between what is required (unknown) and what is given (known).

It is often necessary to determine intermediate angles before solving the problem.

Example

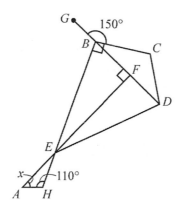

Determine the value of $\angle x$ in the given diagram.

Solution

Create a statement-reason table.

Statement	Reason
$\begin{aligned}\angle CBF &= 180° - \angle GBC \\ &= 180° - 150° \\ &= 30°\end{aligned}$	Property of supplementary angles
$\begin{aligned}\angle EBF &= 90° - \angle CBF \\ &= 90° - 30° \\ &= 60°\end{aligned}$	$\angle CBE$ is a right angle.
$\begin{aligned}\angle FEB &= 180° - (\angle EBF + \angle BFE) \\ &= 180° - (60° + 90°) \\ &= 180° - 150° \\ &= 30°\end{aligned}$	The sum of the interior angles of a triangle is 180°.
$\begin{aligned}\angle AEH &= \angle FEB \\ &= 30°\end{aligned}$	Opposite angle theorem
$\begin{aligned}\angle x &= 180° - (\angle AEH + \angle EHA) \\ &= 180° - (30° + 110°) \\ &= 180° - 140° \\ &= 40°\end{aligned}$	The sum of the interior angles of a triangle is 180°.

Therefore, the measure of $\angle x$ is 40°.

20G.2 Solve problems that involve properties of angles and triangles.

DETERMINING THE MEASURE OF VERTICALLY OPPOSITE ANGLES

A **transversal** is a line that cuts across two **parallel lines**.

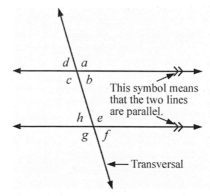

This symbol means that the two lines are parallel.

Transversal

When the transversal intersects two parallel lines, four opposite angles are formed. Opposite angles have the same measure. In the given diagram, $\angle d = \angle b$, $\angle a = \angle c$, $\angle h = \angle f$, and $\angle g = \angle e$ are opposite angles.

If the measure of one opposite angle is known, the measure of its opposite angle must be the same.

Example

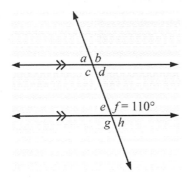

A transversal cuts across two parallel lines, as shown. The measure of $\angle f$ is given.

What is the measure of $\angle g$?

Solution

Step 1
Determine the relationship between the given angle ($\angle f$) and $\angle g$.
Angle g and angle f are opposite angles.

Step 2
Determine the measure of the unknown angle using the relationship of opposite angles.
Opposite angles have the same measure.
If $\angle f = 110°$, then $\angle g = 110°$.
The measure of $\angle g$ is $110°$.

20G.2 Solve problems that involve properties of angles and triangles.

CALCULATING CORRESPONDING ANGLES IN TRANSVERSALS

A transversal is a line that crosses two parallel lines.

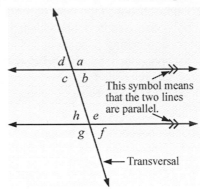

This symbol means that the two lines are parallel.

Transversal

Corresponding angles are pairs of angles that are in the same position relative to each of the parallel lines and the transversal. For example, one pair of corresponding angles in the given diagram is $\angle a$ and $\angle e$. The property of corresponding angles states that corresponding angles are equal. Therefore, $\angle a = \angle e$.

When determining the measure of an unknown angle in a transversal, follow these steps:

1. Determine the relationship between the given angle and the unknown angle.
2. Determine the measure of the unknown angle by using the appropriate relationship.

Example
A diagram is given.

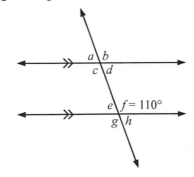

What is the measure of ∠b?

Solution

Step 1
Determine the relationship between the given angle and the unknown angle.
The given angle, *f*, and the unknown angle, *b*, are corresponding angles.

Step 2
Determine the measure of ∠b by using the appropriate relationship.
Since corresponding angles are equal,
∠f = ∠b. Therefore, ∠b = 110°.

20G.2 Solve problems that involve properties of angles and triangles.

CONSTRUCTING PERPENDICULAR BISECTORS

When a line segment is divided into two equal parts by another line, the segment is bisected. *Bi* means two, and *sect* means cut. The line that divides the line segment is called the **bisector**. The line segment is marked with the same number of ticks on each side to indicate that both sides are the same length.

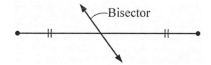

When the bisector is at a right angle to the line segment, it is called a **perpendicular bisector**.

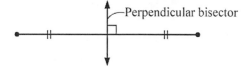

To draw the perpendicular bisector using a compass, follow these steps:

1. Place the pointed end of a compass on one endpoint of the line segment. Draw a large arc that crosses the line segment more than halfway between the two points.
2. Keep the compass exactly the same. Draw another arc from the other endpoint.
3. Draw a line that connects the points where the two arcs cross each other. This is the perpendicular bisector.

Example

Draw the perpendicular bisector of line segment *AB*.

Solution

Step 1
Draw the first arc.
Place the pointed end of the compass on point *A* of the line segment. Draw an arc that crosses the line segment at a distance greater than halfway between the two points.

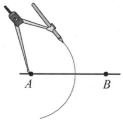

Step 2
Draw the second arc.
Repeat the same process with the pointed end of the compass on point *B* of the line segment. Label the points where the arcs intersect *C* and *D*.

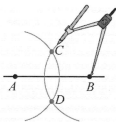

Step 3
Draw the perpendicular bisector.
Use a straightedge to connect points C and D.

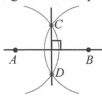

20G.2 Solve problems that involve properties of angles and triangles.

CONSTRUCTING A PERPENDICULAR LINE THROUGH A POINT USING A STRAIGHTEDGE AND COMPASS

Perpendicular lines are two lines in the same plane that intersect at 90° to form a right angle. It is possible to construct a perpendicular line through a point using only a straightedge and a compass.

To construct a perpendicular line using a straightedge and a compass, follow these steps:

1. Use a straightedge to draw a line segment. Draw a point, P, above the line segment but not touching it.
2. Place the compass needle on point P, and open the compass to a width greater than the distance between point P and the line segment.
3. Draw an arc that intersects the line segment to the left of point P. Keeping the width of the compass the same, draw an arc that intersects the line segment to the right of point P.
4. Place the compass needle on the point of intersection on the left, and draw an arc below the line segment.
5. Without adjusting the width of the compass, place the compass needle on the point of intersection on the right, and draw an arc below the line segment that intersects the arc drawn in step 4.
6. Use a straightedge to connect point P to the point of intersection drawn in step 5.

The construction of a perpendicular line through a point is shown here.

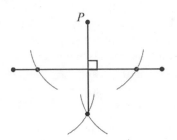

Example
Construct a line segment perpendicular to $\overline{AB}$ through point P.

Solution

Step 1
Use a straightedge to draw $\overline{AB}$. Draw a point, P, above the line segment but not touching it.

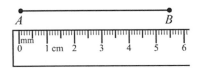

Step 2
Place the compass needle on point P, and open the compass to a width greater than the distance between point P and $\overline{AB}$. The exact width is not important.

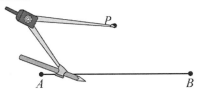

Step 3

Draw an arc that intersects $\overline{AB}$ to the left of point P. Label the point of intersection Q. Keeping the width of the compass the same, draw an arc that intersects $\overline{AB}$ to the right of point P. Label the point of intersection R.

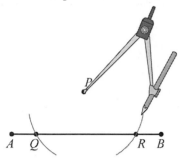

Step 4

Place the compass needle on point Q, and draw an arc below $\overline{AB}$.

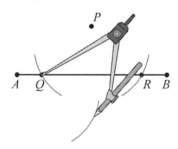

Step 5

Without adjusting the width of the compass, place the compass needle on point R and draw an arc below $\overline{AB}$ that intersects the arc drawn in step 4. Label the point of intersection S.

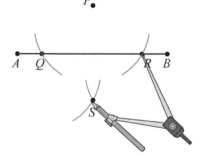

Step 6

Use a straightedge to connect point S to point P.

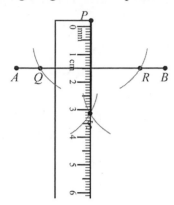

The line segment perpendicular to $\overline{AB}$ through point P is $\overline{PS}$.

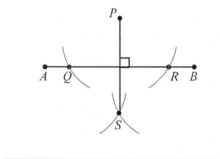

20G.2 Solve problems that involve properties of angles and triangles.

DRAWING A PARALLEL LINE USING A STRAIGHTEDGE AND COMPASS

Parallel lines are straight lines that do not intersect; they remain the same distance apart. You can draw a line parallel to a given line by using a straightedge and compass. To draw a line parallel to a given line AB through a given point P, use the following steps:

1. Use a straightedge to draw a line at an angle through point P and line AB. Label the point of intersection R.
2. Place the compass needle on point R, and set the width to approximately half the length between point R and point P.
3. Draw an arc between both lines. Label the points of intersection C and D. With the compass set to the same width, place the compass needle on point P, and draw a similar arc. Label the point of intersection E.
4. Set the width of the compass by placing the compass needle on point C and the other end at point D. With the compass set to the same width, place the compass needle on point E. Draw an arc and label the point of intersection F.
5. Using a straightedge, draw a line through points P and F.

Example
  A line, AB, and a point, P, are given.

Draw a line parallel to AB.

Solution

Step 1
Use a straightedge to draw a line at an angle through point P and line AB. Label the point of intersection R.

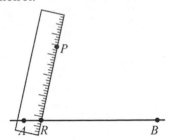

Step 2
Place the compass needle on point R, and set the width to approximately half the length between point R and point P.

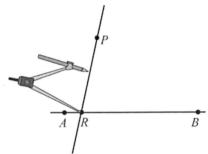

Step 3

Draw an arc between both lines. Label the points of intersection *C* and *D*.

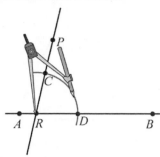

With the compass set to the same width, place the compass needle on point *P*, and draw a similar arc. Label the point of intersection *E*.

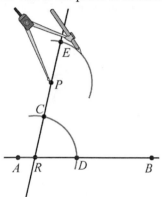

Step 4

Set the width of the compass by placing the compass needle on point *C* and the other end at point *D*.

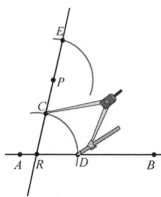

With the compass set to the same width, place the compass needle on point *E*. Draw an arc, and label the point of intersection *F*.

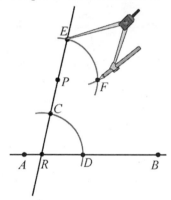

Step 5

Using a straightedge, draw a line through points P and F.

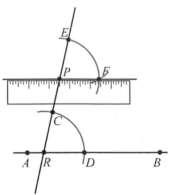

Line PF is parallel to line AB.

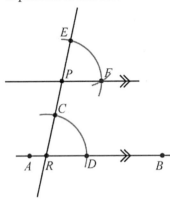

20G.3 Solve problems that involve the cosine law and the sine law, excluding the ambiguous case.

DEVELOPING THE SINE LAW

Any triangle that is not a right-angled triangle is called an **oblique triangle**.

The primary trigonometric ratios can only be applied to solve for a side or an angle of a right triangle, so a new procedure needs to be developed when presented with an oblique triangle.
The primary trigonometric ratios are used to develop a new method called the sine law.

Consider $\triangle ABC$.

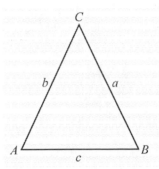

Side BC is opposite angle A and can be denoted by a. Similarly, side AC can be denoted by b, and side AB can be denoted by c.

Draw DC perpendicular to AB in order to form two right triangles, as shown.

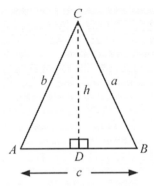

DC is the height, h, of $\triangle ABC$.

There are now two right triangles: $\triangle ADC$ and $\triangle BDC$. Applying the primary trigonometric sine ratio for angle A and angle B gives $\sin A = \dfrac{h}{b}$ and $\sin B = \dfrac{h}{a}$.

Solving for h in each case gives $h = b\sin A$ and $h = a\sin B$.

Since the value of h is identical for $\triangle ADC$ and $\triangle BDC$, $b\sin A = a\sin B$.

The equation $b\sin A = a\sin B$ can be rewritten as $\dfrac{a}{\sin A} = \dfrac{b}{\sin B}$. If a line perpendicular to AC is drawn and the same steps are followed, the equation $\dfrac{a}{\sin A} = \dfrac{c}{\sin C}$ can also be generated.

Combining the derived results gives the equation $\dfrac{a}{\sin A} = \dfrac{b}{\sin B} = \dfrac{c}{\sin C}$. This equation is called the sine law. The sine law can be illustrated by examining each of the following triangles.

The sine law can also be written as $\dfrac{\sin A}{a} = \dfrac{\sin B}{b} = \dfrac{\sin C}{c}$.

Example

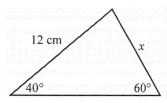

Since the side measuring x cm is opposite the 40°angle, and the side measuring 12 cm is opposite the 60°angle, the following equation is generated:
$$\frac{12}{\sin 60°} = \frac{x}{\sin 40°}.$$

Example

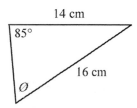

Since the side measuring 14 cm is opposite angle θ, and the side measuring 16 cm is opposite the 85°angle, the following equation is generated:
$$\frac{14}{\sin \theta} = \frac{16}{\sin 85°}.$$

Example

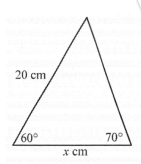

Recall that the sum of the interior angles of a triangle is equal to 180°. Therefore, the angle opposite the side measuring x cm is equal to $180° - 60° - 70° = 50°$. Since the side measuring 20 cm is opposite the 70° angle, the following equation is generated:
$$\frac{x}{\sin 50°} = \frac{20}{\sin 70°}.$$

20G.3 Solve problems that involve the cosine law and the sine law, excluding the ambiguous case.

APPLYING THE SINE LAW USING ACUTE TRIANGLES

The sine law can be used to calculate the measures of unknown side lengths or angles in non-right triangles provided that at least three other measures are given.

Since the sine law uses two ratios at a time, only one unknown and three known quantities must be given.

Either of the following triangles gives enough information to determine the measure of side *a*.

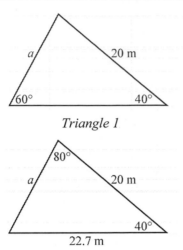

Triangle 1

Triangle 2

In triangle 1, the measure of the angle opposite to side *a* is 40°, and the angle-side pair is 60° and 20 m.

In triangle 2, the measure of the angle opposite to side *a* is 40°, and the angle-side pair is 80° and 22.7 m.

An angle-side pair refers to the measure of an angle and the measure of the side length opposite to it.

In order to solve any problems involving triangles, it is helpful to label the triangle first.

For example, once triangle 1 has been labelled with its known values, make the appropriate substitutions into the sine law, and solve for *a*.

$$\frac{a}{\sin A} = \frac{b}{\sin B}$$

$$\frac{a}{\sin 40°} = \frac{20}{\sin 60°}$$

$$a = \frac{20\sin 40°}{\sin 60°}$$

$$\approx 14.8 \text{ m}$$

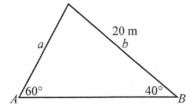

The equation could also be set up as $\frac{\sin A}{a}$

$= \frac{\sin B}{b}$.

The sine law can be used to calculate the measure of an unknown angle in an acute triangle.

In order to determine the measure of an unknown angle, the following information is required:

- The measure of the side opposite the unknown angle
- Another complete angle-side pair

Remember to use the inverse function on your calculator to determine the measure of the unknown angle.

Example

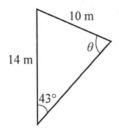

Determine the measure of the unknown angle *θ*, rounded to the nearest tenth of a degree. _____°

Solution

Step 1

Label the diagram with the appropriate variables.

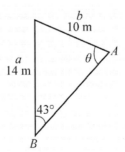

Step 2
Apply the sine law and solve for θ.
$$\frac{\sin A}{a} = \frac{\sin B}{b}$$
$$\frac{\sin \theta}{14} = \frac{\sin 43°}{10}$$
$$\sin \theta = \frac{14\sin 43°}{10}$$
$$\theta = \sin^{-1}(0.9548)$$
$$\theta = 72.71°$$

Rounded to the nearest tenth of a degree, the measure of θ is 72.7°.

The sine law can be used to calculate the measure of a side length in an acute triangle.

In order to determine the measure of a side length, the following information is required:

- The angle opposite to the unknown side
- Another complete angle-side pair

Example

The following triangle is given.

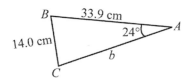

Determine the length of side b, to the nearest tenth centimetre.

Solution

Since a known pair (a side with its corresponding opposite angle) is given, use the sine law.

Step 1
Find $\angle C$ using its corresponding opposite side.
$$\frac{a}{\sin A} = \frac{c}{\sin C}$$
$$\frac{14.0}{\sin 24°} = \frac{33.9}{\sin C}$$
$$14.0(\sin C) = 33.9(\sin 24°)$$
$$\sin C = \frac{33.9(\sin 24°)}{14.0}$$
$$\sin C = 0.984\,883\,7286\ldots$$
$$\angle C = \sin^{-1}(0.984\,883\,7286\ldots)$$
$$\angle C \approx 80.0°$$

Step 2
Find $\angle B$.
Since the sum of the measures of all three angles within a triangle is equal to 180°, the measure of $\angle B$ can be calculated as follows:
$$\angle B = 180° - 80.0° - 24°$$
$$\angle B = 76°$$

Step 3
Find side b by using its corresponding opposite angle B.
$$\frac{a}{\sin A} = \frac{b}{\sin B}$$
$$\frac{14.0}{\sin 24°} = \frac{b}{\sin 76°}$$
$$14.0(\sin 76°) = b(\sin 24°)$$
$$\frac{14.0(\sin 76°)}{\sin 24°} = b$$
$$33.397\,876\,49\ldots = b$$
$$b \approx 33.4$$

Therefore, the length of side b, to the nearest tenth centimetre, is 33.4 cm.

20G.3 Solve problems that involve the cosine law and the sine law, excluding the ambiguous case.

SOLVING PROBLEMS USING THE SINE LAW FOR ACUTE TRIANGLES

Problems involving acute triangles can be solved by following these general steps:

1. Read the problem carefully. Determine which measures are given and which measure needs to be calculated.
2. If a diagram is not given, draw a sketch to represent the situation presented in the problem.
3. Make substitutions into the sine law, and use correct algebraic steps to solve for the unknown value. Avoid or minimize rounding until the last step.
4. Check your calculations.
5. Write a concluding statement.

Example

During hockey practice, players performed the following drill: Player A passed the puck to player B, who was 12 m away. Player B redirected the puck at an angle of $40°$ to player C. Player C then passed the puck back to player A, who was standing 9 m away.

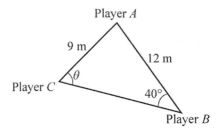

To the nearest degree, determine the measure of angle θ.

Solution

Since it is not a side-side-side situation, apply the sine law. The side measuring 9 m is opposite the $40°$ angle, and the side measuring 12 m is opposite angle θ. Solve for θ as follows:

$$\frac{9}{\sin 40°} = \frac{12}{\sin \theta}$$
$$9\sin \theta = 12\sin 40°$$
$$\frac{9\sin \theta}{9} = \frac{12\sin 40°}{9}$$
$$\sin \theta = \frac{12\sin 40°}{9}$$
$$\theta \approx 58.99°$$

The measure of angle θ, to the nearest degree, is $59°$.

Example

A surveyor needs to find the length, b, of a bridge across a pond in a park.

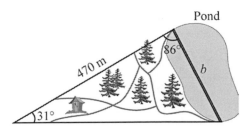

Explain which trigonometric law you would use to find the length of the bridge, b. Then, use the trigonometric law to find the length of the bridge, to the nearest whole metre.

Solution

The missing angle in the triangle can be easily determined, since the sum of the measures of the angles must be equal to $180°$. This will provide a known pair with the side 470 m. Therefore, the sine law would be the correct formula to use to find the length of the bridge, b.

First, find the missing angle, A.
$$\angle A = 180° - 86° - 31° = 63°$$

Next, let side $a = 470$ m and $\angle B = 31°$ in the given triangle. Then, use the sine law to find the value of b.

$$\frac{a}{\sin A} = \frac{b}{\sin B}$$
$$\frac{470}{\sin 63°} = \frac{b}{\sin 31°}$$
$$\frac{470(\sin 31°)}{\sin 63°} = b$$
$$b = 271.679\ 1501$$

The length of the bridge, b, to the nearest whole metre, is 272 m.

20G.3 Solve problems that involve the cosine law and the sine law, excluding the ambiguous case.

APPLYING THE SINE LAW USING OBTUSE TRIANGLES

The sine law states that in triangle ABC, $\frac{\sin A}{a} = \frac{\sin B}{b} = \frac{\sin C}{c}$, where a, b, and c represent the sides of the triangle. The sine law can also be written as $\frac{a}{\sin A} = \frac{b}{\sin B} = \frac{c}{\sin C}$.

In order to solve any problems that involve triangles, it is helpful to label the triangle first.

Since the sine law uses two ratios at a time, three known quantities and only one unknown must be given.

Use the sine law when the measures of two angles and the length of one side are supplied. The measure of the third angle must first be determined using the property that the sum of the measures of the angles in a triangle is 180 °. Then, use the sine law to determine the length of either missing side.

The length of the third side can be determined from either the sine law or the cosine law. If the length of the side between the angles is given, the situation is called angle-side-angle (ASA). If the length of one of the sides that is not between the two angles is given, the situation is called angle-angle-side (AAS).

In order to determine the measure of a side length, you need to know the measure of the angle opposite to the unknown side and another complete angle-side pair.

Example

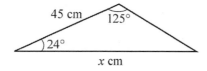

Determine the measure of the missing side, x, rounded to the nearest tenth of a centimetre.

Solution

The angle opposite the unknown side length is given, but the measure of the angle opposite 45 cm is not.

Step 1
Calculate the measure of the unknown angle by subtracting the known angles from 180°.
$$180° - 125° - 24° = 31°$$

Step 2
Apply the sine law.
$$\frac{\sin A}{a} = \frac{\sin B}{b}$$
$$\frac{\sin 125°}{x} = \frac{\sin 31°}{45}$$
$$x\sin 31° = 45\sin 125°$$
$$x = \frac{45\sin 125°}{\sin 31°}$$
$$x \approx 71.57 \text{ cm}$$

Rounded to the nearest tenth of a centimetre, the measure of side x is 71.6 cm.

Use the sine law when the lengths of two sides and the measure of one of the angles that is not between the two given sides are supplied. This is called side-side-angle (SSA). The sine law must be used as the first step to find the measure of a missing angle. However, the solution may not be unique, or there may be no solution. This situation is called the ambiguous case.

In order to determine the measure of an unknown angle, you need to know the measure of the side opposite the unknown angle and another complete angle-side pair.

Example

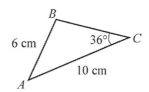

Triangle *ABC* is given.

Determine the measure of ∠*A*, rounded to the nearest degree.

Solution

Step 1
Apply the sine law to determine the measure of ∠*B*.

The side that measures 6 cm is opposite the angle that measures 36°. The side that measures 10 cm is opposite ∠*B*.
$$\frac{6}{\sin 36°} = \frac{10}{\sin ∠B}$$
$$6\sin ∠B = 10\sin 36°$$
$$\sin ∠B = \frac{10\sin 36°}{6}$$
$$∠B = \sin^{-1}\left(\frac{5\sin 36°}{3}\right)$$
$$∠B \approx 78.42°$$

The value determined for ∠*B*, 78.42°, is too small because according to the given diagram ∠*B* is an obtuse angle.

Step 2

Determine the other possible value for ∠B.
Subtract 180° by 78.42° to find the other value of ∠B.

∠B ≈ 180° − 78.42°

∠B ≈ 101.58°

This is a more reasonable measurement for the given diagram.

Step 3

Determine the measure of ∠A.

Apply the property that the sum of the interior angles of a triangle is equal to 180°.

∠A = 180° − (∠B + ∠C)

∠A ≈ 180° − (101.58° + 36°)

∠A ≈ 180° − (137.58°)

∠A ≈ 42.42°

Therefore, rounded to the nearest degree, the measure of ∠A is 42°.

20G.3 Solve problems that involve the cosine law and the sine law, excluding the ambiguous case.

SOLVING PROBLEMS USING SINE LAWS FOR OBTUSE TRIANGLES

Problems involving obtuse triangles can be solved by following these general steps:

1. Read the problem carefully. Determine what measures are given and what measure needs to be calculated.
2. If a diagram is not given, draw a sketch to represent the situation presented in the problem.
3. Make substitutions into the sine law, and use correct algebraic steps to solve for the unknown value. Avoid or minimize rounding until the last step.
4. Check your calculations for the ambiguous case.
5. Write a concluding statement.

Example

The given image shows where three basketball players were standing as they performed a practice drill. One player stood at point *A* and passed the ball to another player standing at point *B*, which was 6 m away. The player standing at *B* then passed it at an angle of 20° to a player standing at point *C*. The player standing at *C* then passed the ball back to the player standing at point *A*, which was 3 m away.

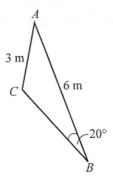

To the nearest degree, determine the measure of ∠A.

Solution

Step 1

Apply the sine law to determine the measure of ∠C.

The side measuring 3 m is opposite the 20° angle, and the side measuring 6 m is opposite ∠C. Solve for ∠C.

$$\frac{3}{\sin 20°} = \frac{6}{\sin ∠C}$$

3sin ∠C = 6sin 20°

sin ∠C = 2sin 20°

∠C = sin⁻¹(2sin 20°)

∠C ≈ 43.16°

Looking at the given diagram, the value determined for ∠C is too small because an obtuse angle is shown in the diagram. This is a scenario where the ambiguous case is possible.

Step 2

Determine the other possible value of ∠C.

Subtract 180° by 43.16° to find the other value of ∠C.

∠C ≈ 180° − 43.16°

∠C ≈ 136.84°

This is a more reasonable measurement for the given diagram.

Step 3

Determine the measure of ∠*A*.

Apply the property that the sum of the interior angles of a triangle is equal to 180°.

$\angle A = 180° - (\angle B + \angle C)$
$\angle A \approx 180° - (20° + 136.84°)$
$\angle A \approx 180° - (156.84°)$
$\angle A \approx 23.16°$

Rounded to the nearest degree, the measure of ∠*A* is 23°.

Example

A golfer at point *T* on the given diagram wishes to sink his golf ball in a hole directly on the other side of a pond at point *H*. The golfer has two options. He can play two low-risk shots (one from point *T* to point *A* and another from point *A* to point *H*) or he can play a high-risk shot and attempt to shoot directly from point *T* to point *H*. The golfer estimates that the distance from point *T* to point *A* is 175 m, the measure of angle *ATH* is 45°, and the measure of angle *TAH* is 95°.

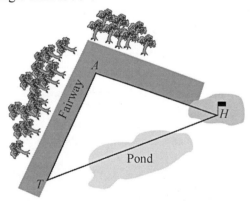

To the nearest metre, what is the distance from point *T* to point *H*?

Solution

Step 1

Determine the measure of angle *AHT*.
$\angle AHT = 180° - (\angle ATH + \angle TAH)$
$\angle AHT = 180° - (45° + 95°)$
$\angle AHT = 40°$

Step 2

Use the sine law to determine the distance from point *T* to point *H*.

$$\frac{TH}{\sin TAH} = \frac{TA}{\sin AHT}$$
$$\frac{TH}{\sin 95°} = \frac{175}{\sin 40°}$$
$$TH = \frac{175\sin 95°}{\sin 40°}$$
$$TH = 271.215\ 6699\ldots$$

Step 3

Round the answer to the neatest metre.

The distance from point *T* to point *H* is about 271 m.

20G.3 Solve problems that involve the cosine law and the sine law, excluding the ambiguous case.

DEVELOPING THE COSINE LAW

Some oblique triangles cannot be solved directly using the law of sines. A new procedure can be developed by applying the Pythagorean theorem and the cosine ratio.

Consider △*ABC*.

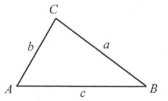

In △*ABC*, draw a segment *DC* perpendicular to *AB* to form two right triangles. Recall that *DC* is the height, *h*, of △*ABC*. Denote side *AD* by *x*. It follows that side *DB* = *c* − *x* as illustrated in the following diagram.

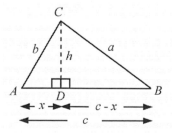

Apply the Pythagorean theorem to both ΔADC and ΔBDC.

In ΔADC, $b^2 = x^2 + h^2$ or $b^2 - x^2 = h^2$.

In ΔBDC, $a^2 = h^2 + (c - x)^2$.

Substitute $b^2 - x^2$ for h^2 in the equation $a^2 = h^2 + (c - x)^2$.

$$a^2 = b^2 - x^2 + (c - x)^2$$

Expand $(c - x)^2$.

$$a^2 = b^2 - x^2 + c^2 - 2cx + x^2$$

Collect like terms.

$$a^2 = b^2 + c^2 - 2cx$$

Also, in ΔADC, $\cos A = \dfrac{x}{b}$ or $b\cos A = x$.

By substituting $b\cos A$ for x in the equation $a^2 = b^2 + c^2 - 2cx$, the equation becomes $a^2 = b^2 + c^2 - 2bc\cos A$. This equation is called the Cosine Law.

Similar equations can be derived that involve $\cos B$ and $\cos C$:

$$b^2 = a^2 + c^2 - 2ac\cos B$$
$$c^2 = a^2 + b^2 - 2ab\cos C$$

The Cosine Law can be used to calculate the measure of an angle in a triangle when the lengths of all three sides of the triangle are known. In this case, one of the following forms of the law of cosines is useful.

$$\cos A = \frac{b^2 + c^2 - a^2}{2bc}$$

$$\cos B = \frac{a^2 + c^2 - b^2}{2ac}$$

$$\cos C = \frac{a^2 + b^2 - c^2}{2ab}$$

The Cosine Law can be illustrated by examining each of the following triangles.

Example

This example illustrates the use of the Cosine Law when a side length is unknown.

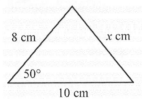

Since the side measuring x cm is opposite the 50° angle, $x^2 = 8^2 + 10^2 - 2(8)(10)\cos 50°$.

Example

This example illustrates the use of the Cosine Law when the measure of an angle is unknown.

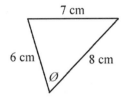

Since the angle measuring θ is opposite the side measuring 7 cm, $\cos \theta = \dfrac{6^2 + 8^2 - 7^2}{2(6)(8)}$.

20G.3 Solve problems that involve the cosine law and the sine law, excluding the ambiguous case.

APPLYING THE COSINE LAW USING ACUTE TRIANGLES

The cosine law can be used to calculate either the measures of unknown side lengths or unknown angles in non-right triangles, provided that at least three other measures are given. Use the cosine law primarily when the measures of an angle-side pair are not given.

An angle-side pair refers to the measure of an angle and the measure of the side length opposite to it.

The measure to be calculated depends on the following information:

- If the measures of all three sides of the triangle are given, the measures of any of the angles can be calculated using the cosine law in the form of $\cos A = \dfrac{b^2 + c^2 - a^2}{2bc}$.

- If the measures of two sides of the triangle and the measure of the angle contained between those sides are given, the measure of the unknown side can be calculated using the cosine law in the form of $a^2 = b^2 + c^2 - 2bc\cos A$.

Example

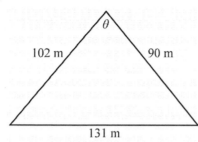

Rounded to the nearest tenth of a degree, calculate the measure of the unknown angle on the given triangle.

Solution

The value of ∠A is θ, the measure of side a is 131 m, and sides b and c are interchangeable.

Substitute the known values into the cosine law and solve for θ:

$$\cos A = \frac{b^2 + c^2 - a^2}{2bc}$$
$$\cos \theta = \frac{102^2 + 90^2 - 131^2}{2(102)(90)}$$
$$\cos \theta = \frac{1\ 343}{18\ 360}$$
$$\theta = \cos^{-1}\left(\frac{1\ 343}{18\ 360}\right)$$
$$\theta \approx 85.805°$$

Rounded to the nearest tenth of a degree, the measure of θ is 85.8°.

20G.3 Solve problems that involve the cosine law and the sine law, excluding the ambiguous case.

SOLVING PROBLEMS USING THE COSINE LAW FOR ACUTE TRIANGLES

Problems involving acute triangles can be solved by following these general steps:

1. Read the problem carefully. Determine which measures are given and which measure needs to be calculated.
2. If a diagram is not given, draw a sketch to represent the situation presented in the problem.
3. Make substitutions into the cosine law formula, and use correct algebraic steps to solve for the unknown value. Avoid or minimize rounding until the last step.
4. Check your calculations.
5. Write a concluding statement.

Example

A radar tracking station locates two boats: a fishing boat at a distance of 3.4 km from the tracking station, and a passenger ferry at a distance of 5.6 km from the tracking station. From the tracking station, the angle between the line of sight to the two boats is 86°. Determine the distance between the two boats to the nearest tenth of a kilometre.

Solution

Draw a diagram representing the situation. Let x represent the distance between the two boats.

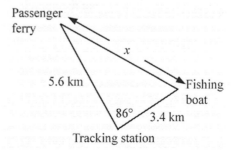

Since the problem is a side-angle-side situation, apply the cosine law. Side x is opposite the $86°$ angle; therefore, solve for x as follows:

$$a^2 = b^2 + c^2 - 2bc\cos A$$
$$x^2 = 5.6^2 + 3.4^2 - 2(5.6)(3.4)\cos 86°$$
$$x^2 \approx 31.36 + 11.56 - 2.66$$
$$x^2 \approx 40.26$$
$$x \approx \sqrt{40.26}$$
$$x \approx 6.345 \text{ km}$$

The distance between the fishing boat and the passenger ferry, to the nearest tenth of a kilometre, is 6.3 km.

_____

Example

To display the Stanley Cup, staff at a hockey arena roped off a triangular area and installed a security camera, as illustrated in the given diagram.

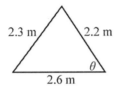

The security camera, located at θ, moves continuously between the two ropes, which measure 2.2 m and 2.6 m, respectively.

To the nearest tenth of a degree, determine the measure of angle θ.

Solution

Since this is a side-side-side situation, apply the cosine law. Angle θ is opposite the side measuring 2.3 m, so solve for θ as follows:

$$\cos A = \frac{b^2 + c^2 - a^2}{2bc}$$
$$\cos \theta = \frac{2.6^2 + 2.2^2 - 2.3^2}{2(2.6)(2.2)}$$
$$\cos \theta = \frac{6.76 + 4.84 - 5.29}{11.44}$$
$$\cos \theta = \frac{6.31}{11.44}$$
$$\theta \approx 56.525°$$

To the nearest tenth of a degree, the measure of angle θ is 56.5°.

_____

20G.3 Solve problems that involve the cosine law and the sine law, excluding the ambiguous case.

APPLYING THE COSINE LAW TO OBTUSE TRIANGLES

The cosine law can be used to calculate either the measures of unknown side lengths or the measures of unknown angles in non-right triangles, provided that at least three other measures are given. You can use the cosine law primarily when the measures of an angle-side pair are not given.

An angle-side pair refers to the measure of an angle and the measure of the side length opposite to it.

The measure to be calculated depends on the following information:

- If the measures of all three sides of the triangle are given, the measures of any of the angles can be calculated by using the cosine law in the form $\cos A = \dfrac{b^2 + c^2 - a^2}{2bc}$.

- If the measures of two sides of the triangle and the measure of the angle contained between those sides are given, the measure of the unknown side can be calculated by using the cosine law in the form $a^2 = b^2 + c^2 - 2bc\cos A$.

Example

Expressing all values to the nearest tenth, solve triangle ABC if $a = 15$ cm, $b = 8$ cm, and $\angle C = 55°$.

Solution

Step 1
Sketch the triangle.
The sketch of the triangle shows that this situation is SAS. The lengths of two sides and the measure of the included angle are given.

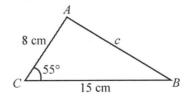

Step 2

Determine the measure of the third side using the cosine law.

$$c^2 = a^2 + b^2 - 2ab\cos C$$
$$c^2 = (15)^2 + (8)^2 - 2(15)(8)\cos 55°$$
$$c^2 \approx 151.34$$
$$c \approx 12.3$$

Step 3

Determine the measure of either $\angle A$ or $\angle B$.

$\angle A$ will be determined using the cosine law.

$$\cos A = \frac{b^2 + c^2 - a^2}{2bc}$$
$$\cos A = \frac{(8)^2 + (12.3)^2 - (15)^2}{2(8)(12.3)}$$
$$\cos A \approx -0.049$$
$$A \approx \cos^{-1}(-0.049)$$
$$A \approx 92.8°$$

Step 4

Determine the measure of $\angle B$.

$$\angle A + \angle B + \angle C = 180°$$
$$92.8° + \angle B + 55° \approx 180°$$
$$\angle B \approx 32.2°$$

The missing measures of triangle ABC are $\angle A = 92.8°$, $\angle B = 32.2°$, and $c = 12.3$ cm.

Example

Expressing all values to the nearest tenth, solve triangle ABC if $a = 13$ cm, $b = 22$ cm, and $c = 11$ cm.

Solution

Step 1

Sketch the triangle.

Since the lengths of all three sides are given, this situation is side-side-side (SSS).

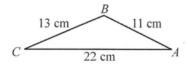

Step 2

Determine the measure of any angle using the cosine law.

$\angle A$ will be determined.

$$\cos A = \frac{b^2 + c^2 - a^2}{2bc}$$
$$\cos A = \frac{(22)^2 + (11)^2 - (13)^2}{2(22)(11)}$$
$$\cos A \approx 0.9008$$
$$A \approx \cos^{-1}(0.9008)$$
$$A \approx 25.7°$$

Step 3

Determine the measure of either $\angle B$ or $\angle C$.

$\angle B$ will be determined using the cosine law.

$$\cos B = \frac{a^2 + c^2 - b^2}{2ac}$$
$$\cos B = \frac{(13)^2 + (11)^2 - (22)^2}{2(13)(11)}$$
$$\cos B \approx -0.6783$$
$$B \approx \cos^{-1}(-0.6783)$$
$$B \approx 132.7°$$

Step 4

Determine the measure of $\angle C$.

$$\angle A + \angle B + \angle C = 180°$$
$$25.7° + 132.7° + \angle C \approx 180°$$
$$\angle C \approx 21.6°$$

The measures of the missing angles are $\angle A = 25.7°$, $\angle B = 132.7°$, and $\angle C = 21.6°$.

20G.3 Solve problems that involve the cosine law and the sine law, excluding the ambiguous case.

SOLVING PROBLEMS USING COSINE LAWS FOR OBTUSE TRIANGLES

Problems that involve obtuse triangles can be solved by following these general steps:

1. Read the problem carefully. Determine which measures are given and which measure needs to be calculated.
2. If a diagram is not given, draw a sketch to represent the situation presented in the problem.
3. Make substitutions into the cosine law formula, and use correct algebraic steps to solve for the unknown value. Avoid or minimize rounding until the last step.
4. Write a concluding statement.

Example

To the nearest tenth of a kilometre, calculate the distance from the sailboat to the harbour.

Solution

Step 1

Draw a diagram.

The sailboat is denoted as B, the lighthouse as A, and the harbour as C.

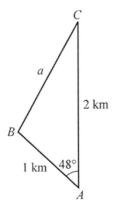

Step 2

Since the triangle is not a right triangle and the measures of two sides and an included angle are known, use the cosine law to solve for a.

$a^2 = b^2 + c^2 - 2bc(\cos A)$
$a^2 = 2^2 + 1^2 - 2(2)(1)\cos 48°$
$a^2 \approx 2.3235$
$\ a \approx 1.5 \text{ km}$

The distance from the sailboat to the harbour is approximately 1.5 km.

Example

From the top of a 100 m fire tower, a fire ranger at point R observes smoke coming from two separate fires. The angle of elevation from Fire A is 5° and from Fire B it is 3°. The angle that the two fires make with the base of the tower, T, is 87°.

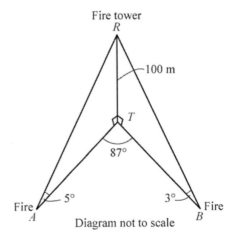

To the nearest metre, what is the distance from Fire *A* to Fire *B*?

Solution

Step 1

Draw a diagram, and label it as shown.

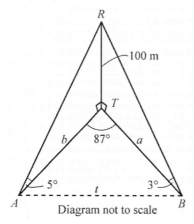

Diagram not to scale

Step 2

Solve for sides *a* and *b*.

Since $\triangle ART$ and $\triangle BRT$ are right triangles, use the primary trigonometric ratios to solve for *a* and *b*.

Solve for *a* using the tangent ratio.

$$\tan \theta = \frac{\text{opposite}}{\text{adjacent}}$$

$$\tan 3° = \frac{100}{a}$$

$$a = \frac{100}{\tan 3°}$$

$$a \approx 1\ 908\text{m}$$

Solve for *b* using the tangent ratio.

$$\tan \theta = \frac{\text{opposite}}{\text{adjacent}}$$

$$\tan 5° = \frac{100}{b}$$

$$b = \frac{100}{\tan 5°}$$

$$b \approx 1\ 143 \text{ m}$$

Step 3

Since two sides and the angle between the two sides are known, solve for *t* in $\triangle ATB$ using the cosine law $t^2 = a^2 + b^2 - 2ab(\cos T)$.

$$t^2 = a^2 + b^2 - 2ab(\cos T)$$

$$t^2 \approx 1\ 908^2 + 1\ 143^2 - 2(1\ 908)(1\ 143)\cos 87°$$

$$t^2 \approx 4\ 946\ 913 - 228\ 273.1123$$

$$t^2 \approx 4\ 718\ 639.888$$

$$t \approx 2\ 172 \text{ m}$$

The distance from Fire *A* to Fire *B* is 2 172 m.

Use the following information to answer the next question.

Triangles *ABC* and *DEF* are given.

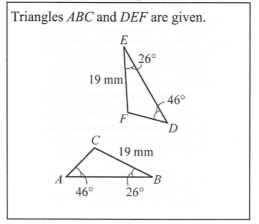

Written Response

1. Determine whether triangle *ABC* is congruent to triangle *DEF*, and explain your answer.

Written Response

2. Prove that same-side exterior angles on a transversal are supplementary.

Use the following information to answer the next question.

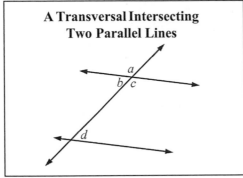

A Transversal Intersecting Two Parallel Lines

3. Which of the following mathematical statements about a transversal intersecting two parallel lines is **false**?

   A. $\angle a = \angle c$

   B. $\angle b = \angle d$

   C. $\angle a + \angle d = 90°$

   D. $\angle c + \angle d = 180°$

Use the following information to answer the next question.

To solve a problem, John needs to find the sum of the interior angles in the given polygon.

4. The sum of the interior angles in the polygon is

   A. 540°   **B.** 1 260°

   C. 1 440°   **D.** 1 620°

Use the following information to answer the next question.

Line segment *GH* is 1.4 dm long.

Written Response

5. Draw the line segment and its perpendicular bisector using a right triangle.

Use the following information to answer the next question.

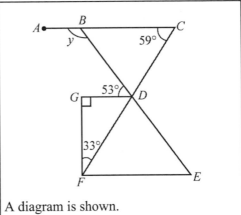

A diagram is shown.

6. What is the measure of $\angle y$?

   A. 108°   **B.** 117°

   C. 129°   **D.** 134°

Use the following information to answer the next question.

A transversal cuts through two parallel lines as shown. The measure of ∠*a* is 30°.

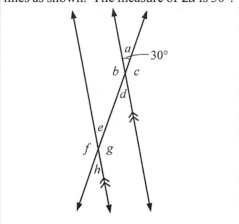

7. What is the measure of ∠*d*?
    A. 30°   **B.** 40°

    C. 140°   **D.** 150°

Use the following information to answer the next question.

$l_1: 2x + 3y - 18 = 0$

$l_2: 5x + \dfrac{15}{2}y - 210 = 0$

Written Response

8. Use algebra to explain whether the two given lines are coincident, parallel, or intersecting.

Use the following information to answer the next question.

Quadrilateral *ABCD* is shown.

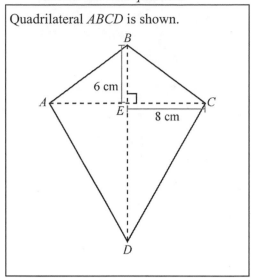

Numerical Response

9. If ∠*CAB* = ∠*ACB*, ∠*DAC* = ∠*DCA*, and the perimeter of quadrilateral *ABCD* is 54 cm, then the length of side *AD* is _____ cm.

Use the following information to answer the next question.

A transversal line intersects two parallel lines. The measure of ∠*u* is 50 °.

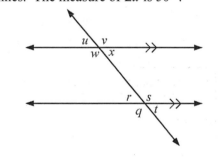

10. What is the measure of ∠*r*?
    A. 25°   **B.** 50°

    C. 80°   **D.** 130°

Use the following information to answer the next question.

The measure of side *p* of Δ*PQR* is 25 cm long. The measure of ∠*P* is 55°, and the measure of ∠*R* is 40°.

Numerical Response

11. The measure of the longest side in Δ*PQR*, expressed to the nearest tenth, is about _____ cm.

Use the following information to answer the next question.

A student is asked to solve Δ*ABC*. In Δ*ABC*, *a* = 15 cm, *b* = 18 cm, and ∠*C* = 48°.

12. After sketching the triangle, the next step in the student's solution is to determine the measure of
   A. side *AB* using the cosine law
   B. angle *A* using the cosine law
   C. side *AB* using the sine law
   D. angle *A* using the sine law

Use the following information to answer the next question.

Triangle *ABC* is shown.

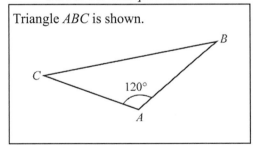

Numerical Response

13. If the length of *BC* is 52 cm and the length of *AB* is 30 cm, the measure of ∠*B*, to the nearest tenth of a degree, is _____°.

Use the following information to answer the next question.

Triangle *ABC* is shown.

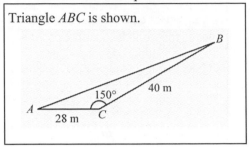

14. What is the length of *AB*?
   A. 65.8 m   **B.** 68.2 m
   C. 70.7 m   **D.** 73.1 m

Use the following information to answer the next question.

The given diagram shows a triangle in three dimensions.

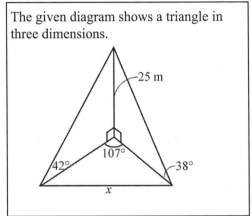

Numerical Response

15. To the nearest tenth of a metre, the length of *x* is _____ m.

Use the following information to answer the next question.

A weather balloon is flying in a field outside of London, Ontario. One end of a lightweight rope is attached to the base of the weather balloon, and the other end of the rope is anchored to the ground at point P. On a windy day, Rachel decides to determine the length of the rope, x, between P and the connection point located at the base of the weather balloon. She locates two points, A and B, that are 200 m apart, and records the measurements shown in the diagram.

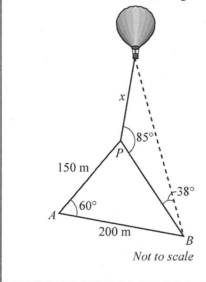

Not to scale

16. The value of x, to the nearest metre, is

    A. 128 m   **B.** 132 m

    C. 136 m   **D.** 140 m

ANSWERS AND SOLUTIONS
GEOMETRY

1. WR	5. WR	9. 17	13. 30.0
2. WR	6. C	10. B	14. A
3. C	7. A	11. 30.4	15. 48.1
4. B	8. WR	12. A	16. B

1. WR

Step 1

Locate the sides or angles that are identified.
Two angles and a side are given.

Step 2

Identify the condition that will prove congruency.
The angle-angle-side condition, or AAS, will prove congruency.

Step 3

Apply the condition.
Verify the corresponding sides and angles are equal.

$\angle A = \angle D$
$\angle B = \angle E$
$BC = EF$

The given triangles satisfiy the condition AAS: two angles of one triangle and a non-included side are equal to the two angles and a non-included side of the other triangle.

Therefore, $\triangle ABC \cong \triangle DEF$.

2. WR

Step 1

Draw a diagram.

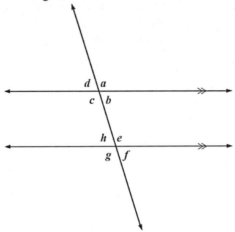

Angles d and g are same-side exterior angles.

Angles a and f are also same-side exterior angles.

Proving the result for one pair is enough because a similar proof can be reconstructed for the second pair of angles.

To prove that angles a and f are supplementary, prove that $\angle a + \angle f = 180°$.

Step 2

Prove the given statement.

Statement	Reason
$\angle b + \angle e = 180°$ Angles b and e are supplementary.	Supplementary interior angles. This is defined by the parallel-line postulate.
$\angle b + \angle a = 180°$ Angles b and a are supplementary.	Angles adjacent to each other on a line are supplementary.
$\angle a = \angle e$	$\angle b + \angle e = 180°$ $= \angle b + \angle a$
$\angle e + \angle f = 180°$ Angles e and f are supplementary.	Angles adjacent to each other on a line are supplementary.
$\angle a + \angle f = 180°$ Angles a and f are supplementary.	By substitution

3. C

Analyze the relations between each pair of angles given in the alternatives.

- Angles a and c are vertically opposite angles; therefore, they are congruent.
- Angles b and d are alternate interior angles; therefore, they are congruent.
- Angles c and d are consecutive interior angles; therefore, they are supplementary, meaning $\angle c + \angle d = 180°$.

By the vertical angle theorem, $\angle a \cong \angle c$.

Therefore, $\angle c + \angle d = 180° \Rightarrow \angle a + \angle d = 180°$.

The statement in choice C is false.

4. B

The sum of the measures of the interior angles in a polygon can be found using the formula $S = 180°(n - 2)$, where n is the number of sides the polygon has.

The given polygon has nine sides, so substitute 9 for n in the formula, and solve.
$S = 180°(9 - 2)$
$S = 180°(7)$
$S = 1\ 260°$

5. WR

Step 1

Draw a line segment.
Plot point G. Measure 1.4 dm, which is equal to 14 cm, and plot point H.
Connect the two points.

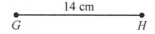

$$\overset{14 \text{ cm}}{\underset{G \qquad\qquad\qquad H}{\rule{4cm}{0.4pt}}}$$

Step 2

Calculate the length of the bisected line segment. Divide the length by 2.
$14 \div 2 = 7$

Step 3

Draw the perpendicular bisector.
Plot point I at a distance of 7 cm from either side.
Place the corner of the right triangle at point I.
Draw a line segment, making sure to extend the line above and below line segment GH.

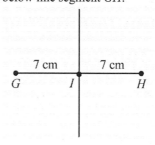

6. C

Create a statement-reason table.

Statement	Reason
$\angle GDF$ $= 180° - (\angle FGD + \angle GFD)$ $= 180° - (90° + 33°)$ $= 180° - 123°$ $= 57°$	The sum of the interior angles of a triangle is 180°.
$\angle BDF = \angle GDF + \angle GDB$ $\angle BDF = 57° + 53°$ $\angle BDF = 110°$	Angle addition postulate
$\angle BDC = 180° - \angle BDF$ $\angle BDC = 180° - 110°$ $\angle BDC = 70°$	$\angle BDC$ and $\angle BDF$ are supplementary.
$\angle y = \angle BDC + \angle BCD$ $\angle y = 70° + 59°$ $\angle y = 129°$	An exterior angle is equal to the sum of the opposite interior angles.

7. A

Step 1

Determine the relationship between $\angle a$ and $\angle d$.

In the diagram shown, $\angle a$ and $\angle d$ are vertically opposite angles.

Step 2

Determine the measure of $\angle d$.

Vertically opposite angles have the same measure. Because $\angle a$ and $\angle d$ are opposite angles, $\angle a = \angle d$. If $\angle a = 30°$, then $\angle d = 30°$.

The measure of $\angle d$ is 30°.

8. WR

Method 1

Step 1

Rewrite the equation of each line in the slope-intercept form $y = mx + b$.

$l_1: 2x + 3y - 18 = 0$
$$3y = -2x + 18$$
$$y = -\frac{2}{3}x + 6$$

$l_2: 5x + \frac{15}{2}y - 210 = 0$
$$\frac{15}{2}y = -5x + 210$$
$$y = \frac{-10}{15}x + \frac{420}{15}$$
$$y = \frac{-2}{3}x + 28$$

Step 2

Compare the slopes (m) and y-intercepts (b) of each line to determine the nature of the lines.

$l_1: m = -\dfrac{2}{3}$
$b = 6$

$l_2: m = -\dfrac{2}{3}$
$b = 28$

Since the slopes of the two lines are the same but their y-intercepts are different, these two lines are parallel.

Method 2

Step 1

Create a system of equations in the form $ax + by = c$.

$l_1: 2x + 3y - 18 = 0$
① $2x + 3y = 18$

$l_2: 5x + \dfrac{15}{2}y - 210 = 0$
② $5x + \dfrac{15}{2}y = 210$

Step 2

Multiply equation (1) by 5 and equation (2) by 2. Then, subtract equation (1) from equation (2).

② $\times 2 \ (10x + 15y = 420)$
① $\times 5 \ \underline{-(10x + 15y = 90)}$
$0x + 0y = 330$

Since there are no solutions (x, y) that satisfy the system, the lines are parallel.

9. 17

Step 1

Determine the length of side BC in triangle BEC by applying the Pythagorean theorem.
$$(BE)^2 + (CE)^2 = (BC)^2$$

Substitute 6 for BE and 8 for CE, and then solve for BC.
$$6^2 + 8^2 = (BC)^2$$
$$36 + 64 = (BC)^2$$
$$100 = (BC)^2$$
$$\sqrt{100} = BC$$
$$10 = BC$$

The length of side BC is 10 cm.

Step 2

Determine the length of side AD.

Since $\angle CAB = \angle ACB$, triangle ABC is an isosceles triangle. It then follows, by the corollary of the isosceles triangle theorem, that $AB = BC$.

Similarly, since $\angle DAC = \angle DCA$, triangle ADC is an isosceles triangle. It then follows, by the corollary of the isosceles triangle theorem, that $AD = CD$.

In order to determine the length of side AD, let $AD = CD = x$. Then, using the fact that the perimeter of quadrilateral $ABCD$ is 54 cm, solve for x.
$$AB + BC + CD + AD = 54$$

Substitute 10 for both AB and BC, and x for both CD and for AD.
$$10 + 10 + x + x = 54$$
$$20 + 2x = 54$$
$$2x = 34$$
$$x = 17$$

The length of side AD is 17 cm.

10. B

Step 1

Determine the relationship between the given angle and the unknown angle.

Angles u and r are corresponding angles.

Step 2

Determine the measure of $\angle r$ using the appropriate relationship.

Since the angles are corresponding angles, $\angle u = \angle r$. Therefore, $\angle r = 50°$.

11. 30.4

Step 1

Sketch the triangle.

The sketch of the triangle shows that this situation is Angle-Angle-Side (AAS). The measures of two angles and the length of a non-included side are given.

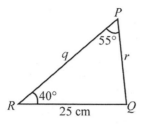

Step 2

Determine the measure of $\angle Q$.

$\angle P + \angle Q + \angle R = 180°$

$55° + \angle Q + 40° = 180°$

$\angle Q = 180° - 55° - 40°$

$\angle Q = 85°$

Step 3

Determine the length of the longest side using the sine law. The longest side is opposite the largest angle. Since $\angle Q$ is the largest angle, PR is the longest side.

$$\frac{q}{\sin Q} = \frac{p}{\sin P}$$

$$\frac{q}{\sin 85°} = \frac{25}{\sin 55°}$$

$$q = \frac{25\sin 85°}{\sin 55°}$$

$$q \approx 30.4$$

The longest side has a measure of about 30.4 cm.

12. A

Step 1

Sketch the triangle.

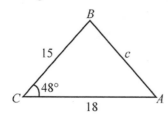

The sketch shows that the situation is side-angle-side (SAS).

Step 2

Determine the next step in the solution.

When the situation is SAS, the next step is to determine the length of the missing side using the cosine law. In this case, side AB will be determined using the cosine law.

13. 30.0

Step 1

Determine the measure of $\angle C$ by applying the sine law.

$$\frac{\sin \angle C}{30 \text{ cm}} = \frac{\sin 120°}{52 \text{ cm}}$$

$$\sin \angle C = \frac{(30 \text{ cm})(\sin 120°)}{52 \text{ cm}}$$

$$\angle C = \sin^{-1}\left(\frac{(30 \text{ cm})(\sin 120°)}{52 \text{ cm}}\right)$$

$$\angle C = \sin^{-1}(0.499\ 63\ldots)$$

$$\angle C \approx 29.9755°$$

Step 2

Determine the measure of $\angle B$.

Since the sum of all angles in a triangle is 180°, subtract the sum of the two known angles from 180°.

$\angle B = 180° - (\angle A + \angle C)$

$\angle B \approx 180° - (120° + 29.9755°)$

$\angle B \approx 180° - 149.9755°$

$\angle B \approx 30.0245°$

$\angle B \approx 30.0°$

To the nearest tenth of a degree, the measure of $\angle B$ is 30.0°.

14. A

Determine the length of AB by using the cosine law.

$AB^2 = BC^2 + AC^2 - 2(BC)(AC)\cos C$

$AB^2 = (40)^2 + (28)^2 - 2(40)(28)\cos 150°$

$AB^2 \approx 4\ 323.8969$

$AB \approx 65.8 \text{ m}$

15. 48.1

Step 1

Determine the lengths of the bases of the vertical triangles using the tangent ratio.

$\tan 42° = \dfrac{25}{y}$

$y = \dfrac{25}{\tan 42°}$

$y \approx 27.77$

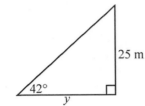

$\tan 38° = \dfrac{25}{z}$

$z = \dfrac{25}{\tan 38°}$

$z \approx 32.00$

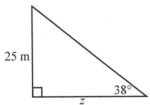

Step 2

Determine x using the cosine law.

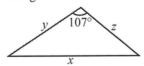

$a^2 = b^2 + c^2 - 2bc\cos A$

$x^2 = y^2 + z^2 - 2(y)(z)\cos 107°$

$x \approx \sqrt{\dfrac{(27.77)^2 + (32.00)^2}{-2(27.77)(32.00)\cos 107°}}$

$x \approx 48.1$

16. B

Step 1

Label the diagram as shown:

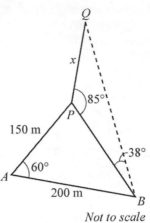

Not to scale

Step 2

Determine the length of BP by applying the cosine law as follows:

$a^2 = b^2 + c^2 - 2bc\cos A$

$(BP)^2 = 150^2 + 200^2 - 2(150)(200)\cos 60$

$(BP)^2 = 22\ 500 + 40\ 000 - 30\ 000$

$(BP)^2 = 32\ 500$

$BP \approx 180.28$ m

Step 3

Calculate the measure of $\angle Q$.

$180° - 85° - 38° = 57°$

Step 4

Calculate the value of x by applying the sine law as follows:

$\dfrac{x}{\sin B} = \dfrac{BP}{\sin Q}$

$\dfrac{x}{\sin 38°} = \dfrac{180.28}{\sin 57°}$

$x = \dfrac{180.28(\sin 38°)}{\sin 57°}$

$x \approx 132.34$ m

The value of x, rounded to the nearest metre, is 132 m.

Answers and Solutions   82   Castle Rock Research

UNIT TEST — GEOMETRY

Use the following information to answer the next question.

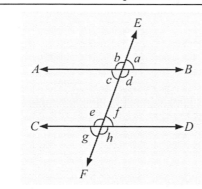

The transversal *EF* intersects lines *AB* and *CD*.

1. If $\angle d + \angle f = 180°$, lines *AB* and *CD*
    A. never intersect
    B. intersect at a point
    C. are perpendicular
    D. are congruent

Use the following information to answer the next question.

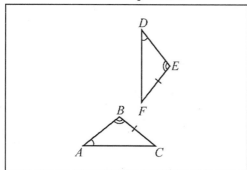

Written Response

2. Determine if the two given triangles are congruent.

Use the following information to answer the next question.

Line segment *EF* is 1 dm long.

Written Response

3. Draw the line segment and its perpendicular bisector using a ruler and a right angle triangle.

Use the following information to answer the next question.

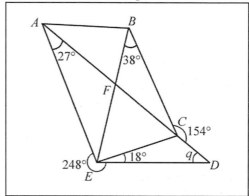

4. What is the measure of $\angle q$ in the figure shown?
    A. 28°   **B.** 41°
    C. 55°   **D.** 66°

Use the following information to answer the next question.

A transversal cuts through two parallel lines, as shown.

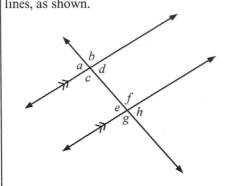

5. If ∠b = 100° and ∠h = 80°, what is the measure of ∠c?

   A. 80°   **B.** 90°

   C. 100°   **D.** 110°

Use the following information to answer the next question.

Triangle *ABC* is an isosceles triangle, where ∠A = ∠B.

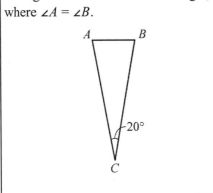

6. What is the measure of ∠A?

   A. 60°   **B.** 70°

   C. 80°   **D.** 90°

Written Response

7. What are the slopes of lines that are parallel and perpendicular to a line with a slope of $m = -\dfrac{1}{5}$?

Use the following information to answer the next question.

In the given figure, lines *AB* and *CD* are parallel. Lines *EG* and *FH* are also parallel and intersect lines *AB* and *CD* at points *P*, *Q*, *R*, and *S*.

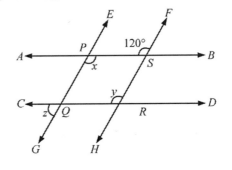

8. What is the measure of ∠y?

   A. 60°   **B.** 75°

   C. 110°   **D.** 120°

Use the following information to answer the next question.

Two different geometrical figures are given.

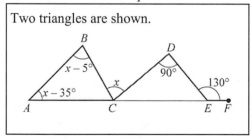

O is the centre of the circle.

Figure 1

Figure 2

9. If *MP* = *NP*, then the measure of ∠*PNM* in figure 2 exceeds the measure of ∠*OAB* in figure 1 by

   A. 23°   **B.** 29°

   C. 32°   **D.** 36°

Use the following information to answer the next question.

Two triangles are shown.

Numerical Response

10. The value of *x* is _____ °.

11. For which of the following triangles can the equation $\dfrac{80}{\sin 50°} = \dfrac{65}{\sin x°}$ be used to determine the measure of angle *x*?

   A.

   B.

   C.

   D.

Use the following information to answer the next question.

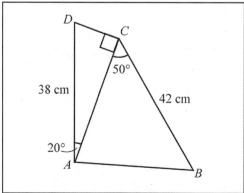

Numerical Response

12. Correct to the nearest centimetre, the perimeter of △*ABC* is _____ cm.

An engineer needs to calculate the distance across a deep canyon. She takes a sighting from a point *A* and then from a point *C*, which are both on the same side of the canyon, to a point *B* on the opposite side of the canyon, as shown in the diagram.

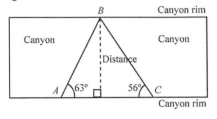

13. If points *A* and *C* are 70 m apart, then the distance across the canyon, correct to the nearest tenth of a metre, is

   A. 51.9 m   B. 59.1 m

   C. 60.3 m   D. 68.7 m

14. Expressed to the nearest tenth, the perimeter of $\triangle ABC$, if $\angle A = 40°$, $\angle B = 35°$, and $c = 15$ cm, is

   A. 32.3 cm   B. 32.8 cm

   C. 33.6 cm   D. 33.9 cm

The measures of the sides of $\triangle ABC$ are $a = 6$, $b = 8$, and $c = 13$.

Numerical Response

15. Expressed to the nearest tenth, the ratio of the measure of the largest angle in $\triangle ABC$ to the sum of the measures of the two smallest angles is _____.

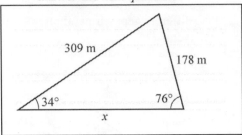

16. An equation that could be used to solve for the length, in metres, of side *x* in the given diagram is

   A. $x = \dfrac{(309)\sin 70°}{\sin 76°}$

   B. $x = \dfrac{(178)\sin 70°}{\sin 76°}$

   C. $x = \sqrt{309^2 + 178^2 - 2(309)(178)\cos 34°}$

   D. $x = \sqrt{309^2 + 178^2 - 2(392)(178)\cos 76°}$

ANSWERS AND SOLUTIONS — UNIT TEST

1. A	5. C	9. A	13. B
2. WR	6. C	10. 80	14. D
3. WR	7. WR	11. B	15. 3.1
4. B	8. D	12. 111	16. A

1. A

Given that the transversal is line *EF* and that $\angle d$ and $\angle f$ are supplementary, the angles are called same-side interior angles, which are formed between the parallel lines *AB* and *CD*.

Since parallel lines never intersect, lines *AB* and *CD* never intersect.

2. WR

Step 1

Identify the given sides or angles.

Two angles and a side are given.

Step 2

Identify the condition that will prove congruency.

The condition that will prove congruency is angle-angle-side (AAS). Two angles and a non-included side of one triangle are equal to two angles and the non-included side of the other triangle.

Step 3

Apply the condition.

Verify that the corresponding angles and sides are equal.

$\angle A = \angle D$
$\angle B = \angle E$
$BC = EF$

Since $\triangle ABC = \triangle DEF$, the condition of AAS is satisfied.

Therefore, the given triangles are proven to be congruent.

3. WR

Step 1

Draw line segment *EF*.

Plot point *E*. Measure 1 dm, which is equal to 10 cm. Then, plot point *F*.

Connect the two points.

E ———————— 10 cm ———————— *F*

Step 2

Calculate the length of the bisected line segment.

Divide the length of line segment *EF* by 2.

10 cm ÷ 2 = 5 cm

Step 3

Draw the perpendicular bisector.

Plot point *D* 5 cm from either point *E* or point *F*.

Place the corner of the right triangle at point *D*. Draw a line segment, making sure to extend the line above and below line segment *EF*.

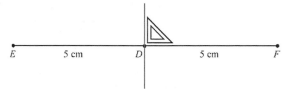

4. B

Create a statement-reason table.

Statement	Reason
$\angle BCD = \angle FBC + \angle CFB$ $154° = 38° + \angle CFB$ $116° = \angle CFB$	An exterior angle is equal to the sum of the opposite interior angles.
$\angle AFE = \angle CFB$ $\angle AFE = 116°$	The vertical angle theorem applies in this case.
$\angle FEA = 180° (\angle EAF + \angle AFE)$ $\angle FEA = 180° (27° + 116°)$ $\angle FEA = 180° - (143°)$ $\angle FEA = 37°$	The sum of the interior angles of a triangle is 180°.
$\angle FEC$ $= 360 - (\angle FEA + \angle AED + \angle CED)$ $= 360 - (37 + 248 + 18)$ $= 360 - (303)$ $= 57$	The sum of the angles around a point is 360°.
$\angle EFC$ $= 180° - \angle CFB$ $= 180° - 116°$ $= 64°$	Angles *EFC* and *CFB* are supplementary.
$\angle DCE$ $= \angle EFC + \angle FEC$ $= 64° + 57°$ $= 121°$	An exterior angle is equal to the sum of the opposite interior angles.
$\angle q = 180° - (\angle CED + \angle DCE)$ $\angle q = 180° - (18° + 121°)$ $\angle q = 180° - (139°)$ $\angle q = 41°$	The sum of the interior angles of a triangle is 180°.

5. **C**

   Step 1

   Determine the relationship between $\angle b$ and $\angle c$.
   In the diagram shown, $\angle b$ and $\angle c$ are vertically opposite angles.

   Step 2

   Determine the measure of $\angle c$.
   Vertically opposite angles have the same measure.
   Because $\angle b$ and $\angle c$ are opposite angles, $\angle b = \angle c$. If $\angle b = 100°$, then $\angle c = 100°$.
   The measure of $\angle c$ is 100°.

6. **C**

   Step 1

   Determine which angle measures are given.
   $\angle C = 20°$

   Step 2

   Substitute the given values into the angle property for a triangle, and simplify.
   Since this is an isosceles triangle, $\angle A$ and $\angle B$ have the same measure.
   Modify the property.
   $$\angle A + \angle B + \angle C = 180°$$
   $$\angle A + \angle A + \angle C = 180°$$
   $$2\angle A + \angle C = 180°$$
   $$2\angle A + 20° = 180°$$
   $$2\angle A + 20° - 20° = 180° - 20°$$
   $$\frac{2\angle A}{2} = \frac{160°}{2}$$
   $$\angle A = 80°$$

   Therefore, $\angle A$ and $\angle B$ each have a measure of 80°.

7. **WR**

   Step 1

   Determine the slope of a line parallel to the slope $m = -\dfrac{1}{5}$.

   Parallel lines have the same slope. Therefore,

   $m_{\parallel} = -\dfrac{1}{5}$ is the slope of a line parallel to the slope

   $m = -\dfrac{1}{5}$.

   Step 2

   Determine the slope of a line perpendicular to the slope $m = -\dfrac{1}{5}$.

   Perpendicular lines have slopes that are negative reciprocals of each other.

   $$m_{\perp} = -1 \times \frac{1}{m}$$
   $$m_{\perp} = -1 \times \left(\frac{1}{-\frac{1}{5}} \right)$$
   $$m_{\perp} = -1 \times (-5)$$
   $$m_{\perp} = 5$$

   Therefore, $m_{\perp} = 5$ is the slope of a line perpendicular

   to the slope $m = -\dfrac{1}{5}$.

8. **D**

   Step 1

   Determine the relationship between the given angle and the unknown angle.
   Angle FSP and angle y are corresponding angles.

   Step 2

   Determine the measure of $\angle y$ by using the appropriate relationship.
   Since the angles are corresponding angles, $\angle FSP = \angle y$.
   Since $\angle FSP$ equals 120°, $\angle y = 120°$.

9. **A**

   Recall that the isosceles triangle theorem states that if two sides of a triangle are congruent, then the angles opposite to them are congruent.

   Step 1

   Determine the measure of $\angle OAB$ in figure 1.
   Since OA and OB are each a radius of the given circle, their respective lengths must be equal.
   Therefore, ΔAOB is an isosceles triangle. It follows, by the isosceles triangle theorem, that $\angle OAB = \angle OBA$.

   In order to determine the measure of $\angle OAB$, let $\angle OAB = \angle OBA = x$ and then apply the triangle angle sum theorem.
   $$\angle OAB + \angle AOB + \angle OBA = 180°$$

   Substitute 110° for $\angle AOB$ and x for both $\angle OAB$ and for $\angle OBA$.
   $$x + 110° + x = 180°$$
   $$2x + 110° = 180°$$
   $$2x = 70°$$
   $$x = 35°$$

   The measure of $\angle OAB$ is 35°.

Step 2

Determine the measure of $\angle NPY$.

$\angle NPY = \angle NPX + \angle YPX$

Substitute 42° for $\angle NPX$ and 74° for $\angle YPX$.

$\angle NPY = 42° + 74°$

$\angle NPY = 116°$

The measure of $\angle NPY$ is 116°.

Step 3

Determine the measure of $\angle PNM$.

Since $MP = NP$, ΔMNP is an isosceles triangle. It follows, by the isosceles triangle theorem, that $\angle PNM = \angle PMN$. Also, by the exterior angle theorem, $\angle YPN = \angle PNM + \angle PMN$.

In order to determine the measure of $\angle PNM$, let $\angle PNM = \angle PMN = x$ and then solve for x.

$\angle YPN = \angle PNM + \angle PMN$

Substitute 116° for $\angle YPN$ and x for both $\angle PNM$ and for $\angle PMN$.

$116° = x + x$

$116° = 2x$

$58° = x$

The measure of $\angle PNM$ is 58°.

Step 4

Determine the angle measurement difference between $\angle PNM$ and $\angle OAB$.

$58° - 35° = 23°$

The measure of $\angle PNM$ exceeds the measure of $\angle OAB$ by 23°.

10. 80

The exterior angle theorem states that the measure of an exterior angle of a triangle is equal to the sum of the measures of the two remote interior angles of the triangle.

Step 1

Determine the measure of $\angle ECD$ by applying the exterior angle theorem.

When the exterior angle theorem is applied to triangle ECD, the resulting equation is $\angle FED = \angle ECD + \angle CDE$.

The measure of $\angle ECD$ can be determined as follows:

$\angle FED = \angle ECD + \angle CDE$

Substitute 130° for $\angle FED$ and 90° for $\angle CDE$.

$130° = \angle ECD + 90°$

$130° - 90° = \angle ECD$

$40° = \angle ECD$

The measure of $\angle ECD$ is 40°.

Step 2

Determine an expression for the measure of $\angle BCD$.

Since $\angle BCE = \angle BCD + \angle ECD$, it follows that, by substitution, the measure of $\angle BCE$ can be expressed as $\angle BCE = x + 40°$.

Step 3

Apply the exterior angle theorem to triangle ABC.

When the exterior angle theorem is applied to triangle ABC, the resulting equation is $\angle BCE = \angle CAB + \angle ABC$. Substituting $x + 40°$ for $\angle BCE$, $x - 35°$ for $\angle CAB$, and $x - 5°$ for $\angle ABC$, the equation $\angle BCE = \angle CAB + \angle ABC$ becomes $x + 40° = x - 35° + x - 5°$.

Step 4

Solve for x in the equation $x + 40° = x - 35° + x - 5°$.

$x + 40° = x - 35° + x - 5°$

$x + 40 = 2x - 40°$

$40° + 40° = 2x - x$

$80° = x$

The value of x is 80°.

11. B

In general, the law of sines states that $\dfrac{a}{\sin A} = \dfrac{b}{\sin B}$.

Thus, in the equation $\dfrac{80}{\sin 50°} = \dfrac{65}{\sin x°}$, the 50° angle must be opposite the side measuring 80 m and the $x°$ angle must be opposite the side measuring 65 m.

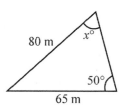

12. 111

In order to determine the perimeter of ΔABC, find the length of each of the three sides of the triangle. The length of side BC is given, but the lengths of side AC and AB must be calculated.

Step 1

Calculate the measure of side AC in ΔDAC.

Use the cosine ratio to solve for side AC.

$\cos \angle DAC = \dfrac{AC}{AD}$

Substitute 20° for $\angle DAC$ and 38 for AD.

$\cos 20° = \dfrac{AC}{38}$

$AC = 38\cos 20°$

$AC = 35.71$ cm

Step 2

Calculate the measure of side *AB* in Δ*ABC*.

Use the law of cosines to determine *AB* as follows:

$(AB)^2 = (AC)^2 + (BC)^2 - 2(AC)(BC)\cos \angle ACB$

Substitute 35.71 for *AC*, 42 for *BC*, and 50° for ∠*ACB*. Then, solve for side *AB*.

$(AB)^2 = (35.71)^2 + (42)^2 - 2(35.71)(42)\cos 50°$

$(AB)^2 = 1\ 111.07$

$AB = 33.33$ cm

Step 3

Calculate the perimeter of Δ*ABC*.

The perimeter of Δ*ABC* is
42 + 35.71 + 33.33 = 111.04 cm.

Rounded to the nearest centimetre, the perimeter of Δ*ABC* is 111 cm.

13. B

Step 1

Label the diagram.

The given diagram can be labelled as shown.

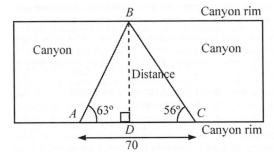

Step 2

Calculate the measure of ∠*B*.

∠*B* = 180° − 63° − 56° = 61°

Step 3

Determine the length of either side *AB* or *CB* by applying the sine law with respect to Δ*ABC*.

The length of *AB* can be determined as follows:

$\dfrac{AB}{\sin C} = \dfrac{AC}{\sin B}$

Substitute 56° for *C*, 70 for *AC*, and 61° for *B*. Solve for *AB*.

$\dfrac{AB}{\sin 56°} = \dfrac{70}{\sin 61°}$

$AB \times \sin 61° = 70 \times \sin 56°$

$AB = \dfrac{70 \times \sin 56°}{\sin 61°}$

$AB \approx 66.35$ m

Step 4

Solve for *BD* by examining Δ*ADB*.

In Δ*ADB*, $\sin A = \dfrac{BD}{AB}$

Substitute 63° for *A* and 66.35 for *AB*.

$\sin 63° = \dfrac{BD}{66.35}$

$BD = 66.35 \times \sin 63°$

$BD = 59.12$ m

To the nearest tenth, the distance across the canyon *BD* is 59.1 m.

A similar procedure can be used to determine the length of side *BC*, and then the sine ratio can be used with respect to Δ*BCD*.

14. D

Step 1

Sketch the triangle.

The sketch of the triangle shows that this situation is ASA, where the measures of two angles and the length of the included side are given.

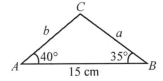

Step 2

Determine the measure of ∠*C*.

∠*A* + ∠*B* + ∠*C* = 180°

40° + 35° + ∠*C* = 180°

∠*C* = 105°

Step 3

Determine the length of one of the missing sides by using the sine law.

The length of $\overline{BC}$ will be determined.

$\dfrac{a}{\sin A} = \dfrac{c}{\sin C}$

$\dfrac{a}{\sin 40°} = \dfrac{15}{\sin 105°}$

$a = \dfrac{15\sin 40°}{\sin 105°}$

$a \approx 9.98$

Step 4

Determine the length of $\overline{AC}$.

$\dfrac{b}{\sin B} = \dfrac{c}{\sin C}$

$\dfrac{b}{\sin 35°} = \dfrac{15}{\sin 105°}$

$b = \dfrac{15\sin 35°}{\sin 105°}$

$b \approx 8.91$

Step 5
Determine the perimeter.
$P = a + b + c$
$P \approx 9.98 + 8.91 + 15$
$P \approx 33.89$
To the nearest tenth, the perimeter of the triangle is approximately 33.9 cm.

15. **3.1**

Since the lengths of all three sides are given, the measure of any angle can be determined using the cosine law.

Step 1
Determine the measure of $\angle A$.

$\cos A = \dfrac{b^2 + c^2 - a^2}{2bc}$

$\cos A = \dfrac{(8)^2 + (13)^2 - (6)^2}{2(8)(13)}$

$\cos A \approx 0.9471$

$\quad A \approx \cos^{-1}(0.9471)$

$\quad A \approx 18.7°$

Step 2
Determine the measure of either $\angle B$ or $\angle C$.
The measure of $\angle B$ is determined using the cosine law.

$\cos B = \dfrac{a^2 + c^2 - b^2}{2ac}$

$\cos B = \dfrac{(6)^2 + (13)^2 - (8)^2}{2(6)(13)}$

$\cos B \approx 0.9038$

$\quad B \approx \cos^{-1}(0.9038)$

$\quad B \approx 25.3°$

Note that the sine law could also have been used to solve for the measure of either angle.

Step 3
Determine the measure of $\angle C$.
$\quad \angle A + \angle B + \angle C = 180°$
$18.7° + 25.3° + \angle C = 180°$
$\quad\quad\quad\quad\quad \angle C = 136.0°$

Step 4
Determine the ratio of the measure of the largest angle to the sum of the measures of the two smallest angles.

$\text{ratio} = \dfrac{136°}{18.7° + 25.3°}$

$\quad\quad = \dfrac{136°}{44.0°}$

$\quad\quad = 3.0909$

Expressed to the nearest tenth, the ratio is 3.1.

16. **A**

Alternative C and D make incorrect use of the Cosine Law because there is no contained angle in between the given sides. To find side x using the Sine Law, the angle opposite of x, plus a side and its opposite angle are used. Therefore, $\dfrac{309}{\sin 76°} = \dfrac{x}{\sin 70°}$.

Then. solving for x:
$x = \dfrac{(309)\sin 70°}{\sin 76°}$

NOTES

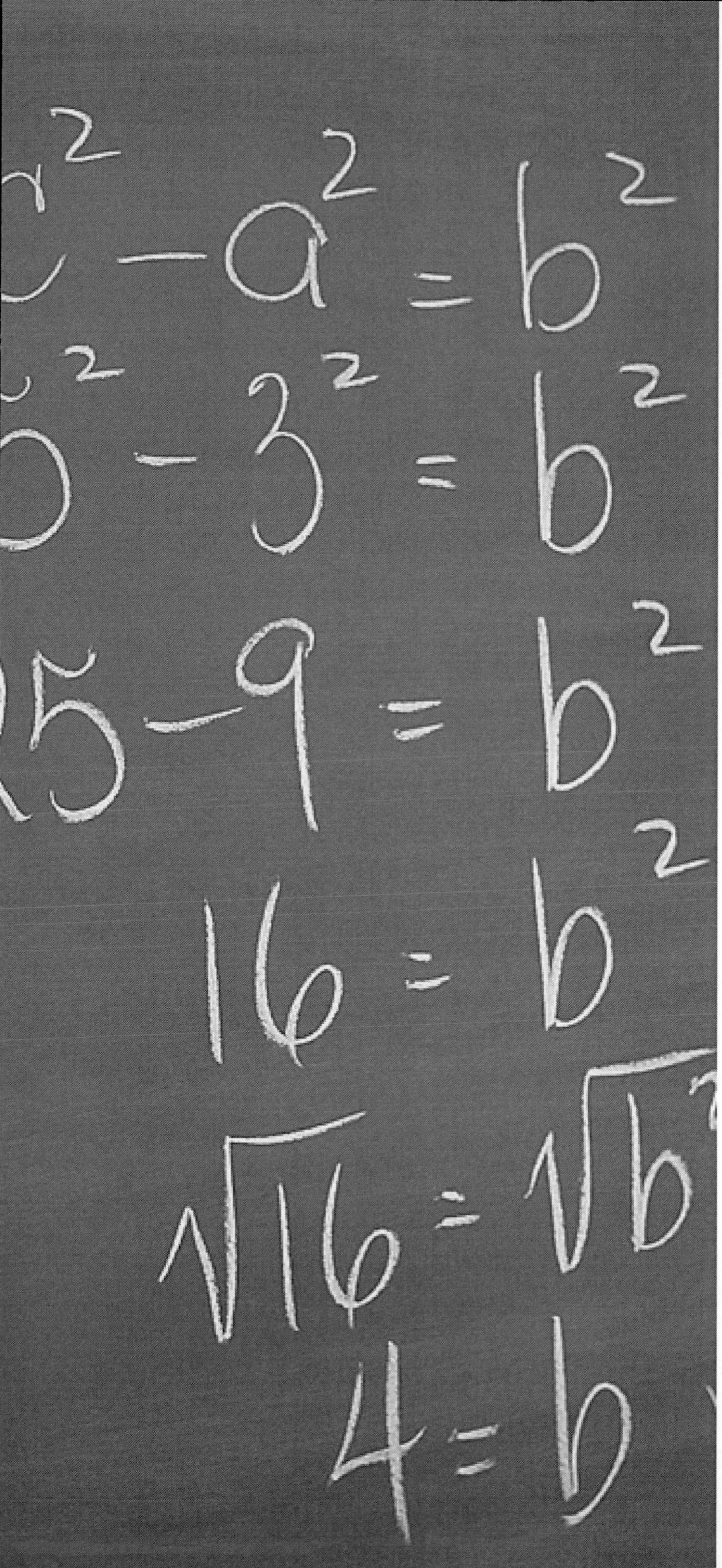

Number and Logic

NUMBER AND LOGIC

Table of Correlations

Outcome		Practice Questions	Unit Test Questions	Practice Test
20NL	Number and Logic			
20NL.1	*Analyze and prove conjectures, using inductive and deductive reasoning, to solve problems.*	1, 2, 3, 4	1, 2, 3, 4	32, 33
20NL.2	*Analyze puzzles and games that involve spatial reasoning, using problem-solving strategies.*	5, 6	5, 6	34, 40
20NL.3	*Solve problems that involve operations on radicals and radical expressions with numerical and variable radicands (limited to square roots).*	7, 8, 9, 10, 11, 12, 13	7, 8, 9, 10, 11, 12, 13	35, 36, 37
20NL.4	*Solve problems that involve radical equations (limited to square roots or cube roots).*	14, 15	14, 15	38, 39

20NL.1 Analyze and prove conjectures, using inductive and deductive reasoning, to solve problems.

APPLYING INDUCTIVE REASONING TO MAKE CONJECTURES

Inductive reasoning is reasoning that is based on an observed pattern or experience. A generalization or prediction is then made. Most day-to-day decisions are based on this kind of reasoning. For example, when you decide what to wear to school, it is likely that your decision is at least partly dependent on a weather forecast. The weather forecast is based on recorded climatic conditions from the past that have produced particular weather systems. When the forecast predicts that similar conditions will produce similar weather, this prediction is an example of inductive reasoning.

Example

This table shows an incomplete display of data.

5	8
4	7
7	10
6	
9	

Use inductive reasoning to complete the given table.

Solution

Step 1

Determine what the problem is asking.

There is a pattern to how the numbers are changing. Determine the pattern, and apply it to the next two numbers in the chart.

Step 2

Plan your strategy.

One option is to determine by how much the numbers are increasing. Also, determine the relationship each number has to the number in the column to the left of it, above it, and below it. Test the relationship on the other examples. If the test proves positive, use the relationship to fill in the next two boxes.

Step 3

Solve the problem.

Determine the relationship between the numbers in each row. Subtract the numbers in the column on the left from the numbers in the column on the right.

$8 - 5 = 3$
$7 - 4 = 3$
$10 - 7 = 3$

The first number is 3 less than the second number, so add 3 to the first number in the next two rows.

$6 + 3 = 9$
$9 + 3 = 12$

The missing data are shown in the completed table.

5	8
4	7
7	10
6	9
9	12

Step 4

Check your solution.

Redo the addition to make sure that it is correct. Add 3 to each number in the first column to get the second column.

$5 + 3 = 8$
$4 + 3 = 7$
$7 + 3 = 10$

Using the numbers above and below a given number can also be used to check the accuracy of the relationship. Notice that 5 is paired with 8. Since the number 6 is one higher than 5, its pair should be one higher than 8. This is also correct since 6 is paired with 9.

20NL.1 Analyze and prove conjectures, using inductive and deductive reasoning, to solve problems.

PROVING CONJECTURES BY APPLYING DEDUCTIVE REASONING

Inductive reasoning is often the first type of reasoning used when a pattern is observed. A conjecture is the outcome of that type of reasoning. After stating a conjecture, an attempt is often made to show that the conjecture is correct in every case through **deductive reasoning**. In mathematics, a demonstration through deductive reasoning that a conjecture is true is called a **proof**. This conjecture is called a **theorem**.

Example

$$1^2 - 0^2 = 1$$
$$2^2 - 1^2 = 3$$
$$3^2 - 2^2 = 5$$
$$4^2 - 3^2 = 7$$

A student studying this pattern makes the conjecture that the difference of the squares of consecutive whole numbers is equal to the sum of the numbers.

Use deductive reasoning to show that the student's conjecture is true.

Solution

Step 1
Let n and $n + 1$ represent any two consecutive whole numbers.

Step 2
Determine the expression for the difference of squares of the two numbers.
$$(n + 1)^2 - n^2 = n^2 + 2n + 1 - n^2$$
$$= 2n + 1$$

Step 3
Determine the expression for the sum of the two consecutive whole numbers.
$$(n + 1) + n = 2n + 1$$

Step 4
Make a conclusion.
Since both equations are equal to $2n + 1$, the conjecture is true.

Example

$$0^2 + 1^2 = 1$$
$$1^2 + 2^2 = 5$$
$$2^2 + 3^2 = 13$$
$$3^2 + 4^2 = 25$$

A student studying this pattern makes the conjecture that the sum of the squares of consecutive whole numbers is always an odd number.

Use deductive reasoning to show that the student's conjecture is true.

Solution

Step 1
Let n and $n + 1$ represent any two consecutive whole numbers.

Step 2
Write and simplify an expression for the sum of the squares of $n + 1$ and n.
$$(n + 1)^2 + n^2 = n^2 + 2n + 1 + n^2$$
$$= 2n^2 + 2n + 1$$

Step 3
Determine if the sum of the squares is an odd or an even number.

Since an even number is one that is divisible by 2, any even number n such that $\frac{n}{2} = k$ may be represented as $2k$. Also, if n is an even number, then $n - 1$ and $n + 1$ must be odd numbers. Therefore, an odd number is of the form $n + 1 = 2k + 1$.

Factor the number 2 from the first two terms.
$$2n^2 + 2n + 1 = 2(n^2 + n) + 1$$
Interpret the expression.

The expression $2(n^2 + n) + 1$ is of the form $2k + 1$, where $k = n^2 + n$. The number $2k$ is even because it is divisible by 2: $\frac{2k}{2} = k$.

Therefore, the expression $2k + 1$ represents an odd number.

The conjecture that the sum of the squares of two consecutive whole numbers is always an odd number is true.

Example

Prove that the product of two consecutive even numbers is divisible by 4.

Solution

Let $2n$ and $2n + 2$ represent any two consecutive even numbers.

It follows that their product is
$$(2n)(2n + 2) = 4n^2 + 4n$$
$$= 4(n^2 + n).$$

Since 4 is a factor of the product, the product is divisible by 4. Therefore, the product of any two consecutive even numbers is divisible by 4.

20NL.1 Analyze and prove conjectures, using inductive and deductive reasoning, to solve problems.

DISPROVING CONJECTURES BY APPLYING COUNTEREXAMPLES

A conjecture is a statement, conclusion, or prediction that is the result of experimentation or observation. It is what seems to be true about an entire set of data. For example, with respect to the topic of weather, a weather forecast is a conjecture.

Conjectures may or may not prove to be true. For example, everyone has experienced hearing a weather forecast that later turned out to be wrong.

An example or situation that contradicts a conjecture, thereby showing that the conjecture is false, is called a counterexample.

Example

All world cities with populations over ten million are in Asia.

Give two examples that support this conjecture and one counterexample that shows it is false.

Solution

The following examples support this conjecture:

- Moscow has a population over ten million and is in Asia.
- Delhi has a population over ten million and is in Asia.

The following counterexample disproves this conjecture:

- São Paulo has a population over ten million and is not in Asia.

Since there is a counterexample disproving the conjecture, the conjecture is false.

Example

The values of y (the range) for $y = -x^2 + 4x$ are all less than 4.

Give two examples that support this conjecture and one counterexample that shows it is false.

Solution

Two examples that support this conjecture are the ordered pairs $(0, 0)$ and $(1, 3)$, giving y-values of 0 and 3, respectively. These points can be determined by graphing the equation on a graphing calculator and tracing the points or looking at the corresponding table of values.

One counterexample that shows that this conjecture is false is the ordered pair $(2, 4)$. The y-value is 4, not less than 4.

Example

$26 \times 11 = 286$
$35 \times 11 = 385$
$12 \times 11 = 132$
$27 \times 11 = 297$

Use the given data to make a conjecture, and then extend the pattern by writing two more examples.

Solution

Conjecture: The product of a two-digit number and 11 is a three-digit number that begins and ends with the digits of the two-digit number and has a middle digit that is the sum of the digits in the two-digit number.

Two additional extensions of the pattern are given as follows:
$32 \times 11 = 352$
$61 \times 11 = 671$

Example

Find a counterexample that shows that the conjecture below is false:

Conjecture: The product of a two-digit number and 11 is a three-digit number that begins and ends with the digits of the two-digit number and has a middle digit that is the sum of the digits in the two-digit number.

Solution

In this case, it is necessary to find an example that contradicts the conjecture.

There are many possibilities. For example, $59 \times 11 = 649$.

The first digit in 649 is not 5, and 4 is not the sum of 5 and 9.

Another counterexample is $98 \times 11 = 1\ 078$.

In this example, the product is a four-digit number, which contradicts the conjecture.

Sometimes, it is possible to modify an initial conjecture to create a new conjecture that will either include the counterexamples for the initial conjecture or exclude them from being possible examples.

Example

Conjecture: The product of a two-digit number and 11 is a three-digit number that begins and ends with the digits of the two-digit number and has a middle digit that is the sum of the two digits.

Revise the conjecture so that the counterexamples are excluded.

Solution

The counterexamples are two-digit numbers where the sum of the first digit and last digit is 10 or greater. The conjecture can be revised to exclude these numbers.

Revised conjecture: For two digit numbers where the sum of the digits is less than 10, the product of the number and 11 is a three-digit number that begins and ends with the digits of the two-digit number and has a middle digit that is the sum of the two digits.

20NL.1 Analyze and prove conjectures, using inductive and deductive reasoning, to solve problems.

DRAWING CONCLUSIONS USING DEDUCTIVE REASONING

In a court of law, defence lawyers will often base their arguments on agreed-upon facts.
The following example shows a defence argument based on deductive reasoning.

In this case, the accused has pleaded not guilty, and his lawyer is arguing that the accused could not have committed the crime for the following reasons:

1. The crime happened between 8 P.M. and 9 P.M. in Edmonton.
2. At 6 P.M., the accused was in Fort McMurray.
3. Fort McMurray is a four-hour drive from Edmonton.
4. On the day of the crime, there were no direct flights from Fort McMurray to Edmonton.

Based on these four facts, the accused is innocent, since he could not have been in Edmonton when the crime was committed.

The type of argument presented in the given example is based on deductive reasoning.

DEDUCTIVE REASONING

Deductive reasoning is based on statements that are accepted as true. With this type of reasoning, if certain statements can be shown to be true, then other statements can be developed from them. The final statement is considered to be a conclusion. In the case of the lawyer's argument, the four facts together form the first statement from which he makes his conclusion that the accused is innocent. If the statements are true and the reasoning is correct, there cannot be a counterexample.

For example, consider the following two statements and the conclusion:

• Edmonton is in Alberta.
• Alberta is in Canada.

Conclusion: Edmonton is in Canada.

If the first two statements are accepted as being true, then the conclusion is correct and logical.

Example
  • Jim lives in Fort McMurray.
  • Fort McMurray is in Alberta.

  Use deductive reasoning to develop a conclusion from the two given statements.

Solution
  Conclusion: Jim lives in Alberta.

Example
  • The sum of any two prime numbers greater than 2 is an even number.
  • The numbers 3 and 5 are two prime numbers greater than 2.

  Use deductive reasoning to develop a conclusion from the two given statements.

Solution
  Conclusion: The sum of 3 and 5 is an even number.

Example
  Consider the following two statements and the conclusion:

  • A right triangle has two acute angles.
  • Triangle *ABC* has two acute angles.

  Conclusion: Triangle *ABC* is a right triangle.

  Does the conclusion follow logically from the two statements?

Solution
  The conclusion does not follow logically from the statements because triangles can have two acute angles without the third angle being a right angle. For example, triangle *ABC* may have acute angles of 30° and 40°, which means the third angle is 110°, which is not a right angle.

The conclusions made using deductive reasoning are different than the conjectures made using inductive reasoning. With deductive reasoning, the conclusions are true for all cases, and this can be proven. With inductive reasoning, the conjectures may appear to be true, but cannot be tested and proven for all cases.

20NL.1 Analyze and prove conjectures, using inductive and deductive reasoning, to solve problems.

PROVING THEOREMS AND CONJECTURES USING POSTULATES

When working with geometric shapes and figures, it is important to be able to establish relationships such as congruence and equality. Additionally, it is important to be able to determine the measures of sides or angles of various shapes without using measurement instruments.

Geometers follow these steps to establish different relationships and determine measures using logic and reasoning:

- Understand the problem.
- Draw a diagram, taking care not to draw special cases such as equilateral triangles or squares unless these shapes are given in the problem.
- Label the diagram.
- State what is required to establish a relationship.
- Build a pathway of reasoning from the given information to the required result using known relationships and propositions.

Example

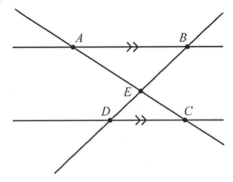

Two parallel lines are intersected by two transversal lines so that two triangles are formed in the interior, as shown in the given diagram.

Prove that the two triangles in the interior are similar.

Solution

Step 1
State what is required for the proof.
The two shapes in the interior are $\triangle ABE$ and $\triangle CDE$. Both shapes are triangles. To prove that the triangles are similar, it is necessary to prove that measures of corresponding angles are equal.

Step 2
Apply known properties and postulates to prove that $\triangle ABE$ and $\triangle CDE$ are similar.

Statement	Reason
$\angle BAC = \angle DCA$	Measures of alternate interior angles are equal.
$\angle ABD = \angle CDB$	Measures of alternate interior angles are equal.
$\angle AEB = \angle CED$	Measures of vertical opposite angles are equal.
$\triangle ABE \sim \triangle CDE$	Measures of corresponding angles are equal.

Example

Use postulates and properties of parallel lines to prove that the sum of the interior angles of a trapezoid is equal to 360°.

Solution

Step 1
Draw and label a diagram.

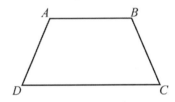

Step 2
State the requirement for the proof.
To prove that the sum of the interior angles is equal to 360°, show that
$\angle ABC + \angle BCD + \angle CDA + \angle DAB = 360°$.

Step 3
Prove the result.

Statement	Reason
$AB \parallel CD$	Bases of a trapezoid are parallel.
AD and BC are transversal.	Line segments intersecting parallel lines
$\angle BAD$ and $\angle CDA$ are supplementary.	Parallel line postulate
$\angle BAD + \angle CDA = 180°$	Sum of the supplementary angles
$\angle ABC$ and $\angle DCB$ are supplementary.	Parallel line postulate
$\angle ABC + \angle DCB = 180°$	Sum of the supplementary angles
The sum of the interior angles is 360°.	Sum of two pairs of supplementary angles

20NL.1 Analyze and prove conjectures, using inductive and deductive reasoning, to solve problems.

UNDERSTANDING GEOMETRIC PROOFS

Before the invention of rulers, protractors, lasers, and other tools, mathematicians used a **straight edge** and a **compass** to draw shapes, cut line segments into equal sections, and build perpendicular lines. Considering that they had so few tools, ancient mathematicians were able to achieve incredible precision. This was due in part to following the logic of geometric construction. This logic has been transformed into a style for geometric proofs.

A geometric proof mainly uses axioms and postulates. Existing objects and new imagined points and lines can also be used to build a logical connection from the available information to a particular conclusion. Each step in the connection is supported by a self-evident truth, given information, a postulate, or any other known result.

It is common to write a geometric proof in two side-by-side columns. One column contains statements, while the other column contains justifications for each statement, such as known postulates or given information.

Example
   Prove that vertically opposite angles have equal measures.

Solution
   Step 1
   Draw a diagram.

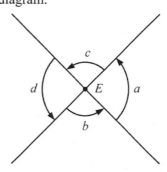

The diagram shows two lines that intersect at point *E*. Angles *a* and *d* and *b* and *c* are vertically opposite.
Proof for only one of the pairs of vertically opposite angles is required because the proof for the second pair would be constructed in an identical way.

Step 2

Prove that the measure of angle *a* is equal to the measure of angle *d*.

Statement	Reason
Angles *a* and *c* are supplementary. $a + c = 180°$	This is true by the definition of supplementary angles.
Angles *d* and *c* are supplementary. $d + c = 180°$	This is true by the definition of supplementary angles.
$a + c = d + c$ $a = d$ The measure of angle *a* is equal to the measure of angle *d*.	Each angle is supplementary with the same angle *c*.

20NL.2 Analyze puzzles and games that involve spatial reasoning, using problem-solving strategies.

APPLYING A VARIETY OF MATHEMATICAL PROBLEM-SOLVING TECHNIQUES

You can apply a variety of mathematical techniques to help you solve problems. One of these problem-solving techniques is guess and check. For this technique, you determine a reasonable guess, select a number, and then check to see if the number is correct by substituting it into the equation.

Example

Laura is asked to find the value of *x* in the equation $84.25 + x = 102$ by using guess and check.

The steps in Laura's partial solution for determining the value of *x* are shown:

1. Round the decimal number in the equation to the nearest whole number.
   $84 + x = 102$
2. Since $84 + 18 = 102$, a reasonable guess is a number less than 18.
3. A possible number could be 17. Substitute 17 for *x*.
   $84.25 + 17 = 101.25$ The guess of 17 gives a number less than 102.

Complete Laura's partial solution to find the value of *x*.

Solution

Since the guess of 17 gives a number less than 102, a reasonable number for *x* will be between 17 and 18.

Step 1

Add 0.75 to the last guess of 17.
$17 + 0.75 = 17.75$

Step 2

Substitute for *x*.
$84.25 + 17.75 = 102$

The value of *x* in the given equation is 17.75.

Another problem-solving technique is to identify the relevant information from the given information and write a simple equation to solve the problem.

Example

Kyle wants to build a rectangular pool and would like it to fit in his backyard. His backyard has an area of 252 m² and a width that is 9 m less than its length. The width of the pool is 3 m. The length of the pool is two times the width of the pool, and the depth of the pool is half the width. Along the perimeter of the pool, there is a walking path that is 2 m longer than the length and width of the pool.

Write and solve an equation to determine the total volume of water that Kyle will need to fill his swimming pool.

Solution

To find the volume of water needed to fill the pool, find the volume of the rectangular pool.

Step 1

Identify the relevant information.

To find the volume of the rectangular pool, only the length, width, and depth of the pool are needed.

The given diagram shows the relevant information, where l is the length, w is the width, and d is the depth.

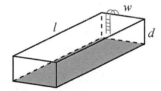

Step 2

Write an equation.

Since the shape of the pool is a rectangular prism, use the formula for the volume of a rectangular prism, which is $V_{rectangular\ prism} = lwh$. Thus, $V_{pool} = lwd$.

The width of the pool equals 3 m. The length of the pool is two times the width, so $l = 2 \times 3 = 6$ m.

The depth of the pool is half the width, so $d = \frac{1}{2}(3) = 1.5$ m. Substitute the values into the equation $V_{pool} = lwd$.

$V_{pool} = 3(6)(1.5)$

Step 3

Determine the volume of the pool by solving the equation.

$V_{pool} = 3(6)(1.5)$

$\quad\ = 27$ m³

The volume of water that Kyle will need to fill the pool is 27 m³.

20NL.2 Analyze puzzles and games that involve spatial reasoning, using problem-solving strategies.

APPLYING A VARIETY OF VISUAL PROBLEM-SOLVING STRATEGIES

You can use a variety of visual strategies to solve problems. Some of these visual strategies include drawing a diagram, making a chart, and creating a table. These problem-solving strategies can make it easier for you to find solutions to various problems.

Example

The first four diagrams in a series of diagrams that form a particular pattern are given.

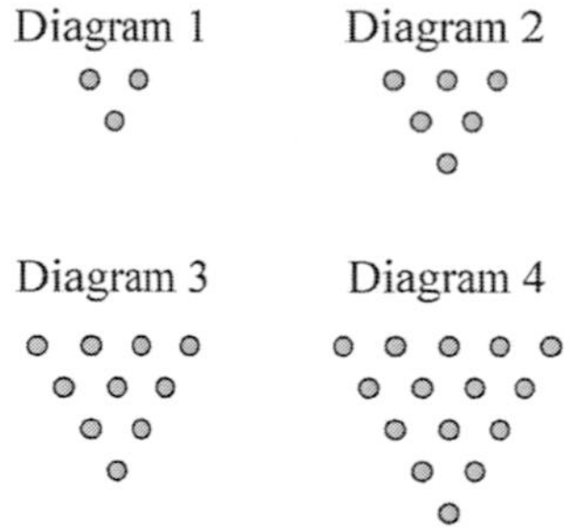

Diagram 1

Diagram 2

Diagram 3

Diagram 4

If the pattern continues, determine how many dots there will be in diagram 5.

Solution

Step 1

Create a table to organize the information from the given diagrams.

Diagram	Number of Dots
1	3
2	6
3	10
4	15

Step 2

Identify the pattern from the given diagrams. From the table, the number of dots in diagram 2 increases by 3 from the number of dots in diagram 1 ($3 + 3 = 6$). The number of dots increases by 4 in diagram 3 ($6 + 4 = 10$). The number of dots in diagram 4 increases by 5 ($10 + 5 = 15$).

The pattern is that the number of dots added to each diagram increases by 1, or is 1 more than the number of dots added to the previous diagram. For example, 5 dots were added from diagram 3 to diagram 4. Therefore, 6 dots will be added to diagram 5.

$15 + 6 = 21$

Diagram 5 will have 21 dots.

Diagram 5

Example

John and Sara are going to have a 60 m race at lunch hour. They want to set up pylons every 8 m to see who can make it to each pylon first.

Which visual problem-solving strategy would John and Sara **most likely** use to determine how many pylons they need for their race?

Solution

Step 1

Choose an appropriate problem-solving strategy.

An effective way to solve this problem is to draw a picture. Drawing a picture can limit the calculations that need to be made, so there is less chance of making an error. Seeing this problem visually will simplify the solution.

Step 2

Draw the picture.

Begin by drawing a line to represent the 60 m race.

Place a pylon that is 8 m away from the start line, the start line being 0.

Next, add another pylon 8 m from the first pylon's location. To identify where the second pylon should be, calculate $8 + 8 = 16$. The second pylon will be 16 m from the start line.

For the third pylon, add another 8 m from the second pylon's location, which is $16 + 8 = 24$. Continue in this way until you reach 60 m.

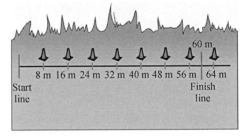

At 56 m, it is not necessary to place another pylon 8 m away, but doing so will help clarify how many pylons will be within the 60 m race.

Step 3

Count the number of pylons.

There are 7 pylons in the 60 m race.

John and Sara would most likely choose to draw a picture to solve this problem because the specific objects, the pylons, and the straight line can be easily drawn in a diagram. The picture also limits the calculations needed to solve this problem. Visually seeing this question makes it easy to simply count the pylons that are within the 60 m.

20NL.3 Solve problems that involve operations on radicals and radical expressions with numerical and variable radicands (limited to square roots).

EXPRESSING A MIXED RADICAL AS AN ENTIRE RADICAL

Radicals can be simplified by writing them as mixed radicals with the smallest possible radicand. This procedure is reversed to write mixed radicals as entire radicals. To reverse a square root, square the factor in front of the radical sign and multiply the result by the original radicand.

Example

Write the expression $3\sqrt{2}$ as an entire radical.

Solution

Bring the 3 under the square root, and simplify. To bring a value under a square root, the value must be squared.

$3\sqrt{2}$
$= \sqrt{3^2 \times 2}$
$= \sqrt{9 \times 2}$
$= \sqrt{18}$

Example

Write an equivalent form of the number 11 as an entire radical under a square root.

Solution

Put the number 11 under a square root, and simplify.

To bring a value under a square root, the value must also be squared.

$11 = \sqrt{11^2}$
$ = \sqrt{121}$

The procedure is similar for roots of higher order. The only difference is that the higher power of the factor in front of the radical sign is used as the multiplier of the original radicand.

Example

Write the expression $2\sqrt[3]{6}$ as an entire radical.

Solution

Bring the 2 under the cube root, and simplify. To bring a value under a cube root, the value must be cubed.

$2\sqrt[3]{6}$
$= \sqrt[3]{2^3 \times 6}$
$= \sqrt[3]{8 \times 6}$
$= \sqrt[3]{48}$

20NL.3 Solve problems that involve operations on radicals and radical expressions with numerical and variable radicands (limited to square roots).

EXPRESSING AN ENTIRE RADICAL AS A MIXED RADICAL

An **entire radical** is a radical in the form $\sqrt[n]{x}$, in which $x \geq 0$ if n is an even number and $x \in \mathbb{R}$ if n is an odd number. For example, $\sqrt{15}$ and $\sqrt{\dfrac{2}{5}}$ are entire radicals.

A **mixed radical** is a radical in the form $m\sqrt[n]{x}$.

For example, $4\sqrt{3}$ and $\frac{1}{3}\sqrt{\frac{2}{5}}$ are mixed radicals.

To convert entire radicals of the form $\sqrt{x}$ to mixed radicals, follow these steps:

1. Determine two numbers that have a product equal to the value of the radicand, one of which must be a perfect square.
2. Express the radicand as a product of these two numbers.
3. Separate the expression to isolate the perfect square.
4. Take the square root of the perfect square, and place this value in front of the remaining radical.

Example

Express $\sqrt{75}$ as a mixed radical.

Solution

Step 1
Determine two numbers that have a product of 75, one of which is a perfect square.
Since 25 is a perfect square, 75 can be expressed as 25×3.

Step 2
Substitute 25×3 for 75 in the expression $\sqrt{75}$.
$\sqrt{75} = \sqrt{25 \times 3}$
Express the radicand as a product of these two numbers.

Step 3
Separate the expression to isolate the perfect square.
$$\sqrt{75} = \sqrt{25 \times 3}$$
$$= \sqrt{25} \times \sqrt{3}$$

Step 4
Take the square root of the perfect square, and place this value in front of the remaining radical.
$$\sqrt{25} \times \sqrt{3} = 5 \times \sqrt{3}$$
$$= 5\sqrt{3}$$

The procedure for expressing an entire radical of the form $\sqrt[3]{x}$ in mixed radical form is almost identical to that for simplifying $\sqrt{x}$. The difference is that it is necessary to determine two numbers that have a product of the radicand, one of which is a perfect cube.

Example

Write the radical $\sqrt[3]{320}$ in simplest mixed radical form.

Solution

Step 1
Determine two numbers that have a product equal to the value of the radicand, one of which must be a perfect cube.
These numbers are 64 and 5.

Step 2
Express the radicand as a product of these two numbers.
$$\sqrt[3]{320} = \sqrt[3]{64 \times 5}$$

Step 3
Separate the expression to isolate the perfect cube.
$$\sqrt[3]{320} = \sqrt[3]{64} \times \sqrt[3]{5}$$

Step 4
Take the cube root of the perfect cube, and place this value in front of the remaining radical.
$$\sqrt[3]{64} \times \sqrt[3]{5} = 4 \times \sqrt[3]{5}$$
$$= 4\sqrt[3]{5}$$

This holds true for radicals with higher indexes. For $\sqrt[n]{x}$, it is necessary to determine two numbers that have a product of the radicand, one of which is a perfect nth root.

It is important to note that radical expressions such as $\sqrt{15}$ cannot be simplified further because no two numbers, with one being a perfect square, have a product of 15.

20NL.3 Solve problems that involve operations on radicals and radical expressions with numerical and variable radicands (limited to square roots).

LOCATING IRRATIONAL NUMBERS ON A NUMBER LINE

The approximate location of an irrational number on a real number line can be determined.

Example

$$\{\sqrt[3]{-43},\ \sqrt{10},\ 2\sqrt{3},\ -2\sqrt[4]{13}\}$$

A set of irrational numbers is given.

Use a number line to order the given set of irrational numbers.

Solution

Step 1

Convert all the irrational numbers into the same format.

Convert mixed radicals into entire form.

$$2\sqrt{3} = \sqrt{2^2 \times 3}$$
$$= \sqrt{4 \times 3}$$
$$= \sqrt{12}$$
$$-2\sqrt[4]{13} = -\sqrt[4]{2^4 \times 13}$$
$$= -\sqrt[4]{16 \times 13}$$
$$= -\sqrt[4]{208}$$

Step 2

Calculate their estimated position between roots of neighbouring perfect powers.

- The irrational number $\sqrt[3]{-43}$ lies about halfway between the perfect cubes -27 and -64. Since $\sqrt[3]{-27} = -3$ and $\sqrt[3]{-64} = -4$, its estimated value is -3.5.

- The irrational number $\sqrt{10}$ is slightly more than $\sqrt{9}$, and $\sqrt{9} = 3$, so its estimated value is 3.1.

- The irrational number $\sqrt{12}$ lies about halfway between the perfect squares 9 and 16. Since $\sqrt{9} = 3$ and $\sqrt{16} = 4$, its estimated value is 3.5.

- The irrational number $-\sqrt[4]{208}$ lies between the perfect powers of 256 and 81. Since $-\sqrt[4]{256} = -4$ and $-\sqrt[4]{81} = -3$, and $-\sqrt[4]{208}$ is closer to $-\sqrt[4]{256}$ than it is to $-\sqrt[4]{81}$, its estimated value is -3.8.

Step 3

Place each irrational number in ascending order on a number line.

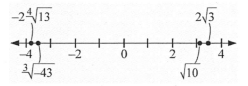

20NL.3 Solve problems that involve operations on radicals and radical expressions with numerical and variable radicands (limited to square roots).

ADDITION AND SUBTRACTION OF RADICALS

When working with polynomials, the sum or difference of like terms can be simplified by applying the distributive property. For example, $5x + 7x = (5 + 7)x = 12x$ and $8xy^2 - 3xy^2 = (8 - 3)xy^2 = 5xy^2$. However, the sum of $2x$ and $3y$ is $2x + 3y$ because $2x$ and $3y$ are not like terms. The distributive property can also be used to add or subtract like radicals. Like radicals are radicals that have the same index and the same radicand. For example, $3\sqrt{7} + 5\sqrt{7} = (3 + 5)\sqrt{7} = 8\sqrt{7}$ and $9\sqrt[4]{5} - 2\sqrt[4]{5} = (9 - 2)\sqrt[4]{5} = 7\sqrt[4]{5}$. It follows that the sum of $4\sqrt{10}$ and $5\sqrt[3]{10}$ is $4\sqrt{10} + 5\sqrt[3]{10}$ because the radicals have a different index and therefore are not like radicals.

In the radical $\sqrt[3]{7}$, the number 3 is called the index, and the number 7 is called the radicand.

When adding or subtracting radicals, always check first to see whether any of the radicals can be simplified. For instance $\sqrt{2}$ and $\sqrt{8}$ do not appear to be like terms. However $\sqrt{8}$ can be written as $\sqrt{4 \times 2} = \sqrt{4} \times \sqrt{2} = 2\sqrt{2}$. Thus, the sum of $\sqrt{2}$ and $\sqrt{8}$ is $\sqrt{2} + 2\sqrt{2} = 3\sqrt{2}$.

Example

Simplify the expression $\sqrt{27} + \sqrt{75}$.

Solution

Step 1

Write each radicand as the product of two numbers, one of which must be a perfect square.
$$\sqrt{27} + \sqrt{75} = \sqrt{9 \times 3} + \sqrt{25 \times 3}$$

Step 2

Simplify each term.
$$\sqrt{9 \times 3} + \sqrt{25 \times 3}$$
$$= \sqrt{9} \times \sqrt{3} + \sqrt{25} \times \sqrt{3}$$
$$= 3 \times \sqrt{3} + 5 \times \sqrt{3}$$
$$= 3\sqrt{3} + 5\sqrt{3}$$

Step 3

Collect like terms by applying the distributive property.
$$3\sqrt{3} + 5\sqrt{3} = (3 + 5)\sqrt{3}$$
$$= 8\sqrt{3}$$

Example

Simplify the expression
$7\sqrt{18} + 3\sqrt{20} - \sqrt{50} + \sqrt{80}$.

Solution

Step 1

Write each radicand as the product of two numbers, one of which must be a perfect square.
$$7\sqrt{18} + 3\sqrt{20} - \sqrt{50} + \sqrt{80}$$
$$= 7\sqrt{9 \times 2} + 3\sqrt{4 \times 5} - \sqrt{25 \times 2} + \sqrt{16 \times 5}$$

Step 2

Simplify each term.
$$7\sqrt{9 \times 2} + 3\sqrt{4 \times 5} - \sqrt{25 \times 2} + \sqrt{16 \times 5}$$
$$= 7(\sqrt{9} \times \sqrt{2}) + 3(\sqrt{4} \times \sqrt{5}) - \sqrt{25} \times \sqrt{2}$$
$$+ \sqrt{16} \times \sqrt{5}$$
$$= 7(3 \times \sqrt{2}) + 3(2 \times \sqrt{5}) - 5 \times \sqrt{2} + 4 \times \sqrt{5}$$
$$= 7(3\sqrt{2}) + 3(2\sqrt{5}) - 5\sqrt{2} + 4\sqrt{5}$$
$$= 21\sqrt{2} + 6\sqrt{5} - 5\sqrt{2} - 4\sqrt{5}$$

Step 3

Collect like terms by applying the distributive property.
$$21\sqrt{2} + 6\sqrt{5} - 5\sqrt{2} - 4\sqrt{5}$$
$$= (21 - 5)\sqrt{2} + (6 - 4)\sqrt{5}$$
$$= 16\sqrt{2} + 2\sqrt{5}$$

Example

Simplify the expression $7\sqrt[3]{3} + 4\sqrt[3]{24} - 9\sqrt[3]{81}$.

Solution

Step 1

Where possible, write each radicand as the product of two numbers, one of which must be a perfect cube.
$$7\sqrt[3]{3} + 4\sqrt[3]{24} - 9\sqrt[3]{81}$$
$$= 7\sqrt[3]{3} + 4\sqrt[3]{8 \times 3} - 9\sqrt[3]{27 \times 3}$$

Step 2

Where possible, simplify each term.
$$7\sqrt[3]{3} + 4\sqrt[3]{8 \times 3} - 9\sqrt[3]{27 \times 3}$$
$$= 7\sqrt[3]{3} + 4(\sqrt[3]{8} \times \sqrt[3]{3}) - 9(\sqrt[3]{27} \times \sqrt[3]{3})$$
$$= 7\sqrt[3]{3} + 4(2 \times \sqrt[3]{3}) - 9(3 \times \sqrt[3]{3})$$
$$= 7\sqrt[3]{3} + 4(2\sqrt[3]{3}) - 9(3\sqrt[3]{3})$$
$$= 7\sqrt[3]{3} + 8\sqrt[3]{3} - 27\sqrt[3]{3}$$

Step 3

Collect like terms by applying the distributive property.
$$7\sqrt[3]{3} + 8\sqrt[3]{3} - 27\sqrt[3]{3}$$
$$= (7 + 8 - 27)\sqrt[3]{3}$$
$$= -12\sqrt[3]{3}$$

20NL.3 Solve problems that involve operations on radicals and radical expressions with numerical and variable radicands (limited to square roots).

MULTIPLYING RADICALS

You can find the product of $\sqrt{9}$ and $\sqrt{4}$ by multiplying the square roots of the two numbers. Since 9 and 4 are perfect squares, the solution can be found by multiplying 3 (the square root of 9) by 2 (the square root of 4) to arrive at the answer of 6.

However, if you were asked to find the product of $\sqrt{5}$ and $\sqrt{3}$, you would not be able to use the same method. Since neither 5 nor 3 is a perfect square, you need to use a different procedure for multiplying two or more radicals.

It was shown that $\sqrt{9} \times \sqrt{4} = 6$, and 36 is the product of 9 and 4. The number 6 is also the square root of 36. Similarly, the product of $\sqrt{5}$ and $\sqrt{3}$ can be expressed as $\sqrt{5 \times 3} = \sqrt{15}$.

The procedure for determining the product of two radicals, such as $7\sqrt{5}$ and $4\sqrt{3}$, is as follows:

$7\sqrt{5} \times 4\sqrt{3}$

$= 7 \times \sqrt{5} \times 4 \times \sqrt{3}$

$= (7 \times 4) \times (\sqrt{5} \times \sqrt{3})$

$= 28 \times \sqrt{15}$

$= 28\sqrt{15}$

When multiplying radicals, multiply the numbers in front of the radicals first, and then multiply the radicands. The general rule for multiplying two radicals can be stated as
$a\sqrt{x} \times b\sqrt{y} = (a \times b)\sqrt{x \times y}$ or simply
$a\sqrt{x} \times b\sqrt{y} = ab\sqrt{xy}$. Multiplying radicals forms a new radicand. This new radicand can often be simplified.

Example

Simplify $7\sqrt{6} \times 5\sqrt{2}$.

Solution

$7\sqrt{6} \times 5\sqrt{2} = (7 \times 5)\sqrt{6 \times 2}$
$= 35\sqrt{12}$
$= 35\sqrt{4 \times 3}$
$= 35(2\sqrt{3})$
$= 70\sqrt{3}$

Example

Determine the product of $5\sqrt[3]{32}$ and $2\sqrt[3]{108}$.

Solution

Notice that cube roots are involved in this question. Since each radicand can be simplified further, the multiplication process will be much easier if the radicands are fully simplified before the multiplication takes place.

$5\sqrt[3]{32} \times 2\sqrt[3]{108}$
$= 5\sqrt[3]{8 \times 4} \times 2\sqrt[3]{27 \times 4}$
$= 5(2\sqrt[3]{4}) \times 2(3\sqrt[3]{4})$
$= 10\sqrt[3]{4} \times 6\sqrt[3]{4}$
$= (10 \times 6)\sqrt[3]{4 \times 4}$
$= 60\sqrt[3]{16}$
$= 60\sqrt[3]{8 \times 2}$
$= 60(2\sqrt[3]{2})$
$= 120\sqrt[3]{2}$

The given example illustrates the use of the distributive property when multiplying radicals.

Example

Simplify $\sqrt{3}(3\sqrt{3} - 2\sqrt{2})$.

Solution

Step 1
Apply the distributive property.
$\sqrt{3}(3\sqrt{3} - 2\sqrt{2}) = \sqrt{3}(3\sqrt{3}) - \sqrt{3}(2\sqrt{2})$

Step 2
Simplify the expression.
$\sqrt{3}(3\sqrt{3}) - \sqrt{3}(2\sqrt{2})$
$= 3(\sqrt{3})(\sqrt{3}) - 2(\sqrt{3})(\sqrt{2})$
$= 3\sqrt{9} - 2\sqrt{6}$
$= 3(3) - 2\sqrt{6}$
$= 9 - 2\sqrt{6}$

The given example illustrates the use of the FOIL method when multiplying radicals.

Example

Expand and simplify $(4\sqrt{3} + 6\sqrt{2})(5\sqrt{3} - \sqrt{2})$.

Solution

Step 1

Apply the FOIL multiplication procedure.
$(4\sqrt{3} + 6\sqrt{2})(5\sqrt{3} - \sqrt{2})$
$= (4\sqrt{3})(5\sqrt{3}) - (4\sqrt{3})(\sqrt{2}) + (6\sqrt{2})(5\sqrt{3})$
$- (6\sqrt{2})(\sqrt{2})$

Step 2

Simplify the expression.
$(4\sqrt{3})(5\sqrt{3}) - (4\sqrt{3})(\sqrt{2}) + (6\sqrt{2})(5\sqrt{3})$
$- (6\sqrt{2})(\sqrt{2})$
$= (4 \times 5)\sqrt{3 \times 3} - 4\sqrt{3 \times 2} + (6 \times 5)\sqrt{2 \times 3}$
$- 6\sqrt{2 \times 2}$
$= 20\sqrt{9} - 4\sqrt{6} + 30\sqrt{6} - 6\sqrt{4}$
$= 20(3) - 4\sqrt{6} + 30\sqrt{6} - 6(2)$
$= 60 - 4\sqrt{6} + 30\sqrt{6} - 12$

Step 3

Collect like terms.
$= 60 - 4\sqrt{6} + 30\sqrt{6} - 12$
$= 48 + 26\sqrt{6}$

20NL.3 Solve problems that involve operations on radicals and radical expressions with numerical and variable radicands (limited to square roots).

DIVIDING RADICALS

The general rule for dividing two radicals is
$$\frac{a\sqrt{x}}{b\sqrt{y}} = (a \div b)\sqrt{x \div y}.$$

For example, the quotient of $\sqrt{36}$ divided by $\sqrt{4}$ can be found by dividing the square roots of the two numbers. Since 36 and 4 are perfect squares, the solution can be found by dividing 6 (the square root of 36) by 2 (the square root of 4) to arrive at the answer of 3.

The answer can also be obtained as follows:
$\dfrac{\sqrt{36}}{\sqrt{4}}$
$= \sqrt{\dfrac{36}{4}}$
$= \sqrt{9}$
$= 3$

Example

The quotient of $75\sqrt{64}$ divided by $25\sqrt{4}$ can be determined in several ways.

One way is to eliminate the radical signs and simplify.
$\dfrac{75\sqrt{64}}{25\sqrt{4}}$
$= \dfrac{75 \times 8}{25 \times 2}$
$= \dfrac{600}{50}$
$= 12$

Another way is to divide the numbers in front of the radical sign first. Then, divide the radicands and simplify.
$\dfrac{75\sqrt{64}}{25\sqrt{4}}$
$= (75 \div 25)\sqrt{64 \div 4}$
$= 3\sqrt{16}$
$= 3 \times 4$
$= 12$

Example

Divide $16\sqrt{55}$ by $4\sqrt{11}$.

Solution

Apply the general rule for dividing radicals.

$$\frac{16\sqrt{55}}{4\sqrt{11}} = (16 \div 4)\sqrt{55 \div 11}$$
$$= 4\sqrt{5}$$

To divide a radical binomial by a radical monomial, split the binomial into its individual terms and divide each term by the monomial.

Example

Divide the binomial $12\sqrt{60} - 14\sqrt{21}$ by the monomial $2\sqrt{3}$.

Solution

$$\frac{12\sqrt{60} - 14\sqrt{21}}{2\sqrt{3}}$$
$$= \frac{12\sqrt{60}}{2\sqrt{3}} - \frac{14\sqrt{21}}{2\sqrt{3}}$$
$$= (12 \div 2)\sqrt{60 \div 3} - (14 \div 2)\sqrt{21 \div 3}$$
$$= 6\sqrt{20} - 7\sqrt{7}$$
$$= 6\sqrt{4 \times 5} - 7\sqrt{7}$$
$$= 6(2\sqrt{5}) - 7\sqrt{7}$$
$$= 12\sqrt{5} - 7\sqrt{7}$$

20NL.3 Solve problems that involve operations on radicals and radical expressions with numerical and variable radicands (limited to square roots).

SIMPLIFYING RADICALS

The following examples illustrate that $\sqrt[n]{x \times y} = \sqrt[n]{x} \times \sqrt[n]{y}$, when x and $y \geq 0$.

- $\sqrt{36} = 6$ and $\sqrt{4} \times \sqrt{9} = 2 \times 3 = 6$
- $\sqrt{900} = 30$ and $\sqrt{9} \times \sqrt{100} = 3 \times 10 = 30$
- $\sqrt{20} \approx 4.472$ and $\sqrt{4} \times \sqrt{5} = 2 \times \sqrt{5} \approx 4.472$
- $\sqrt[3]{216} = 6$ and $\sqrt[3]{27} \times \sqrt[3]{8} = 3 \times 2 = 6$

An expression in the form of $\sqrt[n]{A}$ is called an entire radical. An expression in the form of $a\sqrt[n]{b}$ is called a mixed radical. A radical is in its simplest form when it is written as a rational number or mixed radical with the smallest possible radicand.

When simplifying radicals involving square roots, look for factors of the radicand that are perfect squares. When the radicals involve cube roots, look for factors that are perfect cubes, and so forth.

Example

Simplify the expression $\sqrt{81}$.

Solution

$\sqrt{81} = 9$

Example

Simplify the expression $5\sqrt{49}$.

Solution

$5\sqrt{49} = 5 \times 7$
$5\sqrt{49} = 35$

Example

Simplify the expression $\sqrt{60}$.

Solution

Step 1

Factor the radicand such that it has a perfect square factor.
$\sqrt{60} = \sqrt{4 \times 15}$

Step 2

Apply the $\sqrt[n]{x \times y} = \sqrt[n]{x} \times \sqrt[n]{y}$ property.
$\sqrt{60} = \sqrt{4} \times \sqrt{15}$
$\sqrt{60} = 2\sqrt{15}$

Note: Once you have factored the radicand such that it has a perfect square factor, you can use mental math to go immediately to the next step.
$\sqrt{4 \times 15} = 2\sqrt{15}$

For square roots, if the largest perfect square is not used as a factor initially, additional factoring using perfect squares is required to give the smallest possible radicand.

Example

Simplify the expression $3\sqrt{72}$.

Solution

Step 1

Factor the perfect square 9 from the radicand of the expression $3\sqrt{72}$.

$3\sqrt{72}$
$= 3\sqrt{9 \times 8}$
$= 3 \times 3 \times \sqrt{8}$
$= 9\sqrt{8}$

This mixed radical is not in simplest form because 8 also has a perfect square factor of 4.

Step 2

Factor the perfect square 4 from the radicand in the expression $9\sqrt{8}$.

$9\sqrt{8}$
$= 9\sqrt{4 \times 2}$
$= 9 \times 2 \times \sqrt{2}$
$= 18\sqrt{2}$

Therefore, the expression $3\sqrt{72}$ can be expressed in its simplest form as $18\sqrt{2}$.

Example

Simplify the expression $7\sqrt[3]{16}$.

Solution

$7\sqrt[3]{16} = 7\sqrt[3]{8 \times 2}$
$= 7 \times \sqrt[3]{8} \times \sqrt[3]{2}$
$= 7 \times 2 \times \sqrt[3]{2}$
$= 14\sqrt[3]{2}$

Example

Simplify the expression $4\sqrt{12} + \sqrt{8} \times 2\sqrt{6}$.

Solution

Step 1

Factor the radicands where possible to include a perfect square factor.

$4\sqrt{12} + \sqrt{8} \times 2\sqrt{6}$
$= 4\sqrt{4 \times 3} + \sqrt{4 \times 2} \times 2\sqrt{6}$
$= 4 \times 2\sqrt{3} + 2\sqrt{2} \times 2\sqrt{6}$
$= 8\sqrt{3} + 2\sqrt{2} \times 2\sqrt{6}$

Step 2

Use the order of operations to simplify the expression.

$8\sqrt{3} + (2\sqrt{2} \times 2\sqrt{6})$
$= 8\sqrt{3} + (2 \times 2)(\sqrt{2 \times 6})$
$= 8\sqrt{3} + (4\sqrt{12})$

This mixed radical is not in simplest form because 12 also has a perfect square factor of 4.

$8\sqrt{3} + 4\sqrt{4 \times 3}$
$= 8\sqrt{3} + 4(2\sqrt{3})$
$= 8\sqrt{3} + 8\sqrt{3}$

Step 3

Collect like terms by applying the distributive property.

$8\sqrt{3} + 8\sqrt{3} = (8 + 8)\sqrt{3}$
$\qquad\qquad = 16\sqrt{3}$

The expression $4\sqrt{12} + \sqrt{8} \times 2\sqrt{6}$ can be expressed in its simplest form as $16\sqrt{3}$.

20NL.3 Solve problems that involve operations on radicals and radical expressions with numerical and variable radicands (limited to square roots).

RATIONALIZING THE DENOMINATOR OF A RADICAL EXPRESSION

The process of rationalizing the denominator of a radical expression means to write the given expression in an equivalent form with a rational number as the denominator.

Consider the radical expression $\dfrac{\sqrt{5}}{\sqrt{2}}$.

The denominator of this expression is $\sqrt{2}$, which is not a rational number. However, an equivalent form of the expression $\dfrac{\sqrt{5}}{\sqrt{2}}$ can be arrived at by using a procedure similar to that of creating equivalent fractions. This is when both the numerator and denominator of the given fraction are multiplied or divided by the same number.

The expression $(\sqrt{2})^2 = 2$ is a rational number; thus, the denominator of the expression $\dfrac{\sqrt{5}}{\sqrt{2}}$ can be rationalized as follows:

$$\begin{aligned}
\frac{\sqrt{5}}{\sqrt{2}} &= \frac{\sqrt{5}}{\sqrt{2}} \times \frac{\sqrt{2}}{\sqrt{2}} \\
&= \frac{\sqrt{5 \times 2}}{(\sqrt{2})^2} \\
&= \frac{\sqrt{10}}{2}
\end{aligned}$$

Example

Rationalize the denominator of the expression $\dfrac{3\sqrt{7}}{2\sqrt{5}}$.

Solution

Although the denominator of the given expression can be rationalized by multiplying both its numerator and denominator by $2\sqrt{5}$, it is only necessary to multiply both the numerator and denominator by $\sqrt{5}$, as follows:

$$\begin{aligned}
\frac{3\sqrt{7}}{2\sqrt{5}} &= \frac{3\sqrt{7}}{2\sqrt{5}} \times \frac{\sqrt{5}}{\sqrt{5}} \\
&= \frac{3\sqrt{7 \times 5}}{2(\sqrt{5})^2} \\
&= \frac{3\sqrt{35}}{2(5)} \\
&= \frac{3\sqrt{35}}{10}
\end{aligned}$$

The following example illustrates what steps need to be taken when the numerator consists of an expression.

Example

Express $\dfrac{6\sqrt{2} + 3\sqrt{7}}{5\sqrt{3}}$ in the simplest radical form with a rational denominator.

Solution

Multiply both the numerator and denominator of the given expression by $\sqrt{3}$, and simplify as follows:

$$\begin{aligned}
\frac{6\sqrt{2} + 3\sqrt{7}}{5\sqrt{3}} &= \frac{6\sqrt{2} + 3\sqrt{7}}{5\sqrt{3}} \times \frac{\sqrt{3}}{\sqrt{3}} \\
&= \frac{\sqrt{3}(6\sqrt{2} + 3\sqrt{7})}{\sqrt{3}(5\sqrt{3})} \\
&= \frac{6\sqrt{2 \times 3} + 3\sqrt{7 \times 3}}{5(\sqrt{3})^2} \\
&= \frac{6\sqrt{6} + 3\sqrt{21}}{5(3)} \\
&= \frac{6\sqrt{6} + 3\sqrt{21}}{15}
\end{aligned}$$

In the previous two examples, each of the denominators was a monomial. If the denominator is a binomial and it is necessary to rationalize the denominator of a given radical expression, a different approach is required.

This approach involves multiplying both the numerator and the denominator of the given radical expression by the conjugate of the denominator. The product of the two binomials in the denominator can then be determined by applying the difference of squares factoring procedure in reverse.

In general, $a\sqrt{x} + b\sqrt{y}$ and $a\sqrt{x} - b\sqrt{y}$, in which $x > 0$ and $y > 0$, are conjugate radical expressions.

Example

Rationalize the denominator of the expression $\dfrac{5\sqrt{3}+4\sqrt{7}}{2\sqrt{3}-\sqrt{7}}$.

Solution

Step 1

Determine the conjugate of the denominator of the given expression.

Since the denominator of the expression is $2\sqrt{3}-\sqrt{7}$, the conjugate of the denominator is $2\sqrt{3}+\sqrt{7}$.

Step 2

Multiply both the numerator and the denominator of the given expression by the conjugate.

$$\frac{5\sqrt{3}+4\sqrt{7}}{2\sqrt{3}-\sqrt{7}} = \frac{5\sqrt{3}+4\sqrt{7}}{2\sqrt{3}-\sqrt{7}} \times \frac{2\sqrt{3}+\sqrt{7}}{2\sqrt{3}+\sqrt{7}}$$

Step 3

Simplify the expression.

$$\frac{(5\sqrt{3}+4\sqrt{7})(2\sqrt{3}+\sqrt{7})}{(2\sqrt{3}-\sqrt{7})(2\sqrt{3}+\sqrt{7})}$$

The product of $5\sqrt{3}+4\sqrt{7}$ and $2\sqrt{3}+\sqrt{7}$ can be determined by applying the FOIL rule for the multiplication of two binomials. The product of $2\sqrt{3}-\sqrt{7}$ and $2\sqrt{3}+\sqrt{7}$ can be determined by applying the difference of squares factoring procedure (in reverse), in which $a^2-b^2=(a+b)(a-b)$.

$$= \frac{\begin{array}{c}(5\sqrt{3})(2\sqrt{3})+(5\sqrt{3})(\sqrt{7})\\ +(4\sqrt{7})(2\sqrt{3})+(4\sqrt{7})(\sqrt{7})\end{array}}{(2\sqrt{3})^2-(\sqrt{7})^2}$$

$$= \frac{10(3)+5\sqrt{21}+8\sqrt{21}+4(7)}{12-7}$$

$$= \frac{30+5\sqrt{21}+8\sqrt{21}+28}{12-7}$$

Collect like terms.

$$= \frac{58+13\sqrt{21}}{5}$$

20NL.4 Solve problems that involve radical equations (limited to square roots or cube roots).

PERFORMING INVERSE OPERATIONS USING SQUARES AND SQUARE ROOTS

When solving equations, it is often necessary to undo an operation in order to move a number from one side of the equals sign to the other. This means that the opposite or inverse of the operation is applied to both sides of the equation.

For example,

- adding is the inverse of subtracting
- subtracting is the inverse of adding
- multiplying is the inverse of dividing
- dividing is the inverse of multiplying

SQUARES AND SQUARE ROOTS

Solving an equation involving the square of a number (x^2) or the square root of a number $(\sqrt{x})$ will require the use of inverse operations.

When **squaring** a number, it means that the number is multiplied by itself.

Example

What is the square of 7?

Solution

$$7^2 = 7 \times 7 = 49$$

The inverse operation of squaring a number is the **square root** of the result.

Taking the square root of a number is expressed by writing a radical sign $(\sqrt{})$ over the number of which you wish to take the square root.

Example

Determine the square root of 9.

Solution

To take the square root of 9, find a number that is equal to 9 when multiplied by itself. The square root of 9 is written as $\sqrt{9}$. Since $3 \times 3 = 9$, it follows that $\sqrt{9} = \sqrt{3 \times 3} = 3$.

SOLVING EQUATIONS USING SQUARES AND SQUARE ROOTS

Perform the opposite operation, squaring, to eliminate the square root sign $(\sqrt{})$ in an equation.

Example

Solve the equation $\sqrt{k} = 7$ for k.

Solution

The inverse of taking the square root of a number is to square the number. Square each side of the equation to eliminate the radical sign.

$$(\sqrt{k})^2 = 7^2$$
$$k = 49$$

Other equations are solved by taking the square root of both sides, to eliminate the square (^{2}) in an equation.

If an equation involves a squared variable, such as $x^2 = 9$, be careful to consider both possible solutions for x:

$x = 3$, since $3^2 = 9$ and $x = -3$, since $(-3)^2 = 9$.

Therefore, when square rooting both sides of an equation with a squared variable, remember to find the positive and negative square roots, $\pm\sqrt{}$, of the number.

Example

Solve the equation $x^2 + 8 = 44$.

Solution

Step 1

Isolate the variable by performing the inverse operation to both sides of the equation. Isolate x by subtracting 8 from both sides of the equation.

$$x^2 + 8 = 44$$
$$x^2 + 8 - 8 = 44 - 8$$
$$x^2 = 36$$

Step 2

Remove the square by performing the inverse operation to both sides of the equation.

The opposite operation of squaring is to take the square root of both sides, which means taking the positive and negative square roots, $\pm\sqrt{}$, of the value.

$$\sqrt{x^2} = \pm\sqrt{36}$$
$$x = \pm 6$$

The $\pm$ sign means positive or negative. There are two possible answers: 6 or -6.

20NL.4 Solve problems that involve radical equations (limited to square roots or cube roots).

SOLVING RADICAL EQUATIONS INVOLVING SQUARE ROOTS ALGEBRAICALLY AND GRAPHICALLY

A radical equation is one in which the variable appears under a radical sign.

It is important to remember that the square root sign, $\sqrt{}$, means the **positive** or **principal** square root only; for example, $\sqrt{9} = +3$ only. If the negative square root is required, then there must be a negative sign in front of the square root sign; for example, $-\sqrt{9} = -3$. If both roots are required, then both signs must appear; for example, $\pm\sqrt{9} = \pm 3$. Radical equations can be solved algebraically or graphically.

Solving Radical Equations Involving Square Roots

Algebraically

The algebraic method involves isolating the radicals and squaring both sides of the equation. When squaring both sides of an equation, you do not always get an equivalent equation. Although the new equation will always contain the roots of the original equation, it may also contain roots that are not roots of the original equation.

These are called extraneous roots and are not part of the solution.

The following example illustrates this situation.

Example

Solve $\sqrt{x} + 5 = 0$ algebraically.

Solution

Because the sum of two positive numbers cannot be 0, there is no solution. However, when the variable is isolated and both sides are squared, the result will be as follows:
$$\sqrt{x} + 5 = 0$$
$$\sqrt{x} = -5$$
$$x = 25$$

Check this answer by substituting into the original equation.
$$\sqrt{25} + 5 = 0$$
$$5 + 5 = 0$$
$$10 \neq 0$$

Therefore, there is no solution. Indicate that there is no solution with an empty set $\{\}$, which is also symbolized by $\varnothing$. The equations with extraneous solutions will not always be as obvious as $\sqrt{x} + 5 = 0$. Always verify that the solution values satisfy the original equation.

The symbol for the empty set, , is not the Greek letter Phi.

Example

Solve $\sqrt{x + 5} = x + 3$ algebraically.

Solution

Square both sides of the equation.
$$(\sqrt{x + 5})^2 = (x + 3)^2$$
$$x + 5 = x^2 + 6x + 9$$

Rearrange the equation to leave 0 on one side and a polynomial on the other:
$$0 = x^2 + 6x + 9 - x - 5$$
$$0 = x^2 + 5x + 4$$

Factor and solve:
$$0 = x^2 + 5x + 4$$
$$0 = (x + 1)(x + 4)$$
$$x = -1 \text{ or } x = -4$$

Verify these solutions by substituting back into the original equation.

x = −1		x = −4	
LHS	**RHS**	**LHS**	**RHS**
$\sqrt{-1 + 5}$	$-1 + 3$	$\sqrt{-4 + 5}$	$-4 + 3$
$\sqrt{4}$	2	$\sqrt{1}$	-1
2	2	1	-1

From the verifications, $x = -1$ is a solution value, but $x = -4$ is extraneous. Therefore, the solution set is $\{-1\}$.

Solving Radical Equations Involving Square Roots

Graphically

Each side of a radical equation represents the equation of a line. When solving radical equations using a graph, the solution is the point of intersection of the two graphs of the equations. If there is more than one point of intersection, then multiple solutions are possible.

The graphical method is applicable to any equation, but is especially useful when the algebraic method produces an equation that is not easily solvable.

Example

Use a graphing calculator to solve
$\sqrt{2x + 3} = x + 1$, and round the solution values
to the nearest tenth.

Solution

Press $\boxed{Y =}$, and enter the equations
$Y_1 = \sqrt{(2x + 3)}$ and $Y_2 = x + 1$.

Press $\boxed{ZOOM}$, and select 4:ZDecimal from the
menu. The following graph will result.

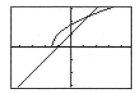

Press $\boxed{2nd}$ $\boxed{TRACE}$, and select 5:Intersect
from the menu to find the points of intersection.

It can be seen that there is only one point of
intersection.

The *x*-coordinate of the point of intersection,
rounded to the nearest tenth, is 1.4.

Therefore, the solution set is {1.4}.

---

*Use the following information to
answer the next question.*

Four students were each asked to use
deductive reasoning to develop a logical
conclusion from two given statements.

Jacob

1. The difference of the squares of two
   consecutive whole numbers is equal to
   the sum of the numbers.
2. An example of two consecutive whole
   numbers is 7 and 8.

Jacob concluded that the difference of the
squares of 7 and 8 is equal to $7 + 8 = 15$.

Alec

1. Perpendicular lines are two lines that
   intersect to form a 90° angle.
2. Lines l_1 and l_2 are perpendicular.

Alec concluded that lines l_1 and l_2 intersect
at a right angle.

Emily

1. The area of rectangle *ABCD* is equal to
   the area of rectangle *EFGH*.
2. The length of rectangle *ABCD* is 6 m,
   and its width is 4 m.

Emily concluded that the length of
rectangle *EFGH* is 6 m, and its width is
4 m.

Angela

1. The sum of the internal angles of a
   triangle equals 180°.
2. In triangle *ABC*, $\angle A = 70°$ and
   $\angle C = 20°$.

Angela concluded that triangle *ABC* is a
right triangle because
$\angle B = 180° - 70° - 20° = 90°$.

1. Which student has reached a conclusion
   that does **not** follow logically from their
   given statements?
   A. Jacob   B. Alec
   C. Emily   D. Angela

Use the following information to answer the next question.

In the given diagram, $AC \cong DB$ and $\angle ACB \cong \angle DBC$.

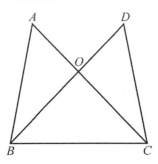

Peter was asked to use this information to prove that $\angle ABC \cong \angle DCB$.

2. Which of the following statements would be **most useful** to Peter in constructing his proof?

    A. $\angle AOB = \angle DOC$

    B. $\angle AOB + \angle BOC = 180°$

    C. The angles in a triangle add up to 180°.

    D. $\triangle ABC$ is congruent to $\triangle DBC$ by the SAS postulate.

Use the following information to answer the next question.

All major Canadian cities have English as the primary language of communication.

Written Response

3. Give a counterexample to the given conjecture.

Use the following information to answer the next question.

Raj studies the given pattern.
$$9 \times 4 = 36$$
$$7 \times 2 = 14$$
$$13 \times 10 = 130$$
$$21 \times 14 = 294$$
He then makes the conjecture that multiplying any odd number by any even number will result in an even number.

4. If Raj wanted to show by using deductive reasoning that his conjecture is true in every case, which of the following formulas would help him?

    A. $(m + 1) \times (n)$, where $m, n \in I$

    B. $(2m + 1) \times (2n)$, where $m, n \in I$

    C. $(m + 1) \times (n + 1)$, where $m, n \in I$

    D. $(2m + 1) \times (2n + 1)$, where $m, n \in I$

Use the following information to answer the next question.

Blake is asked to find the value of x in the equation $19 + x = 27.65$ by using guess and check.

The steps in Blake's partial solution for determining the value of x are shown.

1. Round the decimal number in the equation.
    $19 + x = 27$
2. Since $19 + 8 = 27$, a reasonable guess is a number less than 8.
3. Substitute 7 for x.
    $19 + 7 = 26$ The guess of 7 gives a number less than 27.65.
4. Substitute 7.65 for x.
    $19 + 7.65 = 26.65$ The guess of 7.65 gives a number less than 27.65.

5. In which step did Blake make his first error?

    A. 1   **B.** 2

    C. 3   **D.** 4

Use the following information to answer the next question.

Rachel is asked to find the number of triangles and the number of squares in Level 5 of the given diagram.

Level 1   Level 2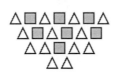

Level 3   Level 4

She recorded her partial results in a table.

Level	Number of Triangles	Number of Squares
1	1	1
2	3	3
3	7	5
4	13	7
5		

6. What are the two numbers that complete Rachel's table?

A. 14, 8   B. 15, 9

C. 21, 9   D. 26, 8

7. What is the simplified form of $(5 + \sqrt{50}) - (8 + \sqrt{4}) + (6 - \sqrt{18})$?

A. $5 + 2\sqrt{2}$ B. $3 + 2\sqrt{7}$

C. $3 + \sqrt{2}$ D. $1 + 2\sqrt{2}$

8. Which of the following expressions is the simplified form of the expression $\dfrac{\sqrt{6} + \sqrt{3}}{2\sqrt{3} + \sqrt{6}}$ with a rational denominator?

A. $\dfrac{1}{2}$ B. $\sqrt{3}$

C. $\dfrac{\sqrt{2}}{2}$ D. $\dfrac{3\sqrt{2}}{2}$

Use the following information to answer the next question.

Carlos and Miguel are asked to divide $12\sqrt{40} + 24\sqrt{54} - 15\sqrt{96}$ by $3\sqrt{2}$. Both solutions are shown.

Carlos' partial solution is as follows:

1. $\dfrac{12\sqrt{40} + 24\sqrt{54} - 15\sqrt{96}}{3\sqrt{2}}$

2. $\dfrac{12\sqrt{40}}{3\sqrt{2}} + \dfrac{24\sqrt{54}}{3\sqrt{2}} - \dfrac{15\sqrt{96}}{3\sqrt{2}}$

3. $4\sqrt{20} + 8\sqrt{27} - 5\sqrt{48}$

4. $4\sqrt{4 \times 5} + 8\sqrt{9 \times 3} - 5\sqrt{16 \times 3}$

5. $16\sqrt{5} + 24\sqrt{3} - 20\sqrt{3}$

Miguel's partial solution is as follows:

1. $\dfrac{12\sqrt{40} + 24\sqrt{54} - 15\sqrt{96}}{3\sqrt{2}}$

2. $\dfrac{12\sqrt{4 \times 10} + 24\sqrt{9 \times 6} - 15\sqrt{16 \times 6}}{3\sqrt{2}}$

3. $\dfrac{24\sqrt{10} + 72\sqrt{6} - 60\sqrt{6}}{3\sqrt{2}}$

4. $\dfrac{24\sqrt{10} + 12\sqrt{6}}{3\sqrt{2}}$

5. $\dfrac{24\sqrt{10}}{3\sqrt{2}} + \dfrac{12\sqrt{6}}{3\sqrt{2}}$

9. Which of the following statements about the two solutions is **true**?

A. Carlos has a correct partial solution, and Miguel has an incorrect partial solution.

B. Carlos has an incorrect partial solution, and Miguel has a correct partial solution.

C. Both Carlos and Miguel have an incorrect partial solution.

D. Both Carlos and Miguel have a correct partial solution.

Numerical Response

10. If $7\sqrt{6} \times 5\sqrt{3} = K\sqrt{2}$, in which K represents an integer, then the value of K is _____.

Use the following information to answer the next question.

Alejandro is asked to determine the product of $4\sqrt{14} - 3\sqrt{2}$ and $5\sqrt{2} + 4\sqrt{14}$. His solution is as shown.

$(4\sqrt{14} - 3\sqrt{2})(5\sqrt{2} + 4\sqrt{14})$

① $= 20\sqrt{28} + 8\sqrt{196} - 15\sqrt{4} - 12\sqrt{28}$

② $= 20\sqrt{4 \times 7} + 8(14) - 15(2) - 12\sqrt{4 \times 7}$

③ $= 40\sqrt{7} + 112 - 30 - 24\sqrt{7}$

④ $= 92 + 16\sqrt{7}$

11. Alejandro's first error occurred in step

    A. 1   **B.** 2

    C. 3   **D.** 4

12. The mixed radical $3\sqrt{6}$ is equivalent to

    A. $\sqrt{9}$ **B.** $\sqrt{18}$

    C. $\sqrt{54}$ **D.** $\sqrt{216}$

13. An equivalent form of the expression $\dfrac{2\sqrt{3} + 12\sqrt{24}}{2\sqrt{3}}$ is

    A. $12\sqrt{2}$ **B.** $24\sqrt{6}$

    C. $1 + 12\sqrt{2}$ **D.** $1 + 24\sqrt{6}$

14. If x is a rational number and satisfies the equation $3x^2 = 147$, what is the value of the principal square root of x^2?

    A. -49 **B.** -7

    C. 7   **D.** 49

| Written Response |

15. Calculate the square root of $m^2 = \sqrt{20 + 2^4}$.

ANSWERS AND SOLUTIONS
NUMBER AND LOGIC

1. C	5. A	9. B	13. C
2. D	6. C	10. 105	14. C
3. WR	7. D	11. A	15. WR
4. B	8. C	12. C	

1. C

The conclusions developed by Jacob, Alec, and Angela are correct; however, Emily's conclusion is incorrect. The area of rectangle $ABCD$ is

6 m × 4 m = 24 m^2. Therefore, the area of rectangle $EFGH$ must also be 24 m^2. The length of rectangle $EFGH$ does not have to be 6 m, and its width does not have to be 4 m. For example, if the length of rectangle $EFGH$ was 8 m and the width was 3 m, the area of the rectangle would still be 24 m^2.

2. D

It is given that $AC \cong DB$ and $\angle ACB \cong \angle DBC$. By observation, it can be seen that side BC is common to both triangle ABC and triangle DBC. Therefore, the statement that will assist Peter in constructing his proof is that $\triangle ABC$ is congruent to $\triangle DBC$ by the side-angle-side (SAS) postulate. It would then follow that $\angle ABC \cong \angle DCB$, since corresponding angles in congruent triangles are congruent.

3. WR

To provide a counterexample to the given conjecture, it is necessary to identify a Canadian city in which the primary language of communication is not English. A possible counterexample is Montreal. In Montreal, the primary language of communication is French.

4. B

Use deductive reasoning to show that Raj's conjecture is true.

Let $2m + 1$ represent any odd numbers and $2n$ represent any even numbers, where $m, n \in I$.

Determine the equation for multiplying any odd number by any even number.
$(2m + 1) \times (2n)$
$= 4mn + 2n$
$= 2(2mn + n)$

Since any number multiplied by 2 is even, it follows that $(2m + 1) \times (2n)$ is even.

Therefore, the expression $(2m + 1) \times (2n)$, where $m, n \in I$, would help Raj prove his conjecture.

5. A

Blake made his first error in step 1. When the decimal number 27.65 is rounded to the nearest whole number, it becomes 28.
$19 + x = 28$

Steps 2 to 5 of a possible solution are therefore as follows:

2. Since $19 + 9 = 28$, a reasonable guess would be a number less than 9.
3. Substitute 8 for x.
   $19 + 8 = 27$
4. The guess of 8 gives a number less than 27.65. Add 0.65 to 8, and substitute the result for x.
   $19 + 8.65 = 27.65$
5. The value of x is 8.65.

6. C

Step 1
Identify the pattern in the number of triangles.

Level	Number of Triangles	Pattern
1	1	
2	3	3 − 1 = 2
3	7	7 − 3 = 4
4	13	13 − 7 = 6

The difference between the number of triangles in one level and the number in the previous level is increasing by 2. Therefore, in Level 5, there will be $13 + 8 = 21$ triangles.

Step 2

Identify the pattern in the number of squares.

Level	Number of Squares	Pattern
1	1	
2	3	$3 - 1 = 2$
3	5	$5 - 3 = 2$
4	7	$7 - 5 = 2$

There is a constant difference of 2 between the number of squares in one level and the number in the previous level. Therefore, in Level 5, there will be $7 + 2 = 9$ squares.

Step 3

Complete the table.

Level	Number of Triangles	Number of Squares
1	1	1
2	3	3
3	7	5
4	13	7
5	21	9

7. D

Step 1

Simplify the radicals.

$(5 + \sqrt{50}) - (8 + \sqrt{4}) + (6 - \sqrt{18})$
$= (5 + \sqrt{25}\sqrt{2}) - (8 + 2) + (6 - \sqrt{9}\sqrt{2})$
$= (5 + 5\sqrt{2}) - (10) + (6 - 3\sqrt{2})$

Step 2

Drop the brackets, and join like terms.

$(5 + 5\sqrt{2}) - (10) + (6 - 3\sqrt{2})$
$= 5 + 5\sqrt{2} - 10 + 6 - 3\sqrt{2}$
$= 1 + 2\sqrt{2}$

8. C

Step 1

Determine the conjugate of the denominator of the given expression.

The denominator of the expression is $2\sqrt{3} + \sqrt{6}$, so the conjugate of the denominator is $2\sqrt{3} - \sqrt{6}$.

Step 2

Multiply both the numerator and the denominator of the given expression by $2\sqrt{3} - \sqrt{6}$.

$\dfrac{\sqrt{6} + \sqrt{3}}{2\sqrt{3} + \sqrt{6}} = \dfrac{\sqrt{6} + \sqrt{3}}{2\sqrt{3} + \sqrt{6}} \times \dfrac{2\sqrt{3} - \sqrt{6}}{2\sqrt{3} - \sqrt{6}}$

Step 3

Simplify $\dfrac{\sqrt{6} + \sqrt{3}}{2\sqrt{3} + \sqrt{6}} \times \dfrac{2\sqrt{3} - \sqrt{6}}{2\sqrt{3} - \sqrt{6}}$.

$\dfrac{(\sqrt{6} + \sqrt{3})(2\sqrt{3} - \sqrt{6})}{(2\sqrt{3} + \sqrt{6})(2\sqrt{3} - \sqrt{6})}$

Use the FOIL rule for the multiplication of 2 binomials to determine the product of $\sqrt{6} + \sqrt{3}$ and $2\sqrt{3} - \sqrt{6}$. Apply the difference of squares factoring procedure (in reverse) where $a^2 - b^2 = (a + b)(a - b)$ to determine the product of $2\sqrt{3} + \sqrt{6}$ and $2\sqrt{3} - \sqrt{6}$.

$= \dfrac{(\sqrt{6})(2\sqrt{3}) - (\sqrt{6})(\sqrt{6}) + (\sqrt{3})(2\sqrt{3}) - (\sqrt{3})(\sqrt{6})}{(2\sqrt{3})^2 - (\sqrt{6})^2}$

$= \dfrac{2\sqrt{18} - 6 + (2)(3) - \sqrt{18}}{12 - 6}$

$= \dfrac{(2)(3)\sqrt{2} - 6 + 6 - 3\sqrt{2}}{12 - 6}$

$= \dfrac{6\sqrt{2} - 6 + 6 - 3\sqrt{2}}{12 - 6}$

Collect like terms.

$= \dfrac{3\sqrt{2}}{6}$

$= \dfrac{\sqrt{2}}{2}$

9. B

Although Carlos and Miguel have used two totally different procedures for dividing $12\sqrt{40} + 24\sqrt{54} - 15\sqrt{96}$ by $3\sqrt{2}$, both approaches are correct.

Step 1

Analyze Carlos' partial solution.

Carlos made an error in step 4. The expression $4\sqrt{4 \times 5} = 4(2\sqrt{5}) = 8\sqrt{5}$ rather than $16\sqrt{5}$.

Step 4 in Carlos' solution should read $8\sqrt{5} + 24\sqrt{3} - 20\sqrt{3}$. After the collection of like terms, this expression becomes $8\sqrt{5} + 4\sqrt{3}$.

Step 2

Analyze Miguel's partial solution.

Miguel's partial solution is correct. The last two steps required to complete his solution would be as follows:

6. $(24 \div 3)\sqrt{10 \div 2} + (12 \div 3)\sqrt{6 \div 2}$

7. $8\sqrt{5} + 4\sqrt{3}$

10. 105

Step 1

Determine the product of $7\sqrt{6}$ and $5\sqrt{3}$.

$7\sqrt{6} \times 5\sqrt{3}$
$= (7 \times 5) \times \sqrt{6 \times 3}$
$= 35\sqrt{18}$
$= 35\sqrt{9 \times 2}$
$= 35(3\sqrt{2})$
$= (35 \times 3)\sqrt{2}$
$= 105\sqrt{2}$

Step 2

Determine the value of K.

It is known that $7\sqrt{6} \times 5\sqrt{3} = K\sqrt{2}$. It has been determined in step 1 that $7\sqrt{6} \times 5\sqrt{3} = 105\sqrt{2}$. Therefore, $K\sqrt{2} = 105\sqrt{2}$. It then follows that $K = 105$.

11. A

Alejandro's first error occurred in step 1. The expanded form of $(4\sqrt{14} - 3\sqrt{2})(5\sqrt{2} + 4\sqrt{14})$ is $20\sqrt{28} + 16\sqrt{196} - 15\sqrt{4} - 12\sqrt{28}$, rather than $20\sqrt{28} + 8\sqrt{196} - 15\sqrt{4} - 12\sqrt{28}$. In particular, 4×4 equals 16, not 8.

Alejandro's solution should have appeared as follows:

1. $(4\sqrt{14} - 3\sqrt{2})(5\sqrt{2} + 4\sqrt{14})$
   $= 20\sqrt{28} + 16\sqrt{196} - 15\sqrt{4} - 12\sqrt{28}$
2. $(4\sqrt{14} - 3\sqrt{2})(5\sqrt{2} + 4\sqrt{14})$
   $= 20\sqrt{4 \times 7} + 16(14) - 15(2) - 12\sqrt{4 \times 7}$
3. $(4\sqrt{14} - 3\sqrt{2})(5\sqrt{2} + 4\sqrt{14})$
   $= 40\sqrt{7} + 224 - 30 - 24\sqrt{7}$
4. $(4\sqrt{14} - 3\sqrt{2})(5\sqrt{2} + 4\sqrt{14}) = 194 + 16\sqrt{7}$

12. C

Step 1

Square the coefficient of the mixed radical, and place this value underneath a radical sign.

$3\sqrt{6} = \sqrt{3^2} \times \sqrt{6}$
$= \sqrt{9} \times \sqrt{6}$

Step 2

Multiply the two radicands.

$3\sqrt{6} = \sqrt{9} \times \sqrt{6}$
$= \sqrt{54}$

13. C

Step 1

Divide the binomial $2\sqrt{3} + 12\sqrt{24}$ by the monomial $2\sqrt{3}$.

$\dfrac{2\sqrt{3} + 12\sqrt{24}}{2\sqrt{3}}$
$= \dfrac{2\sqrt{3}}{2\sqrt{3}} + \dfrac{12\sqrt{24}}{2\sqrt{3}}$
$= (2 \div 2)\sqrt{3 \div 3} + (12 \div 2)\sqrt{24 \div 3}$
$= 1\sqrt{1} + 6\sqrt{8}$
$= 1 + 6\sqrt{8}$

Step 2

Simplify the expression.

Remember that $8 = 4 \times 2$ and that 4 is a perfect square.

$1 + 6\sqrt{8} = 1 + 6\sqrt{4 \times 2}$
$= 1 + 6(2\sqrt{2})$
$= 1 + 12\sqrt{2}$

An equivalent form of the expression $\dfrac{2\sqrt{3} + 12\sqrt{24}}{2\sqrt{3}}$ is $1 + 12\sqrt{2}$.

14. C

Step 1

Determine the value of x by applying inverse operations.

Divide both sides by 3.

$3x^2 = 147$
$\dfrac{3x^2}{3} = \dfrac{147}{3}$
$x^2 = 49$

Take the square root of both sides of the equation.

$\sqrt{x^2} = \sqrt{49}$
$x = \pm 7$

Step 2

Determine the principal square root of x^2.

The principal square root is the positive square root.

The principal square root of x^2 is 7.

15. WR

Step 1

Reduce the expression under the square root sign to its simplest form.

$m^2 = \sqrt{20 + 2^4}$
$= \sqrt{20 + 16}$
$= \sqrt{36}$

Step 2

Calculate the square root of m^2.

Take the square root of both sides.

Round the square root of m to the nearest hundredth.

$$m^2 = \sqrt{36}$$
$$\pm\sqrt{m^2} = \pm\sqrt{6}$$
$$m \approx \pm 2.45$$

UNIT TEST — NUMBER AND LOGIC

Use the following information to answer the next question.

Most cyclists wear helmets. Helmets protect cyclists from head injuries.

1. Which of the following statements logically follows?

A. All cyclists suffer from head injuries.

B. No cyclists suffer from head injuries.

C. All cyclists are protected from head injuries.

D. Most cyclists are protected from head injuries.

Use the following information to answer the next question.

A set of data is illustrated in the given table. Mario's teacher asks him to use inductive reasoning to determine the values of x and y, given that x and y represent whole numbers.

1	0
2	3
3	8
4	15
5	24
6	35
7	x
8	y

2. If Mario correctly determines the values of x and y, he will find that the value of y is

A. 48   B. 55

C. 63   D. 72

Use the following information to answer the next question.

Shreya made the following conjecture:
$a^2b < bc^2$ if $a < c$.
Shreya then determined four sets of values for a, b, and c that might serve as counterexamples to her conjecture.

I. $a = 2, b = 3, c = 4$
II. $a = 3, b = 0, c = 5$
III. $a = -5, b = 2, c = -3$
IV. $a = -7, b = -1, c = -6$

3. Which of Shreya's sets of values serve as counterexamples for her conjecture?

A. I and II

B. II and III

C. III and IV

D. I, II, III, and IV

Use the following information to answer the next question.

The given triangle is called Pascal's triangle. The first six rows are shown.

$$1$$
$$1 \quad 1$$
$$1 \quad 2 \quad 1$$
$$1 \quad 3 \quad 3 \quad 1$$
$$1 \quad 4 \quad 6 \quad 4 \quad 1$$
$$1 \quad 5 \quad 10 \quad 10 \quad 5 \quad 1$$

Numerical Response

4. The sum of the numbers in the seventh row of Pascal's triangle is _____.

Use the following information to answer the next question.

Tom designs a model of a square-based pyramid for a school project. The surface area of the model is 2 160 cm² with a slant height of 30 cm. The side length of the base of the model is 36 cm, and the height of the model is 24 cm. Tom places the pyramid on a rectangular piece of cardboard that is 10 cm longer and wider than the base of the pyramid.

Tom is then asked to find the volume of the pyramid. The steps in his partial solution are as follows:

1. $V_{pyramid} = \frac{1}{3}(A_{base} \times h)$

2. $V_{pyramid} = \frac{1}{3}(36^2 \times 30)$

3. $V_{pyramid} = \frac{1}{3}(38\ 880)$

4. $V_{pyramid} = 12\ 960\,cm^3$

5. In which step did Tom make his first error?

   A. 1   **B.** 2

   C. 3   **D.** 4

Use the following information to answer the next question.

The given image shows the first three diagrams in a series. The series of diagrams illustrates a particular pattern.

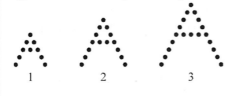

6. How many dots will be in diagram 6?

   A. 20   **B.** 25

   C. 30   **D.** 35

7. If $5\sqrt{18} + \sqrt{98} + k\sqrt{32} = 34\sqrt{2}$, then the value of k is

   A. 3   **B.** 6

   C. 9   **D.** 12

Numerical Response

8. When $\sqrt{432}$ is converted to the simplified mixed radical form $a\sqrt{b}$, the sum of a and b is _____.

Use the following information to answer the next question.

Maya is asked to determine the area of this rectangle.

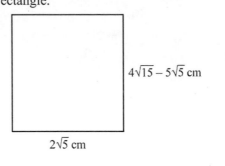

$4\sqrt{15} - 5\sqrt{5}$ cm

$2\sqrt{5}$ cm

9. Assuming Maya's work is correct, which of the following expressions is an expression that she could have obtained for the area of the given rectangle?

   A. $(40\sqrt{3} - 50\sqrt{5})$ cm²

   B. $(13\sqrt{3} - 15\sqrt{5})$ cm²

   C. $(13\sqrt{3} - 15)$ cm²

   D. $(40\sqrt{3} - 50)$ cm²

Use the following information to answer the next question.

Camila is asked to determine an equivalent form of the expression $\dfrac{24\sqrt{160}}{72\sqrt{5}} + \dfrac{15\sqrt{300}}{45\sqrt{6}}$. Her solution is as shown.

1. $\dfrac{24\sqrt{160}}{72\sqrt{5}} + \dfrac{15\sqrt{300}}{45\sqrt{6}}$

   $= \dfrac{1}{3}\sqrt{32} + \dfrac{1}{3}\sqrt{50}$

2. $\dfrac{24\sqrt{160}}{72\sqrt{5}} + \dfrac{15\sqrt{300}}{45\sqrt{6}}$

   $= \dfrac{1}{3}\sqrt{16 \times 2} + \dfrac{1}{3}\sqrt{25 \times 2}$

3. $\dfrac{24\sqrt{160}}{72\sqrt{5}} + \dfrac{15\sqrt{300}}{45\sqrt{6}}$

   $= \dfrac{4}{3}\sqrt{2} + \dfrac{5}{3}\sqrt{2}$

4. $\dfrac{24\sqrt{160}}{72\sqrt{5}} + \dfrac{15\sqrt{300}}{45\sqrt{6}} = 3\sqrt{2}$

10. Which of the following statements about Camila's solution is **true**?

A. Camila made an error in step 1.

B. Camila made an error in step 2.

C. Camila made an error in step 3.

D. Camila did not make any errors.

11. If the expression $\sqrt{75}$ is converted to a mixed radical in the form $a\sqrt{b}$, then the value of a is

A. 3   **B.** 4

C. 5   **D.** 25

12. The expression $8\sqrt{54} - 2\sqrt{150} - \sqrt{24}$ can be simplified to

A. $12\sqrt{6}$ **B.** $10\sqrt{6}$

C. $-4\sqrt{6}$ **D.** $-14\sqrt{6}$

Use the following information to answer the next question.

The radical $\sqrt{1\ 350}$ can be simplified to the mixed radical $k\sqrt{6}$.

Numerical Response

13. The value of k is _____.

14. What is the value of x in the equation $\sqrt{x} - 4 = 2$?

A. 12   **B.** 16

C. 36   **D.** 64

Written Response

15. Solve $\sqrt{2x + 3} = \sqrt{x + 1} + 1$ algebraically, and verify the solution values.

ANSWERS AND SOLUTIONS — UNIT TEST

1. D	5. B	9. D	13. 15
2. C	6. D	10. D	14. C
3. B	7. A	11. C	15. WR
4. 64	8. 15	12. A	

1. D

Assuming that the two statements are true and using deductive reasoning, the statement that follows logically is that most cyclists are protected from head injuries.

2. C

Step 1

Make a conjecture about how each number in the right-hand column is obtained from the corresponding number in the left-hand column. Upon analysis, each number in the right-hand column is obtained by subtracting 1 from the square of the corresponding number in the left-hand column. For example, the number 24 equals $5^2 - 1$, and the number 35 equals $6^2 - 1$.

Step 2

Extend the derived pattern to solve for x and y.

$x = 7^2 - 1 = 48$
$y = 8^2 - 1 = 63$

The value of y is 63.

3. B

Step 1

Determine if the values in set I satisfy the given conjecture.

Since $2 < 4$, $a < c$.

Substitute 2 for a, 3 for b, and 4 for c in the inequality $a^2b < bc^2$ to determine whether the given values for a, b, and c satisfy this inequality.

$2^2 \times 3 < 3 \times 4^2$
$4 \times 3 < 3 \times 16$
$12 < 48$

The values in set I satisfy the inequality.

Step 2

Determine if the values in set II satisfy the given conjecture.

Since $3 < 5$, $a < c$.

Substitute 3 for a, 0 for b, and 5 for c in the inequality $a^2b < bc^2$ to determine whether the given values for a, b, and c satisfy this inequality.

$3^2 \times 0 < 0 \times 5^2$
$0 < 0$

The values in set II do not satisfy the inequality because $0 = 0$.

Step 3

Determine if the values in set III satisfy the given conjecture.

Since $-5 < -3$, $a < c$.

Substitute -5 for a, 2 for b, and -3 for c in the inequality $a^2b < bc^2$ to determine whether the given values for a, b, and c satisfy this inequality.

$(-5)^2 \times 2 < 2 \times (-3)^2$
$25 \times 2 < 2 \times 9$
$50 < 18$

Because 50 is not less than 18, the values in set III do not satisfy the inequality.

Step 4

Determine if the values in set IV satisfy the given conjecture.

Since $-7 < -6$, $a < c$.

Substitute -7 for a, -1 for b, and -6 for c in the inequality $a^2b < bc^2$ to determine whether the given values for a, b, and c satisfy this inequality.

$(-7)^2 \times (-1) < (-1) \times (-6)^2$
$49 \times (-1) < (-1) \times 36$
$-49 < -36$

The values in set IV satisfy the inequality.

Step 5

Determine which sets of values provide counterexamples to Shreya's conjecture.

The values in sets II and III do not satisfy the given set of inequalities, and therefore serve as counterexamples for Shreya's conjecture.

4. 64

Step 1

Make a conjecture about how each number in a particular row of Pascal's triangle is obtained by analyzing the numbers in the previous row.

A possible conjecture is that every number except the first and the last is the sum of the two numbers immediately above it. The first and last numbers are always 1.

For example, in the sixth row, the numbers are 1, $1 + 4 = 5$, $4 + 6 = 10$, $6 + 4 = 10$, $4 + 1 = 5$, and 1.

Step 2

Extend the derived pattern to determine the numbers in the seventh row of Pascal's triangle.

The numbers in the seventh row of Pascal's triangle are 1, $1 + 5 = 6$, $5 + 10 = 15$, $10 + 10 = 20$, $10 + 5 = 15$, $5 + 1 = 6$, and 1.

Step 3

Determine the sum of the numbers.
$1 + 6 + 15 + 20 + 15 + 6 + 1 = 64$

The sum of the numbers in the seventh row of Pascal's triangle is 64.

5. B

Tom made his first error in step 2. The volume, V, of a pyramid can be determined by applying the formula $V = \frac{1}{3}\left(A_{\text{base}} \times h\right)$, where A_{base} is the area of the base and h is the height of the pyramid. Since the pyramid is square-based, the formula becomes $V = \frac{1}{3}\left(s^2 \times h\right)$, where s is the side length of the base and h is the height of the pyramid. Tom used the slant height, 30 cm, instead of the height of the pyramid, which is 24 cm.

The correct solution is as follows:

1. $V = \frac{1}{3}\left(A_{\text{base}} \times h\right)$

2. $V = \frac{1}{3}\left(s^2 \times h\right)$

3. $V = \frac{1}{3}\left(36^2 \times 24\right)$

4. $V = \frac{1}{3}(1\ 296 \times 24)$

5. $V = \frac{1}{3}(31\ 104)$

6. $V = 10\ 368$

The volume of the model of a square-based pyramid is 10 368 cm³.

6. D

Step 1

Make a table to organize the information from the given diagrams.

Diagram	Number of Dots
1	10
2	15
3	20

Step 2

Identify the pattern.

From diagram 1 to diagram 2, there is a difference of 5 dots ($15 - 10 = 5$). From diagram 2 to 3, there is also a difference of 5 dots ($20 - 15 = 5$).

Therefore, the pattern is that 5 dots are added to each diagram.

Step 3

Determine how many dots will be in diagram 6.

Diagram 4 will have $20 + 5 = 25$ dots, and diagram 5 will have $25 + 5 = 30$ dots. Therefore, diagram 6 will have $30 + 5 = 35$ dots.

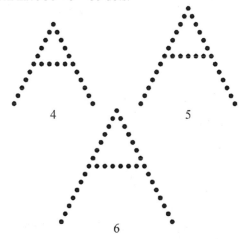

7. A

Since the right side of the equation has a radical of $\sqrt{2}$, then all the other radicals in the equation must be reduced to $\sqrt{2}$.

Step 1

Find the second factor of the radicals on the left side of the equation if the first factor is 2.
$18 \div 2 = 9$
$98 \div 2 = 49$
$32 \div 2 = 16$
The equation becomes
$5\sqrt{9 \times 2} + \sqrt{49 \times 2} + k\sqrt{16 \times 2} = 34\sqrt{2}$.

Step 2

Move all the perfect square values out from the square root, and simplify.

$$(5 \times 3)\sqrt{2} + 7\sqrt{2} + (k \times 4)\sqrt{2} = 34\sqrt{2}$$
$$15\sqrt{2} + 7\sqrt{2} + 4k\sqrt{2} = 34\sqrt{2}$$
$$22\sqrt{2} + 4k\sqrt{2} = 34\sqrt{2}$$

Step 3

Simplify the equation by dividing out $\sqrt{2}$ and solving for k.

$$22\sqrt{2} + 4k\sqrt{2} = 34\sqrt{2}$$
$$22 + 4k = 34$$
$$4k = 34 - 22$$
$$4k = 12$$
$$k = 3$$

8. 15

Step 1

Determine the greatest perfect square of all the factors of 432.

The factors of 432 are 1, 2, 3, 4, 6, 8, 9, 12, 16, 18, 24, 27, 36, 48, 54, 72, 108, 144, 216, and 432. The greatest perfect square is 144.

Step 2

Simplify the entire radical using the factors 144 and 3.

$$\sqrt{432} = \sqrt{144 \times 3}$$
$$= \sqrt{144} \times \sqrt{3}$$
$$= 12 \times \sqrt{3}$$
$$= 12\sqrt{3}$$

Step 3

Determine the value of $a + b$.

When $\sqrt{432}$ is written as $a\sqrt{b} = 12\sqrt{3}$, the sum of a and b is $12 + 3 = 15$.

9. D

In order to determine the area of the rectangle shown, it is necessary to determine the product of $2\sqrt{5}$ and $4\sqrt{15} - 5\sqrt{5}$ because the area of a rectangle is equal to the length multiplied by the width ($A = LW$).

Step 1

Apply the distributive property with respect to the expression $2\sqrt{5}(4\sqrt{15} - 5\sqrt{5})$.

$$2\sqrt{5}(4\sqrt{15} - 5\sqrt{5})$$
$$= 2\sqrt{5}(4\sqrt{15}) - 2\sqrt{5}(5\sqrt{5})$$

Step 2

Simplify the expression $2\sqrt{5}(4\sqrt{15}) - 2\sqrt{5}(5\sqrt{5})$.

$$2\sqrt{5}(4\sqrt{15}) - 2\sqrt{5}(5\sqrt{5})$$
$$= \begin{pmatrix} (2 \times 4) \times (\sqrt{5 \times 15}) \\ -(2 \times 5) \times (\sqrt{5} \times \sqrt{5}) \end{pmatrix}$$
$$= 8\sqrt{75} - 10\sqrt{25}$$
$$= 8\sqrt{25 \times 3} - 10(5)$$
$$= 8(5\sqrt{3}) - 50$$
$$= 40\sqrt{3} - 50$$

The expression that Maya could have obtained for the area of the given rectangle is $(40\sqrt{3} - 50)$ cm^2.

10. D

Although Camila could have shown additional steps in simplifying the given expression, her solution is correct.

11. C

Step 1

Determine two numbers that have a product equal to the value of the radicand, one of which must be a perfect square. These numbers are 3 and 25.

Step 2

Express the radicand as a product of these two numbers, and separate the expression to isolate the perfect square.

$$\sqrt{75} = \sqrt{25 \times 3}$$
$$= \sqrt{25} \times \sqrt{3}$$

Step 3

Take the square root of the perfect square, and place this value in front of the remaining radical.

$$\sqrt{25} \times \sqrt{3} = 5 \times \sqrt{3}$$
$$= 5\sqrt{3}$$

Written in the form $a\sqrt{b}$, the expression $\sqrt{75}$ is $5\sqrt{3}$; therefore, $a = 5$.

12. A

Step 1

Express each radicand as the product of two numbers, one of which must be a perfect square.

$$= 8\sqrt{54} - 2\sqrt{150} - \sqrt{24}$$
$$= 8\sqrt{9 \times 6} - 2\sqrt{25 \times 6} - \sqrt{4 \times 6}$$

Step 2

Simplify each radicand by applying the product rule for radicals.

$$= 8\sqrt{9 \times 6} - 2\sqrt{25 \times 6} - \sqrt{4 \times 6}$$
$$= 8(\sqrt{9} \times \sqrt{6}) - 2(\sqrt{25} \times \sqrt{6}) - \sqrt{4} \times \sqrt{6}$$
$$= 8(3\sqrt{6}) - 2(5\sqrt{6}) - 2(\sqrt{6})$$
$$= (8 \times 3)\sqrt{6} - (2 \times 5)\sqrt{6} - 2\sqrt{6}$$
$$= 24\sqrt{6} - 10\sqrt{6} - 2\sqrt{6}$$

Step 3

Collect like terms.

$$= 24\sqrt{6} - 10\sqrt{6} - 2\sqrt{6}$$
$$= 12\sqrt{6}$$

13. 15

Step 1

Determine the second factor of 1 350 given that one factor is 6.

$$1\ 350 \div 6 = 225$$

The radical $\sqrt{1\ 350}$ can be expressed as $\sqrt{225 \times 6}$.

Step 2

Apply the product rule for radicals.

$$\sqrt{225 \times 6} = \sqrt{225} \times \sqrt{6}$$
$$= 15 \times \sqrt{6}$$
$$= 15\sqrt{6}$$

Therefore, the value of k is 15.

14. C

To find the value of x, isolate the variable x.

$$\sqrt{x} - 4 = 2$$
$$\sqrt{x} = 6$$
$$(\sqrt{x})^2 = 6^2$$
$$x = 36$$

The value of x in the given equation is 36.

15. WR

Step 1

Square both sides of the equation, and simplify the result.

$$\sqrt{2x+3} = \sqrt{x+1} + 1$$
$$(\sqrt{2x+3})^2 = (\sqrt{x+1} + 1)^2$$
$$2x + 3 = x + 1 + 2\sqrt{x+1} + 1$$
$$x + 1 = 2\sqrt{x+1}$$

Step 2

Square both sides of the equation, and rearrange the equation to leave 0 on one side and a polynomial on the other.

$$x + 1 = 2\sqrt{x+1}$$
$$(x+1)^2 = (2\sqrt{x+1})^2$$
$$x^2 + 2x + 1 = 4(x+1)$$
$$x^2 + 2x + 1 = 4x + 4$$
$$x^2 - 2x - 3 = 0$$

Step 3

Solve the equation by factoring.

$$x^2 - 2x - 3 = 0$$
$$(x-3)(x+1) = 0$$

The possible solutions to this equation are $x = 3$ or $x = -1$.

Step 4

Verify these answers by substituting them into the original equation.

$x = 3$

LHS	RHS
$\sqrt{2(3)+3}$	$\sqrt{3+1}+1$
$\sqrt{9}$	$\sqrt{4}+1$
3	3

$x = -1$

LHS	RHS
$\sqrt{2(-1)+3}$	$\sqrt{-1+1}+1$
$\sqrt{1}$	$\sqrt{0}+1$
1	1

Therefore, the solution set is $\{3, -1\}$.

NOTES

Statistics

STATISTICS

Table of Correlations			
Outcome	Practice Questions	Unit Test Questions	Practice Test
20S Statistics			
20S.1 *Demonstrate an understanding of normal distribution, including:*	1, 2, 3, 4, 5, 6, 7, 8	1, 2, 3, 4, 5, 6, 7, 8	7, 8, 9, 10
20S.2 *Interpret statistical data, using:*	9	9, 10	11, 12, 13

20S.1 Demonstrate an understanding of normal distribution, including:

CALCULATING MEAN

When given a set of data, statistical analysis can be performed to determine important information from the data. The mean, median, and mode are three measures of central tendency for a set of data. A set of data is an unordered collection of values. The set is usually within curly brackets { }.

The mean is often referred to as the average of a set of data.

To calculate the mean of a set of numbers, follow these steps:

1. Find the sum of the values.
2. Divide the sum of the values by the number of values.

Example
> {12, 10, 14, 8, 16}
>
> Calculate the mean of the given data set.

Solution
> **Step 1**
> Find the sum of the values.
> $12 + 10 + 14 + 8 + 16 = 60$
>
> **Step 2**
> Divide the sum of the values by the number of values.
> There are five values, so divide the sum by 5.
> $60 \div 5 = 12$
> The mean of the data set is 12.

20S.1 Demonstrate an understanding of normal distribution, including:

CALCULATING VARIANCE AND STANDARD DEVIATION OF A DATA SET

The variance and standard deviation of a data set are both measures of dispersion that represent how the data is spread about the mean. If the data values are spread out, the variance and standard-deviation value will be greater than if the data values are clustered together about the mean.

The variance is the average squared deviation of each number from the mean in a given data set. Variance is denoted by the small Greek letter sigma squared (σ^2). For the set of values $\{x_1, x_2, x_3, \ldots x_{n-1}, x_n\}$, the variance can be calculated as

$$\sigma^2 = \frac{(x_1 - \mu)^2 + (x_2 - \mu)^2 + \ldots + (x_n - \mu)^2}{n}, \text{ in}$$

which μ represents the mean.

The mean of a set of data is calculated by adding all the data values and then dividing by the number of data values in the set. The mean is often referred to as the average.

The standard deviation is the square root of the variance. For the set of values $\{x_1, x_2, x_3, \ldots x_{n-1}, x_n\}$, the standard deviation can be calculated using the following formula:

$$\sigma = \sqrt{\frac{\begin{array}{c}(x_1 - \mu)^2 + (x_2 - \mu)^2 \\ + \ldots + (x_n - \mu)^2\end{array}}{n}}, \text{ in which } \mu = \text{ the mean.}$$

The formulas for variance and standard deviation show why the variance and standard deviation increase as the values become more spread out from the mean. Notice that the values for $(x_1 - \mu)^2$, $(x_2 - \mu)^2$, etc., will increase as the values for x_1, x_2, etc., get farther from μ.

Example

A set of data is collected from 8 students who want to determine whether a new movie is worth seeing. Using a rating scale of 1 to 10, the set of data collected is {5, 7, 8, 5, 7, 6, 3, 9}.

To the nearest hundredth, determine the mean, the variance, and the standard deviation of the given movie ratings.

Solution

The mean is given by the formula

$$\mu = \frac{x_1 + x_2 + \ldots + x_n}{n}.$$

There are 8 data values, so $n = 8$.

Substitute the movie-rating values into the mean formula, and solve.

$$\mu = \frac{5 + 7 + 8 + 5 + 7 + 6 + 3 + 9}{8}$$

$$= \frac{50}{8}$$

$$= 6.25$$

The mean of the data set is 6.25.

Substitute these values (and the data values) into the variance formula

$$\sigma^2 = \frac{(x_1 - \mu)^2 + (x_2 - \mu)^2 + \ldots + (x_n - \mu)^2}{n},$$

and solve.

$$\sigma^2 = \frac{\begin{array}{c}(5 - 6.25)^2 + (7 - 6.25)^2 + (8 - 6.25)^2 \\ +(5 - 6.25)^2 + (7 - 6.25)^2 + (6 - 6.25)^2 \\ +(3 - 6.25)^2 + (9 - 6.25)^2\end{array}}{8}$$

$$\sigma^2 = \frac{\begin{array}{c}(-1.25)^2 + (0.75)^2 + (1.75)^2 \\ +(-1.25)^2 + (0.75)^2 + (-0.25)^2 \\ +(-3.25)^2 + (2.75)^2\end{array}}{8}$$

$$\sigma^2 \approx \frac{25.5}{8}$$

$$\sigma^2 \approx 3.1875$$

The variance of the data is approximately 3.19.

The standard deviation of the set of data is the square root of the variance. Take the square root of the variance.

$$\sigma = \sqrt{\sigma^2}$$

$$\sigma \approx \sqrt{3.1875}$$

$$\sigma \approx 1.79$$

The standard deviation of the data is approximately 1.79.

Recall that the standard deviation is a measure of how spread out the data values are from the mean. The larger the standard deviation, the more spread out the data values are from the mean.

In the original set of data {5, 7, 8, 5, 7, 6, 3, 9}, the mean is 6.25. Since the numbers are reasonably close together, a relatively small standard deviation of 1.79 results.

Compare the original set to the data set {2, 9, 8, 3, 10, 8, 1, 9}. This new set also has a mean of 6.25. However, it has a standard deviation of 3.38. The standard deviation is larger because the data values are more dispersed.

Consider a third set, {6, 6, 7, 5, 6, 6, 7, 7}. It also has a mean of 6.25, but has a standard deviation of 0.66. The data values are much closer together here, so the standard deviation is smaller.

20S.1 Demonstrate an understanding of normal distribution, including:

UNDERSTANDING THE NORMAL CURVE

The normal curve is the graph of the normal distribution.

The normal distribution is an approximation of a frequency or probability distribution that often occurs when examining data generated from real-life situations. Data values that are normally distributed can be represented by a bell-shaped curve, which is symmetric about the mean.

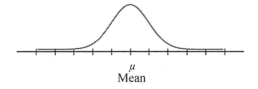

Normal distributions have the following characteristics:

- The mean is at the centre.
- The curve extends indefinitely in both directions, both left and right.
- Most of the data values are near the centre, which means that most of the data is close to the mean.
- Very few data values are far from the mean. Moving away from the mean, the probabilities of the values get closer and closer to 0.
- The normal curve is symmetric about the mean, which means that 50 % of the data lies to the left of the mean and 50 % of the data lies to the right of the mean.
- The mode and median are located at the centre, along with the mean.

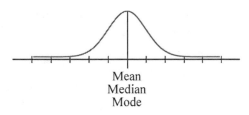

Mean
Median
Mode

The **median** of a set of data is defined as the middle value when the data is sorted in numerical order. The **mode** is defined as the data value or values that occur most frequently.

While the shape of any normal curve is that of a bell, the standard deviation of the data set represented by the curve impacts the height and width of the curve.

Recall that standard deviation measures how the data is dispersed, or spread out, about the mean.

If the standard deviation is small (as in Distribution 1 below), then the data values are bunched together, close to the mean.

Distribution 1:

$\mu = 50, \sigma = 5$

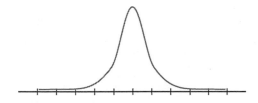

If the standard deviation is large (as in Distribution 2 below), then the data values are spread out, away from the mean.

Distribution 2:

$\mu = 50, \sigma = 15$

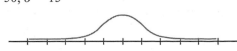

20S.1 Demonstrate an understanding of normal distribution, including:

THE ROLE OF THE MEAN AND STANDARD DEVIATION IN NORMAL DISTRIBUTIONS

The values of the mean and the standard deviation greatly affect the shape and relative position (on the same number line) of normal distributions.

Consider the following three normal distributions:

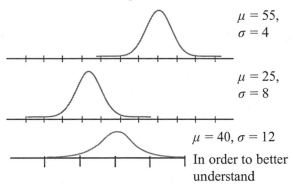

$\mu = 55, \sigma = 4$

$\mu = 25, \sigma = 8$

$\mu = 40, \sigma = 12$

In order to better understand normal distribution, it is useful to learn how to perform calculations involving the mean and standard deviation.

Example

The weights of chickens at a particular farm have a mean of 2.5 kg and a standard deviation of 0.4 kg. Their weights are approximated by a normal distribution, as shown in the diagram.

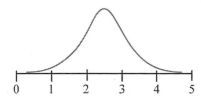

Determine the weight of a chicken that is 1 standard deviation above the mean.

Solution

If the standard deviation is 0.4 kg and the mean is 2.5 kg, then a weight that is 1 standard deviation above the mean will be 2.5 + 0.4, which is equal to 2.9 kg.

The weight of a chicken that is 1 standard deviation above the mean is 2.9 kg.

When the mean and standard deviation of normally distributed data are known, an individual data value can be calculated if the distance from the mean is given in terms of units (or multiples) of the data's standard deviation.

Example

Determine the weight that is 2 standard deviations below the mean.

Solution

To calculate the weight that is 2 standard deviations below the mean, subtract twice the standard deviation from the mean.
2.5 − 2(0.4) = 1.7

The weight of a chicken that is 2 standard deviations below the mean is 1.7 kg.

Determine the weight of a chicken that is 1.3 standard deviations above the mean.

Solution

To determine the weight that is 1.3 standard deviations above the mean, add 1.3(0.4) to 2.5.
2.5 + 1.3(0.4) = 3.02

A chicken's weight of 3.02 kg is 1.3 standard deviations above the mean.

Instead of finding data values given the mean, standard deviation and number of standard deviation units from the mean (as shown in the previous examples), the following two examples show how the number of standard deviation units a data value is from the mean can also be determined.

"Normally distributed" means the data is approximated by a normal distribution.

Example

The scores on a test are normally distributed with a mean of 70 and a standard deviation of 8, as shown in the diagram.

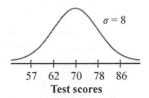

How many units of standard deviation above the mean is a score of 78?

Solution

A score of 78 is 8 marks greater than the mean of 70.

If the standard deviation is 8, then 1 unit of standard deviation is 8. Thus, 78 is 1 standard deviation above the mean.

Example

How many units of standard deviation below the mean is a score of 56?

Solution

A score of 56 is 14 marks below the mean of 70.
70 − 56 = 14

Find how many units of standard deviation correspond to 14 marks.
$\frac{14}{8} = 1.75$ units

Thus, 56 is 1.75 units of standard deviation below the mean.

20S.1 Demonstrate an understanding of normal distribution, including:

UNDERSTANDING THE STANDARD NORMAL DISTRIBUTION CURVE

To see the reason it is necessary to convert data into *z*-scores, consider the following three distributions of the heights of basketball players on three different teams.

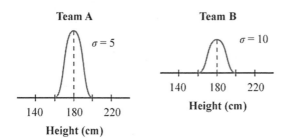

The scale on the vertical axis can represent frequency or probability.

Even though all three teams have a mean height of 180 cm, their distributions differ considerably. This is because the standard deviation is different for each team.

Team A has a small standard deviation, so the heights of the players are not very spread out. Most players have heights that are very close to 180 cm.

Team C, on the other hand, has a large standard deviation, so the heights of the players are more dispersed. Team C has short players and tall players.

Although the distributions are different, one thing is common to all three—they are all normal, meaning they all form a bell-shaped curve. As such, all the graphs can be made to look the same by modifying the scale on the horizontal axis. This can be accomplished by converting each of the above distributions to a **standard normal distribution**, in which the values on the horizontal axis represent *z*-scores (rather than raw data values).

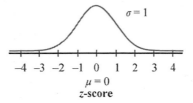

A standard normal distribution is a distribution of the *z*-scores in any normal distribution. For the purpose of simplifying the diagram, the vertical axis has been omitted here.

A standard normal distribution is one in which the mean is 0 and the standard deviation is 1. The curve representing a standard normal distribution is drawn with the following properties:

- The total area under the curve is 1.
- The curve extends infinitely in both directions.
- The mean, median, and mode are all equal to 0.
- The curve is symmetric about the mean, with 50% of the data lying to the left of the mean and 50% lying to the right.

Compare the standard normal distribution curve shown above to the following normal distribution curve:

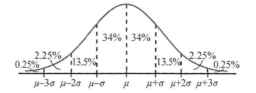

The main difference between the two is that instead of using raw data for the mean and standard deviation with the normal distribution, the standard normal distribution relies solely on the use of *z*-scores. The mean is 0 because at the mean, the *z*-score is 0. Essentially, the use of *z*-scores standardizes the curve.

All of the same problems that could be solved using the raw data from the normal distribution can be solved using the standardized values from the standard normal distribution, but now with greater ease.

20S.1 Demonstrate an understanding of normal distribution, including:

SOLVING PROBLEMS INVOLVING NORMAL DISTRIBUTION

Many real-world situations can be modelled using a normal distribution. Some examples include birth weights of babies in a particular city, household incomes in a particular neighbourhood, or math marks of Grade 12 students in a particular town.

Once data is collected and organized in a frequency table, a normal distribution is evident if the data values are spread evenly on each side of the data mean. The probability histogram of the data will appear to have the bell shape characteristic of a normal distribution.

Example

A manufacturing company produces 355 mL juice boxes. In actuality, not all juice boxes contain exactly 355 mL of juice, but they all must contain a volume of juice within a reasonable range of 355 mL so the company can maintain their business licence. The company performs regular quality testing to ensure that the boxes contain close to 355 mL of juice. The given table shows the results from a test of 100 boxes over one day.

Volume (mL)	Frequency
353	6
354	11
355	59
356	14
357	8
358	2

If the manufacturing company is aiming for 355 mL of juice in each box, most boxes will contain that volume—only a few boxes will have a bit more or a bit less juice.

The data is considered to be close to a normal distribution because the mean is very close to 355 mL and the rest of the data values appear to be spread relatively symmetrically on either side of 355 mL.

The probability histogram of the data has a bell shape. The data values are spread relatively symmetrically on either side of the mean.

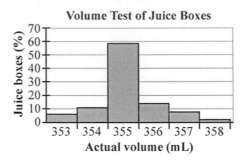

The normal curve can be created by joining the centre point of each bar with a smooth curve.

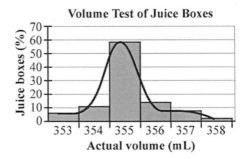

In general, if the data appears to be normally distributed, analyzing the data can be accomplished by sketching a standard normal curve instead of the entire histogram.

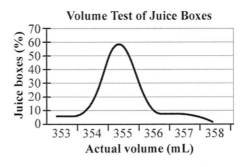

In every normal distribution, the standard deviation divides the population into the same regions, representing approximately the same percentages.

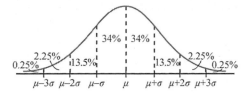

Because all normal curves have the same shape, they possess certain properties. One significant property is that the percentage of scores that fall within certain standard deviation values is known.

- Approximately 68% of the scores fall within one standard deviation of the mean.

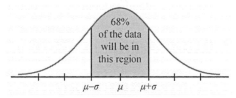

- Approximately 95% of the scores normally land within two standard deviations of the mean.

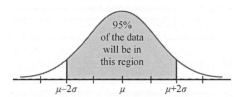

- Approximately 99.5% of the scores normally land within three standard deviations of the mean.

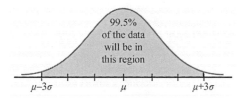

The areas under the normal distribution curve, between any two data values, represent the probability that a data value picked at random is between the two given values. For example, the probability that a data value that lies within two standard deviations from the mean is randomly picked is 95%.

Applying these properties of standard normal curves to real-world data that approximates a standard normal curve allows for the data to be analyzed, and predictions can be made based on the data.

In order to analyze, make predictions, or answer problems based on data that is normally distributed, follow these general steps:

1. Sketch the standard normal curve that represents the given data.
   i. Determine the mean and standard deviation of the given data.
   ii. Sketch a bell-shaped curve. The horizontal base of the curve should be divided into six equally spaced areas, as shown.

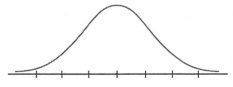

   iii. Label the centre with the data mean, and label the values that are ±1, ±2, and ±3 standard deviations from the mean.
2. Shade the area between any two given boundaries in order to focus on the appropriate standard deviation regions.
3. Determine the probability representing the shaded area by adding the percentages representing each shaded standard deviation region.

It is useful to know that the percentages on either side of the mean are approximately as follows:

Example

A company is producing chocolate bars that are advertised as having a mass of 70 g. During production, the manufacturer tested 320 bars and recorded their true masses, as shown in the given table.

Mass of Sample (g)	Frequency
67	11
68	35
69	40
70	156
71	27
72	21

Approximately what percentage of the chocolate bars have a mass between 68.6 g and 70.8 g?

Solution

Step 1
Sketch the standard normal curve that represents the given data.

Using technology, the mean of the data can be calculated to be 69.7 g, and the standard deviation is approximately 1.1 g.

Label the centre with the mean of the data, and label the values that are ±1, ±2, and ±3 standard deviations from the mean.

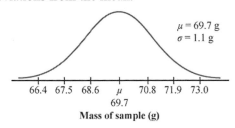

Step 2
Shade the area between the two boundaries given.

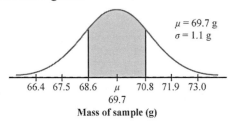

Step 3
Determine the probability representing the shaded area by adding the percentages representing each shaded standard deviation region.

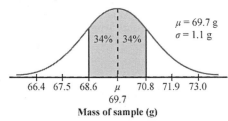

The percentages of each shaded standard deviation region are 34% and 34%, so 34% + 34% = 68% of the data lie within the given mass. Therefore, 68% of the chocolate bars will have a mass between 68.6 g and 70.8 g.

Expressed as a decimal to the nearest thousandth, what is the probability that a randomly selected chocolate bar will have a mass between 68.6 g and 71.9 g?

Solution

Step 1
Sketch the standard normal curve that represents the given data.

Using technology, the mean of the data can be calculated to be 69.7 g, and the standard deviation is approximately 1.1 g.

Label the centre with the data mean, and label the values that are ±1, ±2, and ±3 standard deviations from the mean.

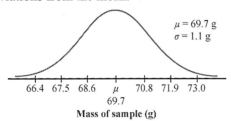

Step 2
Shade the area between the two boundaries given.

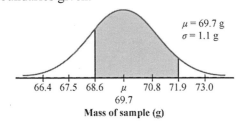

Step 3

Determine the probability represented by the shaded area by adding the percentages representing each shaded standard deviation region.

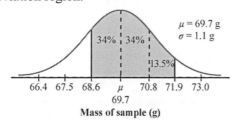

The percentages of each shaded standard deviation region are 34%, 34%, and 13.5%, so 34% + 34% + 13.5% = 81.5% of the data lie within the given mass.

Expressed as a decimal to the nearest thousandth, the probability that a randomly selected chocolate bar will have a mass between 68.6 g and 71.9 g is 0.815.

What percentage of the chocolate bars would be expected to have a mass less than 67.5 g?

Solution

Step 1

Sketch the normal curve that represents the given data.

Using technology, the mean of the data can be calculated to be 69.7 g, and the standard deviation is approximately 1.1 g.

Label the centre with the data mean, and label the values that are ±1, ±2, and ±3 standard deviations from the mean.

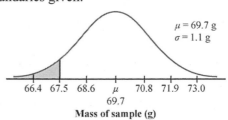

Step 2

Shade the area between the two boundaries given.

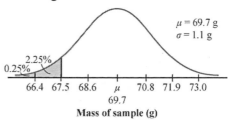

Step 3

Determine the probability representing the shaded area by adding the percentages representing each shaded standard deviation region.

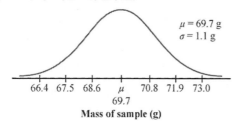

The percentages of each shaded standard deviation region are 0.25% and 2.25%, so 0.25% + 2.25% = 2.5% of the data lie within the given mass.

Therefore, 2.5% of the chocolate bars will have a mass less than 67.5 g.

20S.1 Demonstrate an understanding of normal distribution, including:

UNDERSTANDING *z*-SCORES

When data is normally distributed, it is possible to measure how many units of standard deviation each data value is above or below the mean.

Instead of using phrases such as "this mark is 2.2 units of standard deviation above the mean" or "this weight is 0.9 units of standard deviation below the mean," mathematicians use a shorthand notation for working with units of standard deviation. This shorthand notation is called a *z*-score.

z-score notation greatly simplifies the way in which the relative position of a data value is communicated.

Instead of saying that a test mark is 2.2 units of standard deviation above the mean, it can be said that the test mark has a z-score of 2.2.

Similarly, instead of saying that a child's weight is 0.9 units of standard deviation below the mean, it can be said that the child's weight has a z-score of −0.9.

Reference to Position	z-Score
3.1 units of standard deviation above the mean	3.1
0.6 units of standard deviation below the mean	−0.6
1.7 units of standard deviation above the mean	1.7

z-scores also remove the need to state whether a value is above or below the mean. If a value is above the mean, the z-score is positive. If a value is below the mean, the z-score is negative.

20S.1 Demonstrate an understanding of normal distribution, including:

DETERMINING THE z-SCORE FORMULA

When data is normally distributed, it is possible to measure how many units of standard deviation each data value is above or below the mean. A shorthand notation for this relative position of a data value is a z-score.

The z-score of a particular data value can be calculated when certain information about the data set is known.

Example

On a particular test, marks are normally distributed with a mean of 71 and a standard deviation of 8. If Ariel's mark is 83, what is her corresponding z-score, correct to the nearest tenth?

Solution

Step 1
Determine the difference between Ariel's mark and the mean value.
83 − 71 = 12
Note: Ariel's mark is above the mean and the difference is positive.

Step 2
Determine the position of Ariel's mark relative to the mean with the given standard deviation. If 8 is 1 unit of standard deviation, then 12 is 1.5 units of standard deviation, since
$\dfrac{12}{8} = 1.5.$

So, Ariel's mark of 83 has a corresponding z-score of 1.5.

A specific data value can be determined if the z-score of that particular data value, combined with the mean and standard deviation of the set of data in which the data value lies, are known.

Example

In the month of July, city X has a mean maximum temperature of 23°C, with a standard deviation of 5°C. If, on a certain day, the maximum temperature has a z-score of −1.2, what is the maximum temperature on that day, to the nearest degree?

Solution

A negative z-score means that the temperature is below the mean. It is 1.2 units of standard deviation below the mean.

If 5°C is 1 unit of standard deviation, then 1.2 units of standard deviation will be 1.2 × 5 = 6 or 6°C.

So, the maximum temperature on that day is 6°C below the mean.

The maximum temperature that day is 23° − 6° = 17°C.

The relationship between the **mean** and **standard deviation** of a particular set of data, a **data value** within that set, and its corresponding z-score are constant. As such, a formula can be applied to find any one value when the other three are known.

The corresponding z-score, z, for any data value, x, can be determined by applying the formula
$z = \dfrac{x - \mu}{\sigma}$, in which σ is the standard deviation and μ is the mean.

Example

If the marks on a particular test are normally distributed with a mean of 58 and a standard deviation of 4, what z-score corresponds to a mark of 53?

Solution

To find the z-score, use the formula $z = \dfrac{x - \mu}{\sigma}$.

Substitute 58 for μ, 4 for σ, and 53 for x.

$$z = \frac{53 - 58}{4}$$
$$= \frac{-5}{4}$$
$$= -1.25$$

The z-score is -1.25.

The z-score being negative makes sense, given that the data value, x, lies below the mean.

Example

The height of each player on a basketball team is recorded. The data are normally distributed with a mean of 185 cm. If a height of 194 cm corresponds to a z-score of 1.8, what is the standard deviation of the data?

Solution

To find the standard deviation, use the formula $z = \dfrac{x - \mu}{\sigma}$.

Substitute 185 for μ, 1.8 for z, and 194 for x.

$$1.8 = \frac{194 - 185}{\sigma}$$

Simplify.

$$1.8 = \frac{9}{\sigma}$$

Multiply each side by σ.
$$1.8\sigma = 9$$

Divide each side by 1.8.
$$\sigma = 5$$

The standard deviation is 5 cm.

Example

In Maria's math class, the mean mark is 69 and the standard deviation is 9. In Maria's history class, the mean mark is 66 and the standard deviation is 5. Maria received a mark of 80 in her math class and a mark of 76 in her history class.

In which subject is Maria's mark better when compared with the rest of the class?

Solution

To determine Maria's standing in each subject relative to the rest of each class, it is necessary to calculate her z-score for each subject.

To find the z-score for each subject, use the formula $z = \dfrac{x - \mu}{\sigma}$.

Math	History
Substitute $\mu = 69$, $\sigma = 9$, and $x = 80$	Substitute $\mu = 66$, $\sigma = 5$, and $x = 76$
$z = \dfrac{80 - 69}{9}$ $z \doteq 1.22$	$z = \dfrac{76 - 66}{5}$ $z = 2$

Maria's z-score in math is approximately 1.22, and her z-score in history is 2. This means that Maria's math score is approximately 1.22 units of standard deviation above the mean, and her history mark is 2 units of standard deviation above the mean.

Relative to her peers, Maria's history mark is better than her math mark.

Example

Marks on a chemistry test are normally distributed with a mean of 51 and a standard deviation of 8. Natalie's mark is 63. The teacher decides to adjust the marks by raising the mean to 65 and changing the standard deviation to 10.

What is Natalie's score after the adjustment, assuming her standing relative to her peers remains unchanged?

Solution

Step1

Determine Natalie's original z-score. Since Natalie's standing on the exam, relative to her peers, remains unchanged after the adjustment, she will have the same z-score before and after the adjustment.

Substitute 51 for μ, 8 for σ, and 63 for x in the formula $z = \dfrac{x - \mu}{\sigma}$.

$z = \dfrac{63 - 51}{8}$

$= 1.5$

Natalie's z-score, before and after the adjustment, is 1.5.

Step2

Using the adjusted mean (65) and the adjusted standard deviation (10), determine Natalie's adjusted mark so that her corresponding z-score is still 1.5.

Substitute 1.5 for z, 65 for μ, and 10 for σ in the formula $z = \dfrac{x - \mu}{\sigma}$.

$1.5 = \dfrac{x - 65}{10}$

Multiply each side by 10.

$15 = x - 65$

Add 65 to each side.

$80 = x$

In order for Natalie to retain her z-score of 1.5, her adjusted test mark will be 80.

20S.1 Demonstrate an understanding of normal distribution, including:

FINDING AREAS UNDER THE STANDARD NORMAL CURVE USING z-SCORE TABLES

By converting data into z-scores, areas under a standard normal curve can be determined with the help of z-score tables.

A z-score table is designed to give the area under the Normal curve. In general, a z-score table gives the area under the curve that is to the **left** of a z-score.

Example

Find the area under the standard normal curve that is to the left of the z-score −0.68.

Solution

When solving problems that involve areas under the normal curve, it is a good idea to sketch a normal curve showing the area that is being referred to.

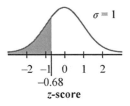

To find the area of the given shaded portion of the normal curve, refer to the following partial z-score table.

z	0.09	0.08	0.07	0.06
-2.9	0.0014	0.0014	0.0015	0.0015
-2.8	0.0019	0.0020	0.0021	0.0021
-2.7	0.0026	0.0027	0.0028	0.0029
-2.6	0.0036	0.0037	0.0038	0.0039
-2.5	0.0048	0.0049	0.0051	0.0052
-2.4	0.0064	0.0066	0.0068	0.0069
-2.3	0.0084	0.0087	0.0089	0.0091
-2.2	0.0110	0.0113	0.0116	0.0119
-2.1	0.0143	0.0146	0.0150	0.0154
-2.0	0.0183	0.0188	0.0192	0.0197
-1.9	0.0233	0.0239	0.0244	0.0250
-1.8	0.0294	0.0301	0.0307	0.0314
-1.7	0.0367	0.0375	0.0384	0.0392
-1.6	0.0455	0.0465	0.0475	0.0485
-1.5	0.0559	0.0571	0.0582	0.0594
-1.4	0.0681	0.0694	0.0708	0.0721
-1.3	0.0823	0.0838	0.0853	0.0869
-1.2	0.0985	0.1003	0.1020	0.1038
-1.1	0.1170	0.1190	0.1210	0.1230
-1.0	0.1379	0.1401	0.1423	0.1446
-0.9	0.1611	0.1635	0.1660	0.1685
-0.8	0.1867	0.1894	0.1922	0.1949
-0.7	0.2148	0.2177	0.2206	0.2236
-0.6	0.2451	0.2483	0.2514	0.2546
-0.5	0.2776	0.2810	0.2843	0.2877
-0.4	0.3121	0.3156	0.3192	0.3228
-0.3	0.3483	0.3520	0.3557	0.3594
-0.2	0.3859	0.3897	0.3936	0.3974
-0.1	0.4247	0.4286	0.4325	0.4364
-0.0	0.4641	0.4681	0.4721	0.4761

This table gives the area under the standard normal curve to the left of each z-score. Each z-score in the table is specified with an accuracy of two decimal places. The areas in the table are rounded to four decimal places.

Since it is required to find the area under the standard normal curve to the left of the z-score −0.68, move vertically down the column labelled z until the number −0.6 is reached.

Then, move horizontally in that row until the row intersects the column titled 0.08, as shown in the given table.

The corresponding area is 0.2483, which means that the area to the left of the z-score −0.68 is 0.2483 (correct to four decimal places).

Another interpretation is that 24.83% (correct to the nearest 0.01%) of normally distributed data values have z-scores less than −0.68.

The area under the standard normal curve to the right of a z-score can also be determined.

Example

Find the area under the standard normal curve that is to the right of the z-score 0.47, correct to two decimal places.

Solution

Draw a diagram of the desired area.

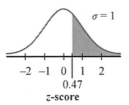

Refer to the z-score table to determine the area that corresponds to a z-score of 0.47. The area listed is 0.6808. However, 0.6808 refers to the area to the left of a z-score of 0.47.

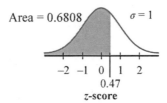

Since the total area under the curve is 1, the area to the right of the z-score 0.47 can be found by subtracting 0.6808 from 1.

The resulting value is
$1 - 0.6808 = 0.3192$.

So, the area to the right of the z-score 0.47 is 0.3192, which means that 31.92% of the data values of a normal distribution have z-scores greater than 0.47.

Rounded to the nearest hundredth, the area is 0.32.

In some instances, rather than being asked to find a particular area, given the z-score, it might be required to find the z-score, given the area.

Example

The shaded area in the following normal distribution graph is 0.1423.

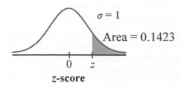

What is the value of the z-score labelled z, to the nearest hundredth? _____

Solution

In this problem the area to the right of the z-score is given. However, the table only provides areas to the left of the z-score.

Step 1
Find the area to the left of the z-score.

Since the total area under the standard normal curve is equal to 1, the area to the left of the z-score can be found by subtracting the area to the right of the z-score from 1.
1 − 0.1423 = 0.8577

Therefore, the area to the left of the z-score is 0.8577.

Step 2
Now, refer to the z-score table to find the z-score corresponding to the given area of 0.8577.

According to the z-score table, the z-score that corresponds to an area of 0.8577 is z = 1.07.

_____

20S.1 Demonstrate an understanding of normal distribution, including:

FINDING AREAS UNDER THE STANDARD NORMAL CURVE USING A GRAPHING CALCULATOR

By converting data into z-scores, areas under a standard normal curve can be determined with the help of a graphing calculator, just as they can using z-score tables.

When using technology, the normalcdf function on a TI-83 plus can be used to find the area under the standard normal distribution curve.

The normalcdf feature can be found on the calculator at $\boxed{\text{2nd}}$ $\boxed{\text{VARS}}$ $\boxed{\text{2:normalcdf(}}$. This feature requires the user to input information about a particular situation into the calculator in a particular order: **normalcdf(left bound, right bound, μ, σ).**
The left bound refers to the left-most z-score for the required area.
The right bound refers to the right-most z-score for the required area.
μ refers to the mean, which for a standard normal distribution is 0.
σ refers to the standard deviation, which for a standard normal distribution is 1.

Note that for a left bound that extends indefinitely to the left, the value to input in the calculator is −1E99. Likewise, the value to input for a right bound that extends indefinitely to the right is 1E99.

For reference and verification purposes, the following examples include the solutions using both the z-score tables and a graphing calculator.

Example

Use a graphing calculator to determine the area under the standard normal curve that is to the left of the z-score 1.83? Round your answer to the nearest hundredth.

Solution

Step 1
Draw a sketch of the standard normal curve, shading the area to the left of a z-score position of 1.83.

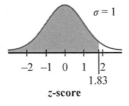

Step 2

Determine the required area.

Use the TI-83 Plus calculator:

Area

$= \text{normalcdf(left bound, right bound, } \mu, \sigma)$

$= \text{normalcdf}(-1E99, 1.83, 0, 1)$

$= 0.966\ 375\ldots$

Therefore, to the nearest hundredth, the area to the left of the z-score 1.83 is 0.97.

___

Example

Marks on a test have a normal distribution. Use a graphing calculator to determine the percentage of marks that have z-scores greater than 1.2. Round your answer to the nearest hundredth of a percent.

Solution

Step 1

Sketch a standard normal curve, shading the area to the right of the z-score 1.2.

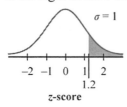

Step 2

Determine the answer using TI 83 Plus calculator.

Area $= \text{normalcdf(left bound, right bound, } \mu, \sigma)$

$= \text{normalcdf}(1.2, 1E99, 0, 1)$

$= 0.115\ 069\ldots$

If the area to the right of the z-score 1.2 is 0.1151, then 11.51% of the test marks have a z-score greater than 1.2.

___

Note that rather than having to subtract the result from 1 when using a graphing calculator to solve (as is the case when using z-score tables), the desired area is communicated through the proper input of the left and right bound values.

In some instances, rather than being asked to find a particular area, given the z-score, it might be required to find the z-score, given the area.

On a TI-83 plus graphing calculator, the command invNorm, accessed by inputting $\boxed{\text{2nd}}$ $\boxed{\text{VARS}}$ $\boxed{3}$, returns the score of the normally distributed data that has the given percentage of data less than the score. It must be entered as follows:

invNorm(area, mean, standard deviation)

Example

The area under the distribution curve to the right of the z-score is 0.0618 in a standard normal distribution.

Determine the value of z using a graphing calculator. Round your answer to the nearest hundredth.

Solution

Step 1

Determine the area under the curve to the left of the z-score.

Since the total area under the standard normal curve is equal to 1, the area to the left of the z-score can be found by subtracting the area to the right of the z-score from 1.

$1 - 0.0618 = 0.9382$

The area to the left of the z-score is 0.9382.

Step 2

Determine z-score.

Use the TI-83 Plus function invnorm(area, μ, σ) to find the z-score.

Using the calculator,

$\text{invNorm}(0.9382, 0, 1) \approx 1.539\ 837\ 37$

Therefore, the z-score is 1.54.

___

20S.1 Demonstrate an understanding of normal distribution, including:

FINDING AREAS BETWEEN TWO z-SCORES

It is possible to determine the area between two z-scores using the same method that is used to find the area under the standard normal curve to the left of a z-score. You can use the z-score table or a graphing calculator to determine the required areas between two data values.

FINDING AREAS UNDER THE NORMAL CURVE USING A CALCULATOR

Graphing calculators have a built-in function that calculates the area under the normal curve between any two data values. The calculator function is labelled **normalcdf**.

Example

To four decimal places, what is the area under the standard normal curve between the z-scores -0.35 and 1.46? _____

Solution

This is a diagram of the area under the standard normal curve between the given z-scores.

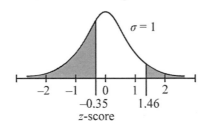

The area between is left clear.

Step 1
Determine areas to the left of each z-score.
The area to the left of $z = 1.46$ from the z-score table is 0.9279.
The area to the left of $z = -0.35$ from the z-score table is 0.3632.

Step 2
Determine the area in between the two z-scores. The area to the left of $z = 1.46$ also includes the area that lies to the left of $z = -0.35$. Thus, if the area to the left of $z = -0.35$ is subtracted from the area to the left of $z = 1.46$, the resulting value is the area between $z = -0.35$ and $z = 1.46$.

The resulting value is
$0.9279 - 0.3632 = 0.5647$.

Therefore, the area between the z-scores -0.35 and 1.46 is 0.5647.

Graphically, the solution can be shown in this way.

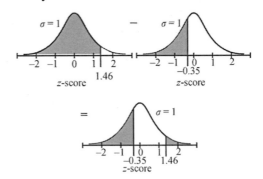

Alternative Solution
Using the calculator, the area under a normal distribution curve may be calculated with normalcdf(left bound, right bound, μ, σ):
Area = normalcdf$(-0.35, 1.46, 0, 1)$
≈ 0.5647

To use the function normalcdf on a graphing calculator, follow these steps:

1. Access DISTR by pressing $\boxed{2^{nd}}$ $\boxed{\text{VARS}}$.

2. Choose 2:normalcdf(.

3. The function normalcdf(is displayed.

4. Enter this information:
   normalcdf (low score, high score, mean, standard deviation)

5. Press $\boxed{\text{ENTER}}$.

6. If the required area is completely on one side or the other of a particular score, use -1×10^{99} as the lower boundary and 1×10^{99} as the upper boundary (since there is virtually no area beyond these values).

If the scores are z-scores, enter 0 for the mean and 1 for the standard deviation. For example, in a problem where the area is between $z = -0.35$ and $z = 1.46$, the normalcdf function can be used to give the results shown on this screen.

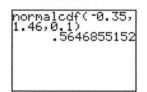

Correct to four decimal places, the area is 0.5647. This is the same answer you would obtain using the z-score table.

If the mean and standard deviation are not entered, the calculator assumes the mean is 0 and the standard deviation is 1 (a standard normal curve). Thus, normalcdf $(-0.35, 1.46)$ gives a result of 0.564 685 5152.

Example

The test marks for a particular test are normally distributed.

To the nearest hundredth, what percentage of the marks lies between $\mu + 0.33\sigma$ and $\mu + 1.81\sigma$? _____

Solution

The expression $\mu + 0.33\sigma$ refers to a data value that is equal to the mean plus 0.33 units of standard deviation. This is equivalent to a z-score of 0.33.

Similarly, $\mu + 1.81\sigma$ is a data value that is 1.81 units of standard deviation above the mean. The corresponding z-score is 1.81.

Thus, it is necessary to determine the area under the standard normal curve that lies between $z = 0.33$ and $z = 1.81$.

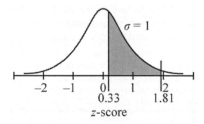

Use a graphing calculator, and enter normalcdf(0.33, 1.81, 0, 1) to give 0.3356 (rounded to four decimal places).

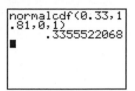

The area between $z = 0.33$ and $z = 1.81$ is approximately 0.3356.

For the particular test marks, approximately 33.56% is between $\mu + 0.33\sigma$ and $\mu + 1.81\sigma$.

FINDING THE z-SCORE FROM THE AREA

Sometimes, you will be given the area between two z-scores and will have to find the z-scores associated with the area.

Example

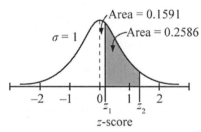

The area of the shaded portion of the standard normal curve is 0.2586, and the area between $z = 0$ and z_1 is 0.1591.

For the given standard normal curve, what are the values of z_1 and z_2?

Solution

Step 1

Find the value of z_1.

The area under the curve between the mean and z_1 is 0.1591. Since the standard normal curve is symmetric about the mean, the area to the left of the mean is 0.5.

Therefore, the total area to the left of z_1 is $0.5 + 0.1591 = 0.6591$.

Use either the z-score table or a graphing calculator to find the value of z_1.

The value of z_1 is 0.41.

Step 2

Find the value of z_2.

The total area to the left of z_2 is equal to 0.5 (the area to the left of the mean) $+0.1591$ (the area between the mean and z_1) $+0.2586$ (the area between z_1 and z_2).

Thus, the total area to the left of z_2 is $0.5 + 0.1591 + 0.2586 = 0.9177$.

Use either the z-score table or a calculator to determine the z-score that corresponds to an area of 0.9177.

The value of z_2 is 1.39.

20S.1 Demonstrate an understanding of normal distribution, including:

APPLICATIONS OF z-SCORES AND THE NORMAL CURVE

Many real-life situations model arbitrary normal distributions. If the data from these situations is converted to a standard normal distribution by converting the data values into z-scores, the data can then be analyzed, and predictions can be made based on the standard normal distribution.

For example, a set of exam marks that are normally distributed with a mean of 70 and a standard deviation of 10 can be illustrated graphically.

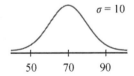
Test mark distribution

Suppose it is necessary to determine the percentage of the students who scored more than 70 on the exam. It is clear from the graph that 50% of the area under the curve lies to the right of the mean, 70. It is logical that approximately 50% of the students scored more than 70.

However, to determine the percentage of students who scored less than 65 is more difficult.

Again, it is necessary to determine the proportional area under the curve, but this time determining the area to the left of 65 is required.

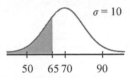
Test mark distribution

The proportional area of the shaded region is difficult to determine from this diagram. In order to find the proportional area, standardize the curve and work with z-scores.

By converting the data value of 65 into its corresponding z-score, it is possible to use the standard normal curve to determine the area.

To convert 65 into its corresponding z-score, apply the z-score formula, $z = \dfrac{x - \mu}{\sigma}$.

Substitute 70 for μ, 10 for σ, and 65 for x.

$$z = \frac{65 - 70}{10}$$
$$= -0.5$$

The corresponding z-score is -0.5. Now, determine the area under the standard normal curve that is to the left of the z-score, -0.5. This can be shown graphically.

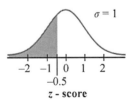
z - score

By referring to the z-score table or by using a calculator, it can be determined that the corresponding area is 0.3085. Thus, the area to the left of the z-score -0.5 is approximately 0.3085.

Approximately 30.9% of the data will have a z-score less than -0.5. This means that out of all the students who wrote the exam, approximately 30.9% of them received marks of less than 65.

This question can also be answered directly using the "normalcdf" function on a calculator.

Enter normalcdf$(-1 \times 10^{99}, 65, 70, 10)$, then press ENTER . The resulting value is 0.3085 (to four decimal places).

The "normalcdf" function on a TI-83 calculator standardizes the distribution and gives results based on the standard normal curve (i.e, on z-scores).

Example

A certain factory makes light bulbs with lifetimes that are normally distributed with a mean of 730 hours and a standard deviation of 40 hours.

To the nearest hundredth, what percentage of light bulbs lasts more than 780 hours? _____%

Solution

Determine the proportional area under the normal curve to the right of 780.

Step 1

Sketch a normal distribution curve that represents the information given in this problem.

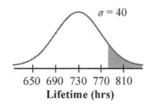

650 690 730 770 810
Lifetime (hrs)

Step 2

Convert 780 into its corresponding z-score by applying the z-score formula.

$$z = \frac{x - \mu}{\sigma}$$

Substitute 780 for x, 730 for μ, and 40 for σ.

$$z = \frac{780 - 730}{40}$$

$$= 1.25$$

The z-score is 1.25.

Step 3

Determine the area under the standard normal curve that is to the right of $z = 1.25$, since the area represents the percentage of light bulbs with a lifetime greater than 780 hours.

A z-score table shows that the area corresponding to $z = 1.25$ is 0.8944, but this is the area to the left of $z = 1.25$. The area that lies to the right of $z = 1.25$ can be found by subtracting 0.8944 from 1.

$1 - 0.8944 = 0.1056$

This question can also be done directly using the normalcdf function on a calculator.

Enter normalcdf$(780, 1 \times 10^{99}, 730, 40)$, and press ENTER to arrive at the value 0.1056 (to four decimal places).

Therefore, the area to the right of $z = 1.25$ is approximately 0.1056.

Step 4

Convert 0.1056 to a percentage.

Approximately 10.56% of light bulbs have lifetimes greater than 780 hours.

Example

The masses of chickens at a certain farm are normally distributed with a mean of 2.9 kg and a standard deviation of 0.5 kg.

To four decimal places, what is the probability that a chicken chosen at random has a mass greater than 2.7 kg and less than 3.5 kg? _____

Solution

Step 1

Sketch a normal distribution curve that represents the given information.

The following diagram illustrates the proportional area under the normal curve that is between the masses of 2.7 kg and 3.5 kg.

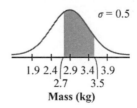

1.9 2.4 2.9 3.4 3.9
2.7   3.5
Mass (kg)

Step 2

Convert 2.7 kg into its corresponding z-score by applying the z-score formula. $z = \dfrac{x - \mu}{\sigma}$

Substitute 2.7 for x, 2.9 for μ, and 0.5 for σ.

$z = \dfrac{2.7 - 2.9}{0.5}$

$\quad = -0.4$

The z-score that corresponds to 2.7 kg is -0.4.

Step 3

Convert 3.5 kg into its corresponding z-score by applying the z-score formula. $z = \dfrac{x - \mu}{\sigma}$

Substitute 3.5 for x, 2.9 for μ, and 0.5 for σ.

$z = \dfrac{3.5 - 2.9}{0.5}$

$\quad = 1.2$

The z-score that corresponds to 3.5 kg is 1.2.

Step 4

Determine the area under the standard normal curve that is between $z = -0.4$ and $z = 1.2$. According to a z-score table, the area to the left of $z = 1.2$ is 0.8849, and the area to the left of $z = -0.4$ is 0.3446.

Thus, the area between $z = -0.4$ and $z = 1.2$ is $0.8849 - 0.3446 = 0.5403$.

This question can also be done directly using the "normalcdf" function on a calculator. Enter normalcdf(2.7, 3.5, 2.9, 0.5), and press $\boxed{\text{ENTER}}$ to get the value 0.5404 (to four decimal places). Although this is 0.0001 more than the answer obtained from the table, it is not a significant difference.

The probability that a chicken has a mass between 2.7 kg and 3.5 kg is approximately 0.5403.

Example

Marks on a certain exam are normally distributed with a mean of 68% and a standard deviation of 11%.

If 20 000 students wrote the exam, approximately how many students scored lower than 50%? _____

Solution

To solve this problem, first find the percentage of students who scored lower than 50%, then calculate the number of students who scored lower than 50%.

Step 1

Sketch a normal distribution curve that represents the given information.

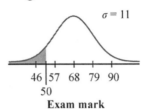

Step 2

Convert 50% into its corresponding z-score by applying the z-score formula. $z = \dfrac{x - \mu}{\sigma}$

Substitute 50 for x, 68 for μ, and 11 for σ.

$z = \dfrac{50 - 68}{11}$

$\quad = -1.64$

The z-score is -1.64 (to two decimal places).

Step 3

Since it is necessary to determine the percentage of marks that are lower than 50%, find the area under the standard normal curve that is to the left of $z = -1.64$.

According to the z-score table, the area corresponding to $z = -1.64$ is 0.0505.

This question can also be done using the "normalcdf" function on a calculator. Enter normalcdf$(-1 \times 10^{99}, 50, 68, 11)$, and press $\boxed{\text{ENTER}}$ to get the value 0.0509 (to four decimal places). The difference between the calculator answer and the table answer is relatively small.

Thus, approximately 5.05% of students got a mark lower than 50% on the exam.

Step 4

Determine the number of students who scored less than 50%.

5.05% of 20 000 = 0.0505 × 20 000 = 1 010

Approximately 1 010 students scored less than 50% on the exam.

Example

There were 5 000 students who wrote a province-wide test. The results were normally distributed, and the mean score was 65.

If 411 students scored over 90, what was the standard deviation to the nearest hundredth?

Solution

Step1

Determine the percentage of students who scored over 90.

Since 411 students out of 5 000 scored over 90 on the test, the percentage of students who scored over 90 is as follows:

$$\frac{411}{5\ 000} = 0.0822$$

Step 2

Sketch a normal distribution curve that represents the given information.

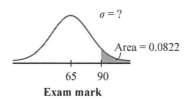

Step 3

Determine the proportional area to the left of 90.

Since the proportional area to the right of 90 is 0.0822, the area to the left of 90 will be 1 − 0.0822 = 0.9178.

Step 4

Determine the z-score that corresponds to an area of 0.9178.

Using a z-score table, the closest area value is 0.9177, which corresponds to a z-score of 1.39.

When using a calculator, the z-score can be found using the "invNorm" feature. The result is invNorm(0.9178) ≐ 1.39.

Step 5

Solve for the standard deviation, σ, by applying the z-score formula. $z = \dfrac{x - \mu}{\sigma}$

Substitute 1.39 for z, 90 for x, and 65 for μ.

$$1.39 = \frac{90 - 65}{\sigma}$$

Now, solve for σ.

$$1.39 = \frac{90 - 65}{\sigma}$$
$$1.39\sigma = 25$$
$$\sigma = 17.99$$

To the nearest hundredth, the standard deviation of the exam marks was 17.99.

Example

A police study measured the speeds of cars on a certain road one day. The study showed that there were 294 cars travelling faster than 90 km/h.

If the speeds of the cars were normally distributed with a mean of 88.6 km/h and a standard deviation of 3.6 km/h, how many cars travelled on the road that day? _____

Solution

Step 1

Sketch a normal distribution curve that represents the information given in the problem. The shaded portion represents cars travelling faster than 90 km/h.

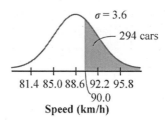

Step 2

Convert 90 km/h into its corresponding z-score by applying the z-score formula.

$$z = \frac{x - \mu}{\sigma}$$

Substitute 90 for x, 88.6 for μ, and 3.6 for σ.

$$z = \frac{90 - 88.6}{3.6}$$

$$z \approx 0.39$$

Thus, a speed of 90 km/h has a corresponding z-score of 0.39.

Step 3

Determine the area to the left of $z = 0.39$.

By referring to a z-score table, the area to the left of $z = 0.39$ is 0.6517.

Step 4

Determine the area to the right of $z = 0.39$. The shaded area to the right of $z = 0.39$ is $1 - 0.6517 = 0.3483$.

If a calculator is used, the area to the right of $x = 90$ can be found to be

normalcdf$(90, 1 \times 10^{99}, 88.6, 3.6) \doteq 0.3487$.

If the calculator was used after finding the z-score of $z = 0.39$, the area can be found as

normalcdf$(0.39, 1 \times 10^{99}, 0, 1) = 0.3483$.

The difference in accuracy is not significant.

Step 5

Determine the number of cars on the road that day.

It is given that 294 cars travelled faster than 90 km/h and it has been determined that 0.3483 or 34.83% of the cars travel faster than 90 km/h. If T represents the total number of cars on the road that day, it follows that

$$\frac{294}{T} = 0.3483 \text{ or } T = \frac{294}{0.3483} = 844.1.$$

Thus, approximately 844 cars travelled on the road that day.

Example

Studies show that the lifetimes of a certain brand of computer monitors are normally distributed with a mean life of 5.1 years and a standard deviation of 0.6 years.

If the manufacturer wants to offer a warranty to buyers so that no more than 5% of the monitors are returned, what should the warranty period be?

Solution

Given the normal distribution of monitor lifetimes with a mean of 5.1 and a standard deviation of 0.6 years, it is necessary to find a warranty period so that only 5% (at most) of the monitors will be returned. In other words, find the lifetime, x, such that only 5% of the data is less than this value.

Step 1

Sketch a normal distribution curve to represent the given information.

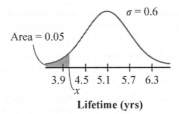

Lifetime (yrs)

Step 2

Determine the z-score that corresponds to an area of 0.05.

Consult the z-score table of areas under the standard normal curve to find the z-score that corresponds to an area of 0.05. This value does not have an exact z-score. The areas 0.0495 and 0.0505 are given.

Remember that, at most, 5% of the monitors are to be returned. The area 0.0505 is equal to 5.05%, which is more than 5%.

Thus, the area of 0.0495 should be selected, which has a corresponding z-score of -1.65. This means that 4.95% of the monitors are to the left of a z-score of -1.65.

Step 3

Solve for the data value, x, by applying the z-score formula. $z = \dfrac{x - \mu}{\sigma}$

Substitute -1.65 for z, 5.1 for μ, and 0.6 for σ.

$-1.65 = \dfrac{x - 5.1}{0.6}$

Solve for x.

$-0.99 = x - 5.1$

$\quad x = 4.11$

Using a calculator, the required x-value can be determined from invNorm(0.05, 5.1, 0.6). The result is 4.11 (to two decimal places), the required warranty period.

Therefore, if the warranty period is 4.11 years, no more than 5% of the monitors will be returned under the warranty. Of course, manufacturers seldom give warranties using fractions of years. If the manufacturer wanted to guarantee the monitors using a whole number of years, the warranty would be for 4 years. This should ensure that close to, but less than, 5% of the monitors are returned.

20S.2 Interpret statistical data, using:

EXPLAINING AND INTERPRETING CONFIDENCE INTERVALS

The **confidence level** is a measure of how confident the statistician is of the results. The three most commonly used confidence levels are 90%, 95%, and 99%. A 95% confidence level means that the statistician is 95% confident of the results. The margin of error, *ME*, establishes the interval for which the confidence level applies. The **confidence intervals** indicate how closely the statistical values calculated from the sample represent the actual population.

A confidence level of C% is the probability that the statistical value derived from a sample will be in a particular interval.

Example

A survey is done that reports that 70% of Canadians prefer watching hockey to football on television. The survey states that it is accurate to within 3 percentage points 95% of the time. This means that if the survey was conducted 100 times, 95 times you would get a result of 70±3%, or between 67% and 73% of the respondents would say they prefer watching hockey.

The general formula for confidence intervals is point estimate ± margin of error. The point estimate is the numerical value of the point estimator or statistic, which could be any one of the sample mean, $\bar{x}$, sample standard deviation, s, or the sample proportion, $\bar{p}$.

The confidence interval for a sample mean, $\bar{x}$, with a known population standard deviation, σ, is

$$\bar{x} \pm z_{\frac{\alpha}{2}} \frac{\sigma}{\sqrt{n}}.$$

The value of $z_{\frac{\alpha}{2}}$ is equal to the critical value $z^{\star}$.

If the margin of error is not given, first calculate the margin of error and then determine the confidence intervals.

Example

A local gym wanted to estimate the average amount of time members spent exercising at their gym each week and surveyed 400 members. The results from the survey showed that on average members spent approximately 0.75 h exercising at their gym (this did not include time playing sports or participating in a class). The standard deviation of the population is 0.25 h, and the population is normally distributed.

Determine the 95% confidence interval for the estimated population mean.

Solution

The confidence interval for a sample mean is

$\bar{x} \pm z_{\frac{\alpha}{2}} \frac{\sigma}{\sqrt{n}}$. Since the margin of error is not

given, first calcluate the margin of error and then find the 95% confidence interval.

Step 1

Determine the margin of error, *ME*.

At a 95% confidence level, the value of $z_{\frac{\alpha}{2}}$, or

the critical value z^{*}, is 1.96. Substitute 1.96 for $z_{\frac{\alpha}{2}}$, 400 for *n*, and 0.25 for σ into the formula

$ME = z_{\frac{\alpha}{2}} \frac{\sigma}{\sqrt{n}}$.

$ME = 1.96 \times \frac{0.25}{\sqrt{400}}$

$ME = 1.96 \times 0.0125$

$ME = 0.0245$

Step 2

Determine the 95% confidence interval.

The confidence interval for a sample mean is

defined by $\bar{x} \pm z_{\frac{\alpha}{2}} \frac{\sigma}{\sqrt{n}}$. The sample mean, $\bar{x}$, is

0.75 and the margin of error is 0.0245. Therefore, the 95% confidence interval is 0.75 ± 0.0245, or between 0.7255 $(0.75 - 0.0245 = 0.7255)$ and 0.7745 $(0.75 + 0.0245 = 0.7745)$.

The surveyor is 95% confident that the average amount of time members spend exercising at the gym is between 0.73 and 0.77 hours.

The confidence interval for a sample proportion,

$\bar{p}$, is $\bar{p} \pm z_{\frac{\alpha}{2}} \sqrt{\frac{\bar{p}(1 - \bar{p})}{n}}$.

Example

A market research company surveyed 950 adults from a normally distributed population. The survey found that 39% of adults prefer camping during the summer months and 61% prefer staying at hotels while on summer vacation.

Determine the 99% confidence interval for the estimated population proportion of adults who prefer camping.

Solution

The confidence interval for a sample proportion,

$\bar{p}$, is $\bar{p} \pm z_{\frac{\alpha}{2}} \sqrt{\frac{\bar{p}(1 - \bar{p})}{n}}$. First calculate the

margin of error and then find the 99% confidence interval.

Step 1

Determine the margin of error, *ME*, for the sample proportion.

Substitute 950 for *n*, 0.39 for $\bar{p}$, and 2.576 for

$z_{\frac{\alpha}{2}}$ in the formula $ME = z_{\frac{\alpha}{2}} \sqrt{\frac{\bar{p}(1 - \bar{p})}{n}}$.

$ME = 2.576 \times \sqrt{\frac{(0.39)(1 - 0.39)}{950}}$

$ME = 2.576 \times \sqrt{\frac{0.2379}{950}}$

$ME \approx 0.040\ 76$

Step 2

Determine the 99% confidence interval.
The confidence interval for a sample proportion

is defined by $\bar{p} \pm z_{\frac{\alpha}{2}}\sqrt{\dfrac{\bar{p}(1-\bar{p})}{n}}$. The sample

proportion, $\bar{p}$, is 0.39 or 39%, and the margin of error is approximately 0.041, or 4.1%.
Therefore, the 99% confidence interval is 0.39 ± 0.041, or $39 \pm 4.1\%$.

According to the results of the survey, it can be said with 99% confidence that between 34.9% and 43.1% of adults prefer camping during the summer months.

20S.2 Interpret statistical data, using:

EXPLAINING AND INTERPRETING MARGIN OF ERROR

When a survey is conducted using a sample of the population, it is unlikely that the sample represents the entire population exactly. If the same survey was conducted on a different sample of the population, the chances are that the results would be at least somewhat different.

The confidence level is a measure of how confident the statistician is of the results. The three most commonly used confidence levels are 90%, 95%, and 99%. A 95% confidence level means that the statistician is 95% confident of the results. The **margin of error**, *ME*, establishes the interval for which the confidence level applies. It indicates how precise the data from the survey of the sample is to the actual population.

A confidence level of C% is the probability that the statistical value derived from the sample will be in a particular interval.

Example

A survey is done that reports that 70% of Canadians prefer watching hockey to football on television. The survey states that it is accurate to within 3 percentage points 95% of the time. This means that if the survey was conducted 100 times, 95 times you would get a result of 70±3%, or between 67% and 73% of the respondents would say they prefer watching hockey.

In general, the larger the sample size, the lower the margin of error. This is because as the sample size increases, it generally represents the population better. The smaller the margin of error, the more precise the data from the survey is to the population.

Point estimators, such as the sample mean, $\bar{x}$, and the sample proportion, $\bar{p}$, can be determined from the results of a survey of a sample of the population. The sample mean estimates the population mean, μ, and the sample proportion estimates the population proportion, p. The margin of error is used to determine how close the point estimators are to the population parameters (population mean and population proportion).

There are many different ways to calculate the margin of error. One way is to find the product of a critical value and the standard error of the data. The critical value is taken from a sampling distribution table and depends on the confidence level used. The standard error depends on the point estimator used.

To determine the margin of error for an estimate of a population mean when given the standard deviation of a population, use the formula

$ME = z_{\frac{\alpha}{2}} \dfrac{\sigma}{\sqrt{n}}$, where n is the sample size, σ is the standard deviation of the population, α is the level of significance, and $z_{\frac{\alpha}{2}}$ is the z-value of the area of

$\dfrac{\alpha}{2}$ in the upper tail of the standard normal distribution curve. The level of significance, α, is equal to 1 - confidence coefficient.

The value of $z_{\frac{\alpha}{2}}$ is equal to the critical value $z^{\star}$.

The confidence coefficient is equal to the confidence level divided by 100. If given a confidence level of 95%, the confidence coefficient is 0.95.

Example

A department store surveyed 200 customers to determine the amount of money each person spent at their store on shoes every three months. The survey found the average amount per person to be $40. The department store's population standard deviation is $15. The population is normally distributed.

Determine the margin of error for the sample mean with a confidence level of 95%, to the nearest thousandth.

Solution

Since the standard deviation of the population is given, you can use the formula $ME = z_{\frac{\alpha}{2}} \dfrac{\sigma}{\sqrt{n}}$ to find the margin of error for the estimate of the population mean, which is the sample mean.

Step 1

Determine the value of $\dfrac{\alpha}{2}$.

At a 95% confidence level, the confidence coefficient is 0.95 and the level of significance, α, is equal to $1 - 0.95 = 0.05$.

Therefore, the value of $\dfrac{\alpha}{2}$ is equal to

$\dfrac{0.05}{2} = 0.025$.

Step 2

Determine the value of $z_{\frac{\alpha}{2}}$.

From the z-score table, the z-value of the area of 0.025 in the upper tail of the standard normal distribution curve is 1.96.

$1 - 0.025 = 0.975$

The number 0.975 is the area to the left of the z-value found on the z-score table.

Step 3

Determine the margin of error for the sample mean.

Substitute 200 for n, 15 for σ, and 1.96 for $z_{\frac{\alpha}{2}}$

into the formula $ME = z_{\frac{\alpha}{2}} \dfrac{\sigma}{\sqrt{n}}$.

$ME = z_{\frac{\alpha}{2}} \dfrac{\sigma}{\sqrt{n}}$

$ME = 1.96 \times \dfrac{15}{\sqrt{200}}$

$ME \approx 2.079$

The margin of error for the sample mean to the nearest thousandth is 2.079.

To determine the margin of error for an estimate of a population proportion, use the formula

$ME = z_{\frac{\alpha}{2}} \sqrt{\dfrac{\bar{p}(1 - \bar{p})}{n}}$, where $\bar{p}$ is the proportion of the sample, n is the sample size, α is the level of significance, and $z_{\frac{\alpha}{2}}$ is the z-value of the area of

$\dfrac{\alpha}{2}$ in the upper tail of the standard normal distribution curve.

The estimate of a population proportion is equal to $\bar{p} = \dfrac{x}{n}$, where x is the value of the desired outcome and n is the sample size.

Example

In a survey of 300 students, representing a normally distributed population, it was found that 165 students rode the bus to school on a regular basis. The estimate of the population proportion, $\bar{p}$, for the number of students who rode the bus to school on a regular basis was calculated to be $\bar{p} = \dfrac{165}{300} = 0.55$.

Using a 99% confidence level, determine the margin of error for the estimate of the population proportion.

Solution

To find the margin of error for the estimate proportion of the population use the formula

$ME = z_{\frac{\alpha}{2}}\sqrt{\dfrac{\bar{p}(1-\bar{p})}{n}}$, where $\bar{p}$ is the proportion

of the sample, n is the sample size, α is the level of significance, and $z_{\frac{\alpha}{2}}$ is the z-value of the area

of $\dfrac{\alpha}{2}$ in the upper tail of the standard normal distribution curve.

Step 1

Determine the value of $\dfrac{\alpha}{2}$.

At a 99% confidence level, the confidence coefficient is 0.99 and the level of significance, α, is equal to $1 - 0.99 = 0.01$.

Therefore, the value of $\dfrac{\alpha}{2}$ is equal to

$\dfrac{0.01}{2} = 0.005$.

Step 2

Determine the value of $z_{\frac{\alpha}{2}}$.

Since 0.005 is the area in the upper tail of the standard normal distribution curve, $1 - 0.005 = 0.995$ is the area to the left and is used to find the z-value.

Using a graphing calculator, press 2nd VARS to access the DISTR menu and select 3:invNorm. Press 0 . 9 9 5 and ENTER.

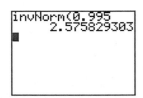

To the nearest thousandth, the z-value of the area of 0.005 in the upper tail of the standard normal distribution curve is 2.576.

For a 99% confidence level, the z-value commonly used is to the nearest thousandth.

Step 3

Determine the margin of error for the estimate population proportion, $\bar{p}$, using the formula

$ME = z_{\frac{\alpha}{2}}\sqrt{\dfrac{\bar{p}(1-\bar{p})}{n}}$.

Substitute 300 for n, 0.55 for $\bar{p}$, and 2.576 for $z_{\frac{\alpha}{2}}$.

$ME = z_{\frac{\alpha}{2}}\sqrt{\dfrac{\bar{p}(1-\bar{p})}{n}}$

$ME = 2.576 \times \sqrt{\dfrac{(0.55)(1-0.55)}{300}}$

$ME = 2.576 \times \sqrt{\dfrac{0.2475}{300}}$

$ME \approx 0.074$

The margin of error for the estimate population proportion is approximately 0.074.

For the common confidence levels 90%, 95%, and 99%, the required z-values are 1.645, 1.96, and 2.576, respectively.

Use the following information to answer the next question.

A standard normal distribution is shown.

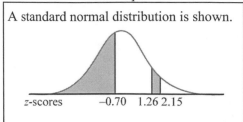

1. To the nearest hundredth, what is the area of the shaded regions?

   A. 0.13   B. 0.15

   C. 0.30   D. 0.33

Written Response

2. Calculate the mean of the data set {125, 300, 150, 175, 50, 450, 150}.

Use the following information to answer the next question.

The table illustrates the percentage of time that a mathematics teacher spends talking to his students in six class periods.

Period	Percentage of Time (%)
1	85
2	78
3	90
4	65
5	82
6	88

Numerical Response

3. To the nearest hundredth, the value of the standard deviation for the percentages is _____.

Use the following information to answer the next question.

On an exam, the raw-score results are normally distributed. The raw scores and corresponding z-scores are shown in the given diagram.

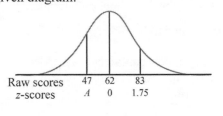

4. Correct to the nearest hundredth, what is the value of *A*?

   A. −1.12   B. −1.25

   C. −1.36   D. −1.50

Use the following information to answer the next question.

Marks on a test have a standard normal distribution.

Numerical Response

5. Using a z-score table, to the nearest hundredth of a percent, the percentage of marks that have z-scores greater than 1.2 is _____.

Numerical Response

6. Using a graphing calculator, determine the area to the left of a z-score of 0.91 to the nearest hundredth. _____

Use the following information to answer the next question.

A discount airline has determined that the mass of passenger luggage is normally distributed with a mean of 16 kg and a standard deviation of 2.5 kg.

7. Correct to the nearest tenth, the percentage of luggage with a mass less than 14 kg is

   A. 24.2%   B. 21.2%

   C. 19.8%   D. 18.7%

Use the following information to answer the next question.

In a certain city, the mean price of diesel fuel is $0.78 /L and the standard deviation is $0.02 /L. At a particular service station in the city, the price of diesel fuel is 1.5 units of standard deviation above the mean.

Numerical Response

8. Assuming a normal distribution, the price per litre of diesel fuel at that service station is $_____.

Use the following information to answer the next question.

A quality control officer for a manufacturer of light bulbs tests 200 bulbs of a particular type and finds the average lifetime of the sample to be 300 h. It is known from previous work that the standard deviation for the lifetimes of all bulbs of that type is 50 h.

9. To the nearest hour, the 95% confidence interval for this sample will be between
   A. 250 and 350 h   **B.** 293 and 307 h

   C. 298 and 310 h   **D.** 300 and 350 h

ANSWERS AND SOLUTIONS
STATISTICS

1. **D**	4. **B**	7. **B**
2. **WR**	5. **11.51**	8. **0.81**
3. **8.28**	6. **0.82**	9. **B**

1. D

Step 1
Use the z-score table to determine the areas under the curve to the left of the z-scores 1.26 and 2.15.
The area under the curve to the left of $z = 1.26$ is 0.8962.
Similarly, the area under the curve to the left of $z = 2.15$ is 0.9842.

Step 2
Find the area between the z-scores 1.26 and 2.15.
The area under the curve between the z-scores 1.26 and 2.15 is the difference between the areas under the curve to the left of $z = 2.15$ and $z = 1.26$.
$0.9842 - 0.8962 = 0.088$.

Step 3
Use the z-score table to find the area under the curve to the left of $z = -0.70$.
The area under the curve to the left of $z = -0.70$ is 0.2420.

Step 4
Add the two areas to find the total shaded area.
$0.088 + 0.2420 = 0.33$
To the nearest hundredth, the area of the shaded regions is 0.33.

2. WR

Step 1
The mean of a set of data is defined as the ratio of the sum of the values to the number of values in the data set (in other words, taking the average of the data set).
Determine the sum of the given values.
$\left(\begin{array}{c} 125 + 300 + 150 + 175 \\ + 50 + 450 + 150 \end{array} \right) = 1\ 400$

Step 2
Divide the total sum by the number of values.
Since there are 7 values, divide by 7.
$1\ 400 \div 7 = 200$
Therefore, the mean of the data set is 200.

3. 8.28

The standard deviation can be determined algebraically.

Step 1
Determine the mean of the data using the formula $\mu = \dfrac{x_1 + x_2 + \ldots + x_n}{n}$.

$\mu = \dfrac{85 + 78 + 90 + 65 + 82 + 88}{6}$

Simplify.
$\mu = \dfrac{488}{6}$
$\mu \approx 81.33$

Step 2
Substitute the required values into the standard deviation formula $\sigma = \sqrt{\dfrac{(x_1 - \mu)^2 + (x_2 - \mu)^2 + \ldots + (x_n - \mu)^2}{n}}$,
where μ = the mean, and solve.

$\sigma = \sqrt{\dfrac{(85 - 81.3\ldots)^2 + \ldots + (88 - 81.3\ldots)^2}{6}}$

$\sigma = \sqrt{\dfrac{411.33\ldots}{6}}$

$\sigma = 8.279\ 828\ 232$

Step 3
Round the answer to the nearest hundredth.
The value of the standard deviation is 8.28.

4. B

Step 1
Substitute 1.75 for z, 83 for x, and 62 for μ in the z-score formula.

$z = \dfrac{x - \mu}{\sigma}$

$1.75 = \dfrac{83 - 62}{\sigma}$

Step 2
Solve for σ.
$1.75\sigma = 83 - 62$
$\qquad = 21$

$\sigma = \dfrac{21}{1.75} = 12$

The standard deviation is 12.

Step 3
Use the standard deviation to determine the z-score of A.

Substitute A for z, 47 for x, 62 for μ, and 12 for σ in the z-score formula.

$$A = \frac{x - \mu}{\sigma}$$
$$= \frac{47 - 62}{12}$$
$$= \frac{-15}{12}$$
$$= -1.25$$

Correct to the nearest hundredth, the value of A is -1.25.

5. 11.51

Step 1
Sketch a standard normal curve, shading the area to the right of the z-score 1.2.

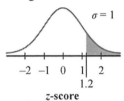

Step 2
Refer to the standard normal distribution table.
First, find the area to the left of the z-score 1.2.
The area to the left of the z-score 1.2 is 0.8849.

Step 3
Determine the area to the right of the z-score 1.2.
Since the total area under the curve is 1, the area to the right of the z-score 1.2 is found by subtracting 0.8849 from 1.
The resulting value is $1 - 0.8849 = 0.1151$.
If the area to the right of the z-score 1.2 is 0.1151, then 11.51% of the test marks have a z-score greater than 1.2.

6. 0.82

Use the normalcdf feature on a TI-83 graphing calculator.
Area = normalcdf(left bound, right bound, μ, σ).

To access this function, press [2nd] [VARS], and select 2:normalcdf(. Enter the data as shown.
A = normalcdf($-1E99$, 0.91, 0, 1)
A = 0.818 588 775...

Therefore, the area to the left of the given z-score is approximately 0.82.

7. B

Two alternative solutions are presented below.

Step 1
Find the z-score corresponding to the given mass of luggage (14 kg).

Use the z-score formula $z = \frac{x - \mu}{\sigma}$ to find the z-score, z, by substituting 14 for x, 16 for μ, and 2.5 for σ.

$$z = \frac{14 - 16}{2.5}$$
$$= -0.8$$

Step 2
Determine the area corresponding to the z-score.
Use the z-score table or a calculator to find the area under the standard normal curve to the left of -0.8.

Step 3
Convert the area value to a percentage.
$0.2119 \times 100 = 21.19\%$
Rounded to the nearest tenth, the percentage of passengers having luggage with a mass less than 14 kg is about 21.2%.

Alternative method. Step 1.
Use TI 83 Plus calculator to determine the area under the normal distribution curve.
Area
= normalcdf(Left bound, Right bound, μ, σ)
= normalcdf(0, 14, 16, 2.5)), (= 0.211 8553...)

Step 2
Convert the area value to a percentage.
$0.211\ 8553 \times 100 = 21.185\ 53\%$
Rounded to the nearest tenth, the percentage of passengers having luggage with a mass less than 14 kg is about 21.2%.

8. 0.81

Determine the price that is 1.5 standard deviation units above the mean.

To determine the price that is 1.5 standard deviations above the mean, add 1.5(0.02) to 0.78.
$0.78 + 1.5(0.02) = 0.81$

The price per litre of diesel fuel at that particular service station is $0.81.

9. B

Step 1

Determine the margin of error, *ME*.

At a 95% confidence level, the value of $z_{\frac{\alpha}{2}}$, or the critical value z^*, is 1.96. Substitute 1.96 for $z_{\frac{\alpha}{2}}$, 200 for *n*, and 50 for σ into the formula $ME = z_{\frac{\alpha}{2}} \frac{\sigma}{\sqrt{n}}$.

$ME = 1.96 \times \frac{50}{\sqrt{200}}$

$ME = 1.96 \times 3.536$

$ME = 6.930$

Rounded to the nearest hour, the margin of error is 7 h.

Step 2

Determine the 95% confidence interval.

The confidence interval for a sample mean is defined by $\bar{x} \pm z_{\frac{\alpha}{2}} \frac{\sigma}{\sqrt{n}}$. The sample mean, $\bar{x}$, is 300, and the margin of error is 7.

Therefore, the 95% confidence interval is 300 ± 7, or between 293 ($300 - 7 = 293$) and 307 ($300 + 7 = 307$).

The 95% confidence interval for this sample is between 293 and 307 h.

UNIT TEST — STATISTICS

1. A set of data is normally distributed and has a mean of $x + y$ and a standard deviation of $2y$. What percentage of the data lies between $x - 3y$ and $x + 5y$?

   A. 99.5%   **B.** 95%

   C. 84%   **D.** 81.5%

Use the following information to answer the next question.

A standard normal distribution is shown.

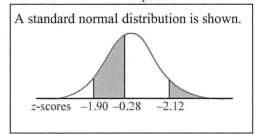

z-scores   −1.90 −0.28   −2.12

2. Correct to the nearest thousandth, the total area of the shaded regions is

   A. 0.344   **B.** 0.350

   C. 0.378   **D.** 0.383

Written Response

3. Calculate the mean of the data set {6, 13, 40, 23, 35, 27, 31}.

Numerical Response

4. A set of 20 numbers has a standard deviation of 7. If 3 is added to each number in the set, the new standard deviation is _____ .

---

5. Which of the following graphs **best** represents data values with a large standard deviation?

   A.
   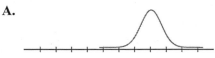

   B.
   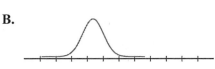

   C.
   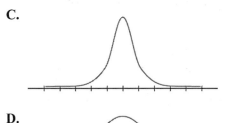

   D.
   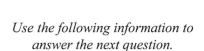

Use the following information to answer the next question.

On a mathematics exam, the class mean was 45% with a standard deviation of 8%. The teacher decides to add an additional 15% to each student's exam score.

6. When the teacher recalculates the mean and standard deviation, she will find that

   A. both the mean and standard deviation increased

   B. the mean increased and the standard deviation decreased

   C. the mean remained the same but the standard deviation increased

   D. the mean increased and the standard deviation remained unchanged

Use the following information to answer the next question.

An examination was written by 10 000 students. The marks were normally distributed, with 5 000 students receiving scores below the mean and 500 students scoring more than a particular *z*-score, *z*, as shown in the given diagram.

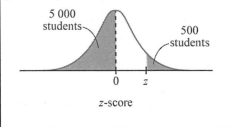

7. Correct to the nearest hundredth, the value of *z* is
   A. 0.13   B. 0.92
   C. 1.64   D. 1.95

Numerical Response

8. Using a graphing calculator, determine the area under a normal curve to the left of a *z*-score of −0.89 to the nearest hundredth. _____

Use the following information to answer the next question.

Some police officers sampled the speeds of 200 drivers on a particular stretch of road in order to determine the proportion of speeders. The officers found that 58% of the sampled drivers were speeding.

9. To the nearest percentage point, what will be the margin of error for a 95% confidence interval when the proportion of speeders on that road is reported?
   A. 6%   B. 7%
   C. 10%   D. 11%

Use the following information to answer the next question.

A coffee distribution company surveyed 700 people to determine how much money people spent on coffee per day. On average, the people surveyed spent approximately $5 per day on coffee. At a 90 % confidence level, the margin of error for the survey's results is $1.75.

10. What conclusion can the coffee distribution company draw based on this survey's results?
    A. The surveyor is 90 % uncertain that the average amount people spend on coffee per day will be between $3.25 and $6.75.

    B. The surveyor is 90 % confident that the average amount people spend on coffee per day is between $3.25 and $6.75.

    C. There is a 90 % chance that the average amount people spend on coffee per day is $5.

    D. There is a 90 % probability that the margin of error for the survey's results is $1.75.

ANSWERS AND SOLUTIONS — UNIT TEST

1. B	4. 7	7. C	10. B
2. C	5. D	8. 0.19	
3. WR	6. D	9. B	

1. B

Step 1

Sketch the standard normal curve that represents the given data.

The mean of the data is given as $x + y$, and the standard deviation is given as $2y$.

Label the centre with the data mean, and label the values that are ± 1, ± 2, and ± 3 standard deviations from the mean.

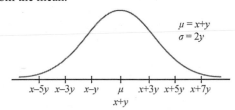

Step 2

Shade the area between the two boundaries given.

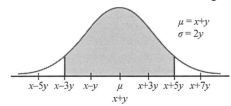

Step 3

By adding the percentages representing each shaded standard deviation region, determine the probability represented by the shaded area.

The percentages of each shaded standard deviation region are 13.5%, 34%, 34%, and 13.5%. Therefore, $13.5 + 34\% + 34\% + 13.5\% = 95\%$ of the data lies between $x - 3y$ and $x + 5y$.

2. C

Step 1

Determine the area between z-scores -1.90 and -0.28.

The area under the curve to the left of $z = -1.90$ is 0.0287. Similarly, the area under the curve to the left of $z = -0.28$ is 0.3897.

The area between the two z-values is $0.3897 - 0.0287 = 0.3610$

Alternatively, you may use TI 83 Plus calculator:
Area
= normalcdf(Left Bound, Right Bound, μ, σ)
= normalcdf(-1.90, -0.28, 0, 1)
= 0.361 022...

Step 2

Determine the area under the curve to the right of the z-score 2.12.

Use the z-score table to determine the area under the curve to the left of 2.12.

The area under the curve to the left of 2.12 is 0.9830.

Since the total area under the curve is 1, the area under the curve to the right of $z = 2.12$ can be found by subtracting the area under the curve to the left of $z = 2.12$ from the area of 1.

That is, $1 - 0.9830 = 0.017$.

Therefore, the area under the curve to the right of $z = 2.12$ is 0.017.

Alternatively, you may use TI83 Plus calculator:
Area
= normalcdf(Left Bound, Right Bound, μ, σ)
= normalcdf(2.12, 1E99, 0, 1)
= 0.017 0029...

Step 4

Determine the total shaded area by adding.
$0.361 + 0.017 = 0.378$

To the nearest thousandth, the total area of the shaded regions is 0.378.

3. WR

Step 1

The mean of a set of data is defined as the ratio of the sum of the values to the number of values in the data set.

Determine the sum of the given values.
$6 + 13 + 40 + 23 + 35 + 27 + 31 = 175$

Step 2

Divide the total sum by the number of values.
Since there are 7 values, divide by 7.
$175 \div 7 = 25$
Therefore, the mean of the data set is 25.

4. 7

Since 3 is added to each number in the set, the spread of the numbers about the mean stays the same. The standard deviation remains 7 because the dispersion of numbers has not changed.

5. D

Standard deviation measures how the data is dispersed or spread out about the mean. If the standard deviation is small, the data values are bunched together and are close to the mean. If the standard deviation is large, the data values are spread out and are distant from the mean.

Graph D best represents data values that are spread out.

6. D

Step 1

Identify the effect of the change in marks on the mean.
When each data value is increased or decreased by a constant, the mean will also increase or decrease by the same constant.
Since the teacher adds an additional 15% to each student's exam score, the mean will increase by 15%.

Step 2

Identify the effect of the change in marks on the standard deviation.
Even though all the exam scores increased by 15%, they are still the same distance from the mean. The standard deviation will not change.

The teacher will find that the mean increased and the standard deviation remained unchanged.

7. C

Step 1

Determine the percentage of students who had z-scores better than z, and find the area to the right of z.
The total number of students writing the exam is 10 000, and 500 students had z-scores better than z.
The percentage of students whose z-scores were better than z can be found by dividing these two values.
$\frac{500}{10\ 000} = 0.05$ or 5%.
The percentage of students who had z-scores better than z is 5%, and the shaded area is 0.05.

Step 2

Find the area to the left of z.
The total area under the standard normal curve is 1, and the area to the right of z is 0.05. The area to the left of z is the difference between these two values.
The area to the left of z is $1 - 0.05 = 0.95$.

Step 3

Use the z-score table to find the z-score.
The area in the table closest to the area of 0.95 is 0.9495. The corresponding z-score for this area is 1.64.
Therefore, $z = 1.64$.

Note: Using a TI-83 Plus calculator, the value of z can be determined using InvNorm(0.95, 0, 1), where 0.95 is the area to the left of the z-value, 0 is the mean value, and 1 is the standard deviation.

8. 0.19

Step 1

Determine the left bound, right bound, μ, and σ of the area being calculated.
Since the curve is a normal curve, the mean is 0 ($\mu = 0$), and the standard deviation is 1 ($\sigma = 1$).
The right bound is given as -0.89. The left bound will be completely to the left of the right bound, so use the value -1×10^{99}.

Step 2

Substitute the values of the left bound, right bound, μ, and σ into the normalcdf(function, and calculate the area.

To calculate the area under the curve with the normalcdf(function, press 2nd VARS 2:normalcdf(.

Area = normalcdf(left bound, right bound, μ, σ)

A = normalcdf$(-1 \times 10^{99}, -0.89, 0, 1)$
$\quad\quad = 0.186\ 732\ 9055$

The area to the left of the given z-score is approximately 0.19.

9. B

Step 1

Determine the value of $\frac{\alpha}{2}$.

At a 95% confidence level, the confidence coefficient is 0.95 and the level of significance, α, is equal to $1 - 0.95 = 0.05$.

Therefore, the value of $\frac{\alpha}{2}$ is equal to $\frac{0.05}{2} = 0.025$.

Step 2

Determine the value of $z_{\frac{\alpha}{2}}$.

From the z-score table, the z-value of the area of 0.025 in the upper tail of the standard normal distribution curve is 1.96.
$1 - 0.025 = 0.975$
The number 0.975 is the area to the left of the z-value found on the z-score table.

Step 3

Determine the margin of error for the estimated population proportion, $\bar{p}$, using the formula
$ME = z_{\frac{\alpha}{2}}\sqrt{\dfrac{\bar{p}(1-\bar{p})}{n}}$.

Substitute 200 for n, 0.58 for $\bar{p}$, and 1.96 for $z_{\frac{\alpha}{2}}$.

$ME = z_{\frac{\alpha}{2}}\sqrt{\dfrac{\bar{p}(1-\bar{p})}{n}}$

$ME = 1.96 \times \sqrt{\dfrac{(0.58)(1-0.58)}{200}}$

$ME = 1.96 \times \sqrt{\dfrac{0.2436}{200}}$

$ME \approx 0.0684$

The margin of error for the proportion of speeders on the road is approximately 0.068, or 6.8%, which rounds to 7%.

10. B

A confidence level of 90 % indicates that the surveyor is 90 % confident of the results and there is a 10 % chance of uncertainty. The margin of error, ME, indicates how precise the data from the survey is to the population. The confidence interval for a sample mean, $\bar{x}$, is in the form $\bar{x} \pm ME$. The confidence interval for the given sample mean is $\$5 \pm 1.75$. Therefore, the surveyor is 90 % confident that the average amount people spend on coffee per day is between $\$5 - \$1.75 = \$3.25$ and $\$5 + \$1.75 = \$6.75$.

NOTES

Relations and Functions

RELATIONS AND FUNCTIONS

Table of Correlations			
Outcome	**Practice Questions**	**Unit Test Questions**	**Practice Test**
20RF Relations and Functions			
20RF.1 *Demonstrate an understanding of the characteristics of quadratic functions, including:*	1, 2, 3, 4, 5, 6, 7, 8, 9	1, 2, 3, 4, 5, 6, 7, 8, 9, 10	1, 2, 3
20RF.2 *Solve problems that involve quadratic equations.*	10, 11, 12, 13, 14, 15, 16, 17	11, 12, 13, 14, 15, 16, 17, 18, 19	4, 5, 6

20RF.1 Demonstrate an understanding of the characteristics of quadratic functions, including:

EVALUATING QUADRATIC FUNCTIONS USING A GRAPH

Function notation can be used to describe values and points on quadratic graphs. On the graph of a quadratic function, the value of $f(x)$ is the corresponding y-value for a given value of x.

Another way of thinking of $f(x)$ is "what is the value of y on the graph for a given value of x?"

Example

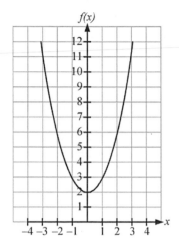

For the given graph, determine $f(-1)$.

Solution

Another way of thinking about $f(-1)$ is "what is the value of y on the graph when $x = -1$?"

This is at the point where y is 3.

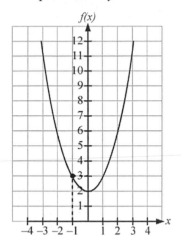

Therefore, $f(-1) = 3$.

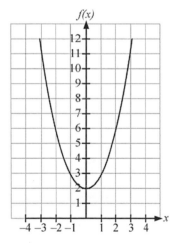

The graph of a function is given. Determine the value of x when $f(x) = 11$.

Solution

Another way of thinking about $f(x) = 11$ is "what are the values for x on the graph when $y = 11$?"

When looking at the graph, observe that there are two values that will satisfy this condition; the points at which $x = \pm 3$.

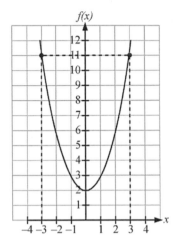

Therefore, $f(3) = 11$ and $f(-3) = 11$.

20RF.1 Demonstrate an understanding of the characteristics of quadratic functions, including:

DETERMINING KEY POINTS ON THE GRAPH OF A QUADRATIC FUNCTION

The key points of a quadratic function can be determined by examining its graph. These points include the x-intercepts, the y-intercept, and the vertex.

The x-intercepts are the points at which the graph crosses the x-axis, where the value of the y-coordinate is 0. These locations are also referred to as the zeros of the function. The zeros of a function of the form $y = ax^2 + bx + c$ are also the solutions, or roots, of the related equation $0 = ax^2 + bx + c$.

The y-intercept is the point at which the graph crosses the y-axis, where the value of the x-coordinate is 0.

The vertex is the maximum or minimum of the graph of a quadratic function.

Example

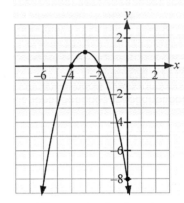

The graph of a function

Determine the coordinates of the x-intercepts, y-intercept, and the vertex of the graph.

Solution

Step 1
Determine the x-intercepts.
The x-intercepts are the points at which the graph crosses the x-axis, where the value of y is 0. This occurs at two locations, $(-4, 0)$ and $(-2, 0)$.

Step 2
Determine the y-intercept.
The y-intercept is the point at which the graph crosses the y-axis, where the value of x is 0. This only happens at one location, $(0, -8)$.

Step 3
Determine the coordinates of the vertex.
The vertex is found at the maximum or minimum of the graph of a quadratic function. There is a maximum for the given graph, and its coordinates are $(-3, 1)$.

You can also find these key points with a graphing calculator. Use the TRACE function to find the coordinates of the y-intercept by entering zero for the value of x. The CALC menu gives the option of finding the zeros and the minimum and maximum values of a graph. This menu can be reached by pressing 2nd TRACE.

Example

Determine the coordinates of the vertex of the function $y = x^2 + 3x - 5$ using a graphing calculator.

Solution

Step 1

Graph the equation $y = x^2 + 3x - 5$ using a graphing calculator.

Enter the equation in the TI-83+ graphing calculator's Y = window.

Select a ZOOM 6:ZStandard window setting, and then press GRAPH.

Step 2

Determine the coordinates of the vertex.

It can been seen from the graph that the vertex is a minimum. Access the CALC menu by pressing 2nd TRACE, and choose 3:Minimum to determine coordinates of the minimum of the graph.

Move the cursor to the left of the vertex when asked for a left bound, and press ENTER.

Move the cursor to the right of the vertex when asked for a right bound, and press ENTER.

Press ENTER a third time, and the result is as given.

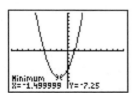

The coordinates of the vertex of the graph of the function $y = x^2 + 3x - 5$ are $(-1.5, -7.25)$.

Step 1

Graph the equation $y = x^2 + 3x - 5$ using a graphing calculator.

Enter the equation in the TI-83+ graphing calculator's Y = window.

Select a ZOOM 6:ZStandard window setting, and then press GRAPH.

Step 2

Determine the coordinates of the vertex.

It can been seen from the graph that the vertex is a minimum. Access the CALC menu by pressing 2nd TRACE, and choose 3:Minimum to determine coordinates of the minimum of the graph.

Move the cursor to the left of the vertex when asked for a left bound, and press ENTER.

Move the cursor to the right of the vertex when asked for a right bound, and press ENTER.

Press ENTER a third time, and the result is as given.

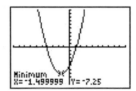

The coordinates of the vertex of the graph of the function $y = x^2 + 3x - 5$ are $(-1.5, -7.25)$.

Step 1

Graph the equation $y = x^2 + 3x - 5$ using a graphing calculator.

Enter the equation in the TI-83+ graphing calculator's Y = window.

Select a ZOOM 6:ZStandard window setting, and then press GRAPH.

Step 2

Determine the coordinates of the vertex.

It can been seen from the graph that the vertex is a minimum. Access the CALC menu by pressing 2nd TRACE , and choose 3:Minimum to determine coordinates of the minimum of the graph.

Move the cursor to the left of the vertex when asked for a left bound, and press ENTER .

Move the cursor to the right of the vertex when asked for a right bound, and press ENTER .

Press ENTER a third time, and the result is as given.

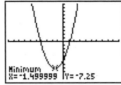

The coordinates of the vertex of the graph of the function $y = x^2 + 3x - 5$ are $(-1.5, -7.25)$.

Step 1

Graph the equation $y = x^2 + 3x - 5$ using a graphing calculator.

Enter the equation in the TI-83+ graphing calculator's Y = window.

Select a ZOOM 6:ZStandard window setting, and then press GRAPH .

Step 2

Determine the coordinates of the vertex.

It can been seen from the graph that the vertex is a minimum. Access the CALC menu by pressing 2nd TRACE , and choose 3:Minimum to determine coordinates of the minimum of the graph.

Move the cursor to the left of the vertex when asked for a left bound, and press ENTER .

Move the cursor to the right of the vertex when asked for a right bound, and press ENTER .

Press ENTER a third time, and the result is as given.

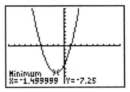

The coordinates of the vertex of the graph of the function $y = x^2 + 3x - 5$ are $(-1.5, -7.25)$.

20RF.1 Demonstrate an understanding of the characteristics of quadratic functions, including:

GRAPHING QUADRATIC FUNCTIONS BY HAND BY FACTORING

When graphing a quadratic function, factoring the function to the form $f(x) = a(x - r)(x - s)$ can provide useful information for sketching the graph.

To use this sketching method, begin by determining the x-intercept(s) and the y-intercept of the graph of the function.

Next, find the vertex of the graph, and use symmetry to complete the sketch.

Example

Without using technology, graph the function $y = -x^2 + x + 6$.

Solution

Step 1

Factor the function.

$y = -x^2 + x + 6$
$y = -(x^2 - x - 6)$
$y = -(x - 3)(x + 2)$

Step 2

Find the x-intercepts by giving y a value of zero.

$0 = -(x - 3)(x + 2)$

$x = 3$

$x = -2$

Step 3

Find the y-intercept by giving x a value of zero.

$y = -(0 - 3)(0 + 2)$

$y = -(-3)(2)$

$y = 6$

Step 4

Find the midpoint of the x-intercepts in order to find the equation of the axis of symmetry.

$$M = \left(\frac{x_1 + x_2}{2}, \frac{y_1 + y_2}{2}\right)$$

$$= \left(\frac{3 + (-2)}{2}, \frac{0 + 0}{2}\right)$$

$$= \left(\frac{1}{2}, 0\right)$$

The equation of the axis of symmetry is $x = \frac{1}{2}$.

Step 5

Find the vertex.

The vertex occurs along the axis of symmetry.

Substitute $\frac{1}{2}$ for x.

$$y = -\left(\frac{1}{2} - 3\right)\left(\frac{1}{2} + 2\right)$$

$$y = \frac{25}{4} \text{ or } y = 6.25$$

The vertex is at point $\left(\frac{1}{2}, \frac{25}{4}\right)$, or $(0.5, 6.25)$.

Step 6

Using the information from steps 2, 3, 4, and 5, sketch the graph of $y = -x^2 + x + 6$.

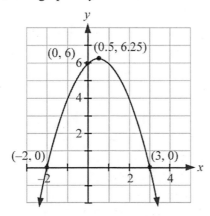

20RF.1 Demonstrate an understanding of the characteristics of quadratic functions, including:

GRAPHING VARIOUS FORMS OF THE QUADRATIC FUNCTION USING TECHNOLOGY

Using technology, such as a TI-83 Plus calculator, to graph a quadratic function requires the use of proper window settings and the appropriate selection of calculator buttons.

To graph a quadratic function on a graphing calculator, follow these steps:

1. Make sure the function is written in terms of the y-variable or unsquared variable.

2. Press the $\boxed{Y =}$ button on your graphing calculator, and type in the function.

3. Set an appropriate WINDOW setting for the graph so that the resulting parabolic graph will be adequately portrayed on the screen. For most quadratic functions, a good starting WINDOW setting can be created by pressing the $\boxed{\text{ZOOM}}$ button and selecting either the 6:ZStandard or 0:Zoom Fit feature.

4. Press the $\boxed{\text{GRAPH}}$ button if necessary to view the parabolic graph representing the quadratic function.

Example

Graph $y = 2(x - 3)^2 - 5$ on a graphing calculator.

Solution

Step 1

Press the $\boxed{Y =}$ button.

Type in the function by pressing the following sequence of buttons:

$\boxed{2} \boxed{(} \boxed{x, T, \theta, n} \boxed{-} \boxed{3} \boxed{)} \boxed{x^2} \boxed{-} \boxed{5}$

Step 2

Set an appropriate WINDOW setting.

Press the ZOOM button, and select the 6:ZStandard feature. This graph should appear on the calculator screen.

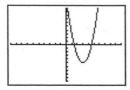

An adequate graph of the parabola representing the function is visible.

Example

Graph $P = -25s^2 + 1\ 010s - 3\ 253$ using technology.

Solution

Step 1

Press the Y = button.

When a function like $P = -25s^2 + 1\ 010s - 3\ 253$ is not defined in terms of x- and y-variables, it can still be entered into a graphing calculator as though it was, namely as $y = -25x^2 + 1\ 010x - 3\ 253$.

Type in the function by pressing the following sequence of buttons:

(–)	2	5	x, T, θ, n	x^2	+	1	0	1	0

x, T, θ, n	–	3	2	5	3

Step 2

Set an appropriate WINDOW setting.

Press the ZOOM button, and select the 0:Zoom Fit feature. This graph should appear on the calculator screen.

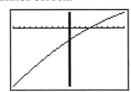

Since there is an inadequate amount of the parabola visible, the WINDOW setting needs to be adjusted manually.

Step 3

Press the WINDOW button.

To see more of the graph, the top and right side of the graph needs to be made more visible. To do so, increase the Xmax value by pressing the down arrow key so that it highlights the Xmax value.

Enter a greater value than 10, such as 50. Then, press ZOOM again, and highlight the 0:Zoom Fit feature again. A more adequate parabola will appear on the screen.

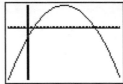

The WINDOW setting can be continually adjusted as necessary by pressing the WINDOW button and entering values for Xmin, Xmax, Xscl, Ymin, Ymac, or Yscl.

Example

Graph $y = -0.5(x - 6)(x + 5)$ using a graphing calculator.

Solution

Step 1

Press the Y = button.

Type in the function by pressing the following sequence of buttons:

(–)	0	.	5	(	x, T, θ, n	–	6	)	(

x, T, θ, n	+	5	)

Step 2

Set an appropriate WINDOW setting.

Press the ZOOM button, and select the 6:ZStandard feature. This graph should appear on the calculator screen.

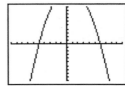

Since the top part of the parabola is not visible, the WINDOW setting needs to be adjusted manually.

Step 3

Press the WINDOW button.

To see more of the upper part of the graph, the Ymax value needs to be increased. Press the down arrow key so that it highlights the Ymax value. Enter a greater value than 10, such as 20.

Then, press the GRAPH button. A more adequate graph of the parabola should appear on the screen.

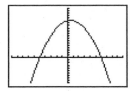

20RF.1 Demonstrate an understanding of the characteristics of quadratic functions, including:

DETERMINING THE VERTEX OF A QUADRATIC FUNCTION'S GRAPH IN FACTORED FORM

To determine the vertex of the function $y = a(x - r)(x - s)$, first find the x-coordinate of the vertex. When the function is written in this form, the x-intercepts can be easily determined from the equation. Since the graph will be symmetrical, the x-coordinate of the vertex will be exactly halfway between the x-intercepts. This position can be found by using the midpoint formula

$M = \left(\dfrac{x_1 + x_2}{2}, \dfrac{y_1 + y_2}{2}\right)$. The x-coordinate can then be substituted back into the equation to solve for the y-coordinate.

To find the vertex of $y = a(x - r)(x - s)$, follow these steps:

1. Determine the x-intercepts.
2. Determine the midpoint of the x-intercepts.
3. Substitute the x-coordinate from the midpoint into the equation to solve for y.

Example

Determine the vertex of the function

$y = \dfrac{1}{2}(x - 2)(x + 5)$.

Solution

Step 1

Determine the x-intercepts.

Set the equation equal to 0, and apply the zero product property.

$0 = \dfrac{1}{2}(x - 2)(x + 5)$

$0 = x - 2$
$2 = x$
$\quad 0 = x + 5$
$-5 = x$

Step 2

Determine the midpoint of the x-intercepts.

$M = \left(\dfrac{x_1 + x_2}{2}, \dfrac{y_1 + y_2}{2}\right)$

$M = \left(\dfrac{-5 + 2}{2}, \dfrac{0 + 0}{2}\right)$

$M = \left(\dfrac{-3}{2}, \dfrac{0}{2}\right)$

$M = \left(-\dfrac{3}{2}, 0\right)$

Step 3

Substitute the x-coordinate from the midpoint into the equation to solve for y.

$y = \dfrac{1}{2}(x - 2)(x + 5)$

$y = \dfrac{1}{2}\left(-\dfrac{3}{2} - 2\right)\left(-\dfrac{3}{2} + 5\right)$

$y = \dfrac{1}{2}\left(-\dfrac{7}{2}\right)\left(\dfrac{7}{2}\right)$

$y = -\dfrac{49}{8}$

The coordinates of the vertex of the function

$y = \dfrac{1}{2}(x - 2)(x + 5)$ are $\left(-\dfrac{3}{2}, -\dfrac{49}{8}\right)$.

20RF.1 Demonstrate an understanding of the characteristics of quadratic functions, including:

DETERMINING THE AXIS OF SYMMETRY OF THE GRAPH OF A QUADRATIC FUNCTION IN FACTORED FORM

In order to determine the axis of symmetry of the function $y = a(x - r)(x - s)$, you must determine the x-coordinate of the vertex. When the equation is given in this form, the x-intercepts can be easily determined from the equation. Since the graph will be symmetrical, the x-coordinate of the vertex will be exactly halfway between the x-intercepts. This position can be found by using the midpoint formula, $M = \left(\dfrac{x_1 + x_2}{2}, \dfrac{y_1 + y_2}{2} \right)$.

To find the axis of symmetry of $y = a(x - r)(x - s)$, follow these steps:

1. Determine the x-intercepts.
2. Determine the midpoint of the x-intercepts.

Example

Determine the axis of symmetry of the function $y = 3(x + 4)(x - 3)$.

Solution

Step 1

Determine the x-intercepts.
Set the equation equal to 0, and apply the zero product property.
$0 = 3(x + 4)(x - 3)$
$0 = x + 4$
$-4 = x$
$0 = x - 3$
$3 = x$

The coordinates of the x-intercepts are $(-4, 0)$ and $(3, 0)$.

Step 2

Determine the midpoint of the x-intercepts.
$$M = \left(\frac{x_1 + x_2}{2}, \frac{y_1 + y_2}{2} \right)$$
$$M = \left(\frac{-4 + 3}{2}, \frac{0 + 0}{2} \right)$$
$$M = \left(-\frac{1}{2}, 0 \right)$$

Since the x-coordinate of the vertex is $-\dfrac{1}{2}$, the equation for the axis of symmetry is $x = -\dfrac{1}{2}$.

20RF.1 Demonstrate an understanding of the characteristics of quadratic functions, including:

DETERMINING THE VERTEX OF THE GRAPH OF A QUADRATIC FUNCTION USING TECHNOLOGY

A characteristic of quadratic functions is that at some point, there will be a minimum or maximum value. This is also called the vertex. A graphing calculator can be used to determine the vertex of a quadratic function. The CALC menu gives the option of finding the minimum or maximum values of a graph. This menu can be accessed by pressing $\boxed{\text{2nd}}\ \boxed{\text{TRACE}}$.

Use the following steps to determine the vertex of a quadratic function:

1. Rearrange the equation in terms of y, if necessary.
2. Graph the function using a graphing calculator.
3. Determine the coordinates of the vertex by finding the minimum or maximum values.

Example

Determine the coordinates of the vertex of the function $y = x^2 + 3x - 5$ using a graphing calculator.

Solution

Step 1

Graph the equation $y = x^2 + 3x - 5$ using a graphing calculator.

Enter the equation in the TI-83+ graphing calculator's $\boxed{Y =}$ window.

Select a $\boxed{ZOOM}$ 6:ZStandard window setting, and then press $\boxed{GRAPH}$.

Step 2

Determine the coordinates of the vertex.

It can been seen from the graph that the vertex is a minimum. Access the CALC menu by pressing $\boxed{2nd}$ $\boxed{TRACE}$, and choose 3:Minimum to determine coordinates of the minimum of the graph.

Move the cursor to the left of the vertex when asked for a left bound, and press $\boxed{ENTER}$.

Move the cursor to the right of the vertex when asked for a right bound, and press $\boxed{ENTER}$.

Press $\boxed{ENTER}$ a third time, and the result is as given.

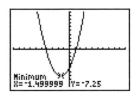

The coordinates of the vertex of the graph of the function $y = x^2 + 3x - 5$ are $(-1.5, -7.25)$.

Step 1

Graph the equation $y = x^2 + 3x - 5$ using a graphing calculator.

Enter the equation in the TI-83+ graphing calculator's $\boxed{Y =}$ window.

Select a $\boxed{ZOOM}$ 6:ZStandard window setting, and then press $\boxed{GRAPH}$.

Step 2

Determine the coordinates of the vertex.

It can been seen from the graph that the vertex is a minimum. Access the CALC menu by pressing $\boxed{2nd}$ $\boxed{TRACE}$, and choose 3:Minimum to determine coordinates of the minimum of the graph.

Move the cursor to the left of the vertex when asked for a left bound, and press $\boxed{ENTER}$.

Move the cursor to the right of the vertex when asked for a right bound, and press $\boxed{ENTER}$.

Press $\boxed{ENTER}$ a third time, and the result is as given.

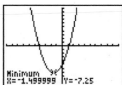

The coordinates of the vertex of the graph of the function $y = x^2 + 3x - 5$ are $(-1.5, -7.25)$.

Step 1

Graph the equation $y = x^2 + 3x - 5$ using a graphing calculator.

Enter the equation in the TI-83+ graphing calculator's $\boxed{Y =}$ window.

Select a $\boxed{ZOOM}$ 6:ZStandard window setting, and then press $\boxed{GRAPH}$.

Step 2

Determine the coordinates of the vertex.

It can been seen from the graph that the vertex is a minimum. Access the CALC menu by pressing $\boxed{\text{2nd}}$ $\boxed{\text{TRACE}}$, and choose 3:Minimum to determine coordinates of the minimum of the graph.

Move the cursor to the left of the vertex when asked for a left bound, and press $\boxed{\text{ENTER}}$.

Move the cursor to the right of the vertex when asked for a right bound, and press $\boxed{\text{ENTER}}$.

Press $\boxed{\text{ENTER}}$ a third time, and the result is as given.

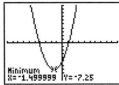

The coordinates of the vertex of the graph of the function $y = x^2 + 3x - 5$ are $(-1.5, -7.25)$.

Step 1

Graph the equation $y = x^2 + 3x - 5$ using a graphing calculator.

Enter the equation in the TI-83+ graphing calculator's $\boxed{\text{Y} =}$ window.

Select a $\boxed{\text{ZOOM}}$ 6:ZStandard window setting, and then press $\boxed{\text{GRAPH}}$.

Step 2

Determine the coordinates of the vertex.

It can been seen from the graph that the vertex is a minimum. Access the CALC menu by pressing $\boxed{\text{2nd}}$ $\boxed{\text{TRACE}}$, and choose 3:Minimum to determine coordinates of the minimum of the graph.

Move the cursor to the left of the vertex when asked for a left bound, and press $\boxed{\text{ENTER}}$.

Move the cursor to the right of the vertex when asked for a right bound, and press $\boxed{\text{ENTER}}$.

Press $\boxed{\text{ENTER}}$ a third time, and the result is as given.

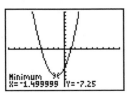

The coordinates of the vertex of the graph of the function $y = x^2 + 3x - 5$ are $(-1.5, -7.25)$.

The axis of symmetry can also be determined using this method. The axis of symmetry is equal to the x-coordinate of the vertex.

Example

Use technology to determine the axis of symmetry of the graph of the quadratic function $\dfrac{y-3}{5} = \dfrac{x}{2}\left(\dfrac{-3x+1}{4}\right)$, and round to the nearest hundredth.

Solution

Step 1

Write the given equation in terms of y.

$$\frac{y-3}{5} = \frac{x}{2}\left(\frac{-3x+1}{4}\right)$$

Multiply both sides of the equation by 5.

$$5\left(\frac{y-3}{5}\right) = 5\left(\frac{x}{2}\left(\frac{-3x+1}{4}\right)\right)$$

$$y-3 = \frac{5}{2}x\left(\frac{-3x+1}{4}\right)$$

Add 3 to each side of the equation.

$$y = \frac{5}{2}x\left(\frac{-3x+1}{4}\right)+3$$

Simplify the equation.

$$y = \frac{-15x^2 + 5x}{8}+3$$

Step 2

Graph the function using a graphing calculator. Press $\boxed{Y=}$, enter $Y_1 = (-15X^2 + 5X)/8 + 3$, and press $\boxed{GRAPH}$. The standard window setting can be used.

The resulting graph is as shown.

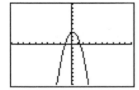

Step 3

Determine the coordinates of the vertex. Since the graph is a parabola that opens downward, the vertex is the maximum point on the graph. Access the CALC menu by pressing $\boxed{2nd}\ \boxed{TRACE}$, and choose 4:maximum to determine the coordinates of the maximum point. Move the cursor to the left of the vertex when asked for a left bound, and press $\boxed{ENTER}$. Move the cursor to the right of the vertex when asked for a right bound, and press $\boxed{ENTER}$. Press $\boxed{ENTER}$ a third time. The resulting graph is shown in the given screen shot.

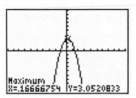

To the nearest hundredth, the coordinates of the vertex are $(0.17,\ 3.05)$.

The axis of symmetry is $x = 0.17$.

20RF.1 Demonstrate an understanding of the characteristics of quadratic functions, including:

DETERMINING THE MAXIMUM OR MINIMUM OF A QUADRATIC FUNCTION IN FACTORED FORM

The maximum or minimum of a quadratic function can be determined from the factored form $y = a(x-r)(x-s)$, where r and s are the x-intercepts.

The y-coordinate of the vertex is equal to the maximum or minimum value of a quadratic function.

To find the value of the maximum or minimum, first find the value of the x-coordinate of the vertex. The x-coordinate of the vertex is located halfway between the x-intercepts and can be calculated by using the formula $x = \dfrac{r+s}{2}$. The y-coordinate can then be determined by substituting the value of the x-coordinate into the original equation.

To determine if the value of the y-coordinate is a maximum or minimum, look at the value of a. If $a > 0$, the parabola opens upward, making the value a minimum. If $a < 0$, the parabola opens downward, making the value a maximum.

Follow these steps to determine the value of the maximum or minimum of a quadratic function:

1. Determine the x-coordinate of the vertex by using the formula $x = \dfrac{r+s}{2}$.

2. Determine the value of the maximum or minimum. Substitute the x-coordinate into the original equation to determine the y-coordinate.

3. Determine if the y-coordinate is a maximum or minimum by looking at the value of a.

Example

Determine the maximum or minimum value of the quadratic function $y = 3(x - 2)(x + 6)$.

Solution

The quadratic function $y = 3(x - 2)(x + 6)$ is in the factored form $y = a(x - r)(x - s)$. Therefore, $a = 3$, $r = 2$, and $s = -6$.

Step 1

Determine the x-coordinate of the vertex.

The x-coordinate of the vertex is located halfway between the x-intercepts and can be calculated by using the formula $x = \dfrac{r+s}{2}$.

Substitute 2 for r and -6 for s.

$$x = \frac{r+s}{2}$$
$$x = \frac{2+(-6)}{2}$$
$$x = \frac{2-6}{2}$$
$$x = \frac{-4}{2}$$
$$x = -2$$

The x-coordinate of the vertex is -2.

Step 2

Determine the value of the maximum or minimum.

The y-coordinate of the vertex is equal to the maximum or minimum value. Substitute the x-coordinate, -2, into the original equation to determine the value of y.

$$y = 3(x - 2)(x + 6)$$
$$y = 3((-2) - 2)((-2) + 6)$$
$$y = 3(-4)(4)$$
$$y = -48$$

The value of the maximum or minimum is -48.

Step 3

Determine whether the y-coordinate is a maximum or minimum.

Look at the value of a. If $a > 0$, the parabola opens upward, so the y-coordinate would be a minimum. If $a < 0$, the parabola opens downward, so the y-coordinate would be a maximum.

The value of a is 3, which is a positive value, so the parabola opens upward. Therefore, the y-coordinate, -48, is the minimum of the quadratic function $y = 3(x - 2)(x + 6)$.

20RF.1 Demonstrate an understanding of the characteristics of quadratic functions, including:

DETERMINING THE DOMAIN AND RANGE OF A QUADRATIC FUNCTION'S GRAPH IN FACTORED FORM

Certain characteristics of the graph of a quadratic function can be determined from its factored form $y = a(x - r)(x - s)$.

The domain of all quadratic functions is $x \in \mathbb{R}$. The range can be determined from the y-value of the vertex and the direction of the graph's opening.

In factored form, or $y = a(x - r)(x - s)$, the x-intercepts of the graph of the quadratic function are equal to the values of r and s. You can use the x-intercepts to find the coordinates of the vertex. They are located halfway between the x-intercepts and can be calculated using the formula $x = \dfrac{r + s}{2}$, where r and s are real numbers.

The x-value can be substituted into the original equation to find the y-value of the vertex.

The graph of a quadratic function will open upward when $a > 0$ and downward when $a < 0$. If the graph opens upward, the y-value of the vertex will be the minimum value of the range. If the graph opens downward, the y-value will be the maximum value of the range.

Use the following general guidelines to determine the range of a quadratic function's graph in the form $y = a(x - r)(x - s)$:

1. Identify the x-intercepts.
2. Find the coordinates of the vertex.
3. Identify the direction of the graph's opening.

Example

State the domain and range of the quadratic function $y = (x - 6)(x + 4)$.

Solution

Step 1

State the domain.

The domain of all quadratic functions is $x \in \mathbb{R}$.

Step 2

Find the coordinates of the vertex.

Since the equation is in the form $y = (x - 6)(x + 4)$, the x-intercepts are 6 and -4.

Find the value of x using the formula $x = \dfrac{r + s}{2}$. Substitute 6 for r and -4 for s.

$$x = \frac{6 + (-4)}{2}$$
$$= \frac{2}{2}$$
$$= 1$$

Find the y-value of the vertex. Substitute 1 for x in the original equation, $y = (x - 6)(x + 4)$.

$$y = (1 - 6)(1 + 4)$$
$$= (-5)(5)$$
$$= -25$$

The coordinates of the vertex are $(1, -25)$.

Step 3

Determine the range.

In this case, the value of $a = 1$. Since a is greater than 0, the graph opens upward. As a result, the minimum y-value is -25.

Therefore, the range of the quadratic function $y = (x - 6)(x + 4)$ is $y \geq -25$.

20RF.1 Demonstrate an understanding of the characteristics of quadratic functions, including:

SKETCHING THE GRAPH OF $y = a(x - r)$ $(x - s)$ USING THE KEY FEATURES

When the graph of a quadratic function has two distinct x-intercepts r and s, the axis of symmetry lies *halfway* between these x-intercepts.
Therefore, the equation of the axis of symmetry, which is defined by the vertex (h, k), is

$x = h = \dfrac{r + s}{2}$, and the vertex, with respect to

the x-intercept, is $\left(\dfrac{r + s}{2}, k\right)$.

Using this understanding, you can sketch the graph of a quadratic function in factored form $f(x) = a(x - r)(x - s)$, where r and s are distinct x-intercepts.

Example

Sketch the graph of $f(x) = -2(x - 3)(x + 1)$ by using the x-intercepts and vertex defined by this function.

Solution

The x-intercepts are zeros of the factors of the function.
$x - 3 = 0$
$\quad x = 3$
and
$x + 1 = 0$
$\quad x = -1$

Therefore, the x-intercepts are 3 and -1.

Find the equation of the axis of symmetry, which is located halfway between the x-intercepts.

$x = h = \dfrac{3 + (-1)}{2}$

$x = 1$

Find the vertex (h, k) by substituting the value of h, corresponding to the equation of the axis of symmetry $x = 1$, into the function to determine the y-coordinate k.
$f(x) = -2(x - 3)(x + 1)$
$\quad k = -2(1 - 3)(1 + 1)$
$\quad k = -2(-2)(2)$
$\quad k = 8$
The vertex is $(1, 8)$.

Sketch the graph of the function using the x-intercepts $(3, 0)$ and $(-1, 0)$ and the vertex $(1, 8)$.

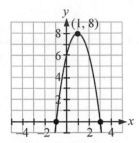

20RF.1 Demonstrate an understanding of the characteristics of quadratic functions, including:

SOLVING REAL-WORLD QUADRATIC PROBLEMS GIVEN A GRAPH

Quadratic functions can be used to model real-world situations and solve problems that require an analysis of the graph of the given quadratic function.

Most real-world problems involving quadratic functions can be solved by analyzing the graph of the corresponding parabola and identifying the y-intercept, the x-intercept, the coordinates of the vertex, or another particular point on the parabola.

Example

The trajectory of a baseball is represented by the given graph.

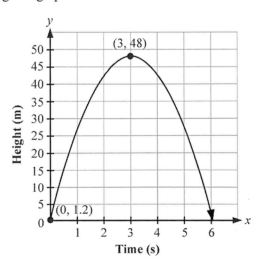

What is the maximum height of the baseball's trajectory?

Solution

The given parabola opens downward and has a vertex at (3, 48).

The maximum value (since the parabola opens downwards) of the quadratic function represented by the given parabola is equal to the *y*-coordinate of the vertex of the parabola.

Therefore, the maximum height of the baseball is 48 m.

What was the initial height of the baseball when it was hit?

Solution

At 0 s, the baseball was at its initial height. This corresponds to the ordered pair (0, 1.2) on the parabola.

Thus, the baseball was hit from an initial height of 1.2 m.

How long does the baseball remain in the air?

Solution

The ball remains in the air until it hits the ground. This occurs at the point where the parabola intersects the *x*-axis after reaching its maximum value.

Since the graph intersects the *x*-axis at 6, the ball remains in the air for 6 s.

20RF.1 Demonstrate an understanding of the characteristics of quadratic functions, including:

SOLVING REAL-WORLD QUADRATIC PROBLEMS GRAPHICALLY WHEN GIVEN AN EQUATION

Quadratic functions can be used to describe real-world situations.

The problems related to the equation can be solved graphically.

Example

A city's population can fluctuate. A small Ontario city that has a declining population is expecting the population to begin increasing in the near future because of the introduction of several industrial development initiatives.

The city planners predict that the city's population can be modelled by the quadratic function $P = 150t^2 - 1\ 200t + 14\ 900$, $t \geq 0$, in which *t* represents the time in years since January 1st, 2006, and *P* represents the population.

Using a graphing calculator, determine the year the city's population will be the lowest.

Solution

Press the $\boxed{\text{Y=}}$ button on your calculator, and enter the equation
$P = 150t^2 - 1\ 200t + 14\ 900$ into the $Y_1 =$ value as follows:
$Y_1 = 150X^2 - 1\ 200X + 14\ 900$.

Press $\boxed{\text{WINDOW}}$, and use settings such as $x: [-5, 12, 2]$ and $y: [7\ 500, 20\ 000, 2\ 500]$.

Use the Minimum feature of your calculator.

Press $\boxed{\text{2nd}}$ $\boxed{\text{TRACE}}$ to access the CALC menu.

Choose 3:minimum from the list. Follow the prompts given by the calculator. Provide a left bound, a right bound, and press $\boxed{\text{ENTER}}$ when prompted for a guess.

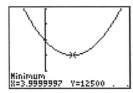

Since the graphing calculator's cursor is at $x \approx 4$, the minimum population will occur at the beginning of $t = 4$, or $2\ 006 + 4 = 2\ 010$.

Using a graphing calculator, determine the first year that the city's population will be more than 24 000.

Solution

Press the $\boxed{\text{Y=}}$ button on your calculator, and enter the equation
$P = 150t^2 - 1\ 200t + 14\ 900$ into the $Y_1 =$ value as follows:
$Y_1 = 150X^2 - 1\ 200X + 14\ 900$.

Use the Intersection feature of your calculator to find the first positive intersection point between this line and the line of the quadratic function,
$Y_1 = 150X^2 - 1\ 200X + 14\ 900$.

Enter the line referring to the population of 24 000 into the $Y_2 =$ value as follows:
$Y_2 = 24\ 000$.

Press $\boxed{\text{WINDOW}}$, and use settings such as $x: [-5, 20, 2]$ and $y: [7\ 500, 35\ 000, 2\ 500]$.

Press $\boxed{\text{2nd}}$ $\boxed{\text{TRACE}}$ to access the CALC menu.

Choose 5:intersect from the list. Follow the prompts given by the calculator. Choose a point near the intersection on the first function (the quadratic function), and a point near the intersection on the second function (the line).

Press $\boxed{\text{ENTER}}$ when prompted for a guess.

The first positive intersection point occurs when $x = 12.76$, as shown in the given diagram.

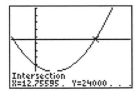

The first year that the population will be more than 24 000 is $2\ 006 + 12.76 = 2\ 018.76$, or 2019.

20RF.2 Solve problems that involve quadratic equations.

FACTORING POLYNOMIALS USING COMMON FACTORS

Polynomials are expressions containing three or more terms.

Factoring is the inverse operation of multiplying, in that the factors of the polynomial are identified through the process of division. Factors are two numbers (or in this case, expressions) that when multiplied result in the original polynomial. When factoring polynomials, first look for a greatest common factor (GCF).

Factoring is the process of expressing polynomials as a product of two or more expressions.

When factoring out the GCF, look at the numbers and variables that are common in each term of the polynomial expression. Once the greatest common factor has been identified, divide it out of each term in the polynomial.

The greatest common factor (GCF) is the largest factor common to two or more numbers.

Example

Take, for example, the binomial, $6x^2 + 8x$. In order to determine its factors, first determine the greatest common factor (GCF) of each term.

- For the term $6x^2$, the factors are 1, 2, 3, 6, x, and x

- For the term $8x$, the factors are 1, 2, 4, 8, and x

Take the greatest number common to both coefficients and the greatest number of x's common to both terms.

The GCF of $6x^2$ and $8x$ is $2x$.

Factor $2x$ out of each term. Divide each term by the GCF, which in this case is $2x$.

$= 6x^2 + 8x$
$= (2x)(3x + 4)$

The factors of $6x^2 + 8x$ are $2x$ and $3x + 4$. When these terms are multiplied, the result will be the original binomial. They are written as a product.

Removing a common factor also applies to polynomial expressions that contain two variables. The same procedure is used as for polynomial expressions that contain one variable.

Follow these steps when removing a common factor from a polynomial expression:

1. Identify the GCF.
2. Divide each term by the GCF.
3. Multiply the GCF (the factor of the original polynomial) by the quotient (the answer to the division question).

Example

Factor $21x^2y - 14xy^2$.

Solution

Step 1
Determine the greatest common factor (GCF) of each term.

- $21x^2y$: 1, 3, 7, 21, x, x, and y.
- $14xy^2$: 1, 2, 7, 14, x, y, and y.

Take the greatest number common to both coefficients and the greatest number of variables common to both terms.
The GCF is $7xy$.

Step 2
Divide each term by the GCF.
$$= \frac{21x^2y}{7xy} - \frac{14xy^2}{7xy}$$
$$= 3x - 2y$$

Step 3
Multiply the GCF (the factor of the original polynomial) by the quotient (the answer to a division question).
$7xy(3x - 2y)$

Apply the same method when factoring a trinomial.

Example

Factor $21x^2y - 14xy^2 + 28x^3y^3$.

Solution

Step 1
Determine the GCF of each term.
$21x^2y$: 1, 3, 7, 21, x, x, and y.
$14xy^2$: 1, 2, 7, 14, x, y, and y.
$28x^3y^3$: 1, 2, 4, 7, 14, 28, x, x, x, y, y, and y.
The GCF is $7xy$

Step 2
Divide each term by the GCF.
$$\frac{21x^2y}{7xy} - \frac{14xy^2}{7xy} + \frac{28x^3y^3}{7xy}$$
$$= 3x - 2y + 4x^2y^2$$

Step 3
Multiply the GCF (the factor of the original polynomial) by the quotient (the answer to the division question).
$$= 21x^2y - 14xy^2 + 28x^3y^3$$
$$= 7xy\left(3x - 2y + 4x^2y^2\right)$$

Factoring a polynomial can also be done by regrouping, or rewriting, the polynomial so that it has an even number of terms. This way, a factor common to two terms in a group can be determined, and a binomial is formed. The factored form of the polynomial is then expressed as a product of two binomials.

To factor a polynomial by grouping, follow these steps:

1. Regroup the polynomial into smaller groups that contain a common factor.
2. Remove the GCF from each group.
3. Factor out the common binomial.
   The remainders form the second binomial.

Example

Factor the expression $x^2 + 2x + x + 2$ using grouping.

Solution

Step 1
Regroup the terms.
$$\left(x^2 + x\right) + (2x + 2)$$

Step 2
Remove the GCF from each group.
The GCF of $x^2 + x$ is x.
The GCF of $2x + 2$ is 2.
$$x(x + 1) + 2(x + 1)$$

Step 3
Factor out the common binomial.
The remaining terms form the second binomial.
$$(x + 1)(x + 2)$$

The factored form of $x^2 + 2x + x + 2$ is $(x + 1)(x + 2)$.

20RF.2 Solve problems that involve quadratic equations.

FACTORING TRINOMIALS OF THE FORM $x^2 + bx + c$

Trinomials are algebraic expressions with three terms.

When factoring trinomials of the form $x^2 + bx + c$, write the trinomial as a product of two binomials, if possible.

Consider the following product of binomials:
$(x + 3)(x - 5)$.
$$= (x)(x) + (x)(-5) + (3)(x) + (3)(-5)$$
$$= x^2 - 5x + 3x - 15$$
$$= x^2 - 2x - 15$$

Use the FOIL method of multiplication.

Notice that the first two terms of the binomials are multiplied to get the first term of the trinomial:
$(x)(x) = x^2$.

The last two terms of the binomials are multiplied to give the last term in the trinomial:
$(3)(-5) = -15$. The product of the coefficient of the first term and the last term in the trinomial is called the **product**.

Since the middle term in the trinomial is found by adding the like terms together, the coefficient of the middle term in the trinomial is called the **sum**.

Example

Factor $x^2 + 6x + 8$.

Solution

Step 1

The product value is the product of the coefficient of the first term and the last term in the polynomial.

Product = 1×8

The sum value is the coefficient of the middle term in the polynomial.

Sum = 6

Step 2

List all the factors of the product until you find two numbers that multiply to a product of 8 and add to a sum of 6.

Product	Sum
$1 \times 8 = 8$	$1 + 8 = 9$
$2 \times 4 = 8$	$2 + 4 = 6$
$-1 \times -8 = 8$	$-1 + (-8) = -9$
$-2 \times -4 = 8$	$-2 + (-4) = -6$

The numbers that add to 6 and have a product of 8 are 4 and 2.

Step 3

Write the factored solution of two binomials.

Since $(x)(x) = x^2$, x is the first term in the binomials.

$(x + \underline{\hspace{1cm}})(x + \underline{\hspace{1cm}})$

Insert one of the numbers in the first binomial and the other number in the second binomial. The order does not matter.

$(x + 2)(x + 4)$

Step 4

Check the solution by using FOIL.

$(x + 2)(x + 4) = x^2 + 4x + 2x + 8$

$(x + 2)(x + 4) = x^2 + 6x + 8$

Verification can also be done using vertical multiplication.

$$
\begin{array}{r}
x + 2 \\
\times \quad x + 4 \\
\hline
4x + 8 \\
x^2 + 2x + 0 \\
\hline
x^2 + 6x + 8
\end{array}
$$

Factor $x^2 - 11x + 18$.

Solution

Step 1

Identify the product and sum values in the trinomial.

The product value is the product of the first term and the last term of the trinomial.

Product = 1×18

The sum value is the coefficient of the middle term of the trinomial.

Sum = -11

Step 2

List all the factors of the product until two numbers are identified that multiply to a product of 18 and add to a sum of -11.

Product	Sum
$1 \times 18 = 18$	$1 + 18 = 19$
$2 \times 9 = 18$	$2 + 9 = 11$
$3 \times 6 = 18$	$3 + 6 = 9$
$-1 \times -18 = 18$	$-1 + (-18) = -19$
$-2 \times -9 = 18$	$-2 + -9 = -11$
$-3 \times -6 = 18$	$-3 + (-6) = -9$

The two numbers that work are -2 and -9.

Step 3

Write the factored solution of two binomials.

Since $(x)(x) = x^2$, x is the first term in the binomials.

$(x\_)(x\_)$

Place one of the numbers in the first set of brackets and the other number in the second set. The order does not matter, but the proper sign of the number must be inserted. Since both numbers are negative, a subtraction sign must be used in each binomial.

The factored answer is $(x - 2)(x - 9)$.

Step 4

Check the solution by using FOIL.

$(x - 2)(x - 9) = x^2 - 9x - 2x + 18$

$\qquad\qquad\qquad = x^2 - 11x + 18$

FACTORING TRINOMIALS OF THE FORM $ax^2 + bx + c$ USING THE DECOMPOSITION METHOD

20RF.2 Solve problems that involve quadratic equations.

It is possible to factor many trinomials of the form $ax^2 + bx + c$ by using the inverse procedure of multiplication, i.e., the decomposition method.

This method will work for factoring all factorable trinomials in the form $ax^2 + bx + c$ into the product of two binomials.

Consider the product of two binomials, $(2x + 3)(x - 2)$.
Using the FOIL procedure, the result is:
$$(2x + 3)(x - 2) = 2x^2 - 4x + 3x - 6$$
$$= 2x^2 - x - 6$$

The inverse procedure would be as follows:
$$2x^2 - x - 6 = 2x^2 - 4x + 3x - 6$$
$$= 2x(x - 2) + 3(x - 2)$$
$$= (2x + 3)(x - 2)$$

For the expression $2x^2 - x - 6$, observe that the product of the coefficient of the x^2-term and the constant term is $2 \times (-6) = -12$. Also, observe that the middle term, $-x$, is decomposed into $-4x + 3x$, and the product of these coefficients is also -12 ($-4 \times 3 = -12$).

Thus, the middle term is decomposed into two terms with coefficients whose product is equal to the product of the coefficient of the x^2-term and the constant term, and with a sum equal to the coefficient of the middle term.

Example

Factor $3x^2 + 10x - 8$ using the decomposition method. Verify the answer using multiplication.

Solution

In $3x^2 + 10x - 8$, the product of the coefficient of x^2 and the constant term is $3 \times (-8) = -24$. The middle term has a coefficient of $+10$. Find two integers that have a product of -24 and a sum of $+10$.

The pairs of integers with a product of -24, along with their respective sums, are as shown:

Product	Sum
$1 \times (-24) = -24$	$1 + (-24) = -23$
$2 \times (-12) = -24$	$2 + (-12) = -10$
$3 \times (-8) = -24$	$3 + (-8) = -5$
$4 \times (-6) = -24$	$4 + (-6) = -2$
$-1 \times 24 = -24$	$-1 + 24 = +23$
$-2 \times 12 = -24$	$-2 + 12 = +10$
$-3 \times 8 = -24$	$-3 + 8 = +5$
$-4 \times 6 = -24$	$-4 + 6 = +2$

The integers required are -2 and $+12$.

Express $10x$ as $-2x + 12x$, and then factor by grouping for a common factor as follows:
$$3x^2 + 10x - 8 = 3x^2 - 2x + 12x - 8$$
$$= x(3x - 2) + 4(3x - 2)$$
$$= (x + 4)(3x - 2)$$

Verify by multiplying the factors (using the FOIL procedure).
$$(x + 4)(3x - 2) = 3x^2 - 2x + 12x - 8$$
$$= 3x^2 + 10x - 8$$

With practice, efficiency at finding the pair of numbers to use for splitting the middle term, without writing all the products and sums, will improve.

Example

Factor $6x^2 - 11x + 3$ using the decomposition method. Verify the answer using multiplication.

Solution

In $6x^2 - 11x + 3$, the product of the coefficient of x^2 and the constant term is $6 \times 3 = 18$. The middle term has a coefficient of -11. Find two integers that have a product of 18 and sum of -11.

The pairs of integers with a product of 18, along with their respective sums, are as shown.

Product	Sum
$1 \times 18 = 18$	$1 + 18 = 19$
$2 \times 9 = 18$	$2 + 9 = 11$
$3 \times 6 = 18$	$3 + 6 = 9$
$(-1) \times (-18) = 18$	$(-1) + (-18) = -19$
$(-2) + (-9) = -11$	$(-2) \times (-9) = 18$
$(-3) \times (-6) = 18$	$(-3) + (-6) = -9$

Thus, the two integers that are required are -2 and -9.

Express $-11x$ as $-2x - 9x$, and then factor by grouping for a common factor as follows:

$$6x^2 - 11x + 3 = 6x^2 - 2x - 9x + 3$$
$$= 2x(3x - 1) - 3(3x - 1)$$
$$= (3x - 1)(2x - 3)$$

Verify by multiplying the factors (using the FOIL procedure).

$$(3x - 1)(2x - 3) = 6x^2 - 9x - 2x + 3$$
$$= 6x^2 - 11x + 3$$

Not all trinomials are factorable. Those that are not factorable are **prime polynomials**. The product and sum values from the method of decomposition can be used to determine whether a trinomial is prime. For example, $2x^2 + x + 5$ is prime because there are no two integers that have a product of 10 and a sum of 1. For some trinomials it is necessary to calculate the product and possible sums in order to verify that the trinomial is prime.

Example

Factor $2x^2 - 3x - 6$ if possible.

If $2x^2 - 3x - 6$ is not factorable, show why the decomposition method does not work.

Solution

In $2x^2 - 3x - 6$ the product of the coefficient of x^2 and the constant term is $2 \times (-6) = -12$. The middle term has a coefficient of -3. If possible, find two integers that have a product of -12 and sum of -3.

The pairs of integers with a product of -12, along with their respective sums, are as shown.

Product	Sum
$1 \times (-12) = -12$	$1 + (-12) = -11$
$2 \times (-6) = -12$	$2 + (-6) = -4$
$3 \times (-4) = -12$	$3 + (-4) = -1$
$-1 \times 12 = -12$	$-1 + 12 = +11$
$-2 \times 6 = -12$	$-2 + 6 = +4$
$-3 \times 4 = -12$	$-3 + 4 = +1$

Since there are no two integers that have a product of -12 and sum of -3, $2x^2 - 3x - 6$ cannot be factored, and it is prime.

20RF.2 Solve problems that involve quadratic equations.

SOLVING QUADRATIC EQUATIONS BY FACTORING

A **quadratic equation** is any equation in the form of $0 = ax^2 + bx + c$, in which a, b, and c are real numbers and $a \neq 0$.

One method of solving a quadratic equation is to factor the equation, then set each factor equal to 0 and solve for the variable.

The solutions of a quadratic equation are also known as the roots of the equation.

Example

Solve the equation $0 = 2x^2 - 11x - 21$.

Solution

This equation can be solved by factoring the trinomial $2x^2 - 11x - 21$.

Step 1

Factor the trinomial in the form of $ax^2 + bx + c$.

Decompose the middle term into two terms by finding two numbers whose product equals ac and whose sum equals b.

$a \times c = 2 \times (-21) = -42$
$b = -11$

Two numbers that have a product of -42 and a sum of -11 are -14 and $+3$.

Decompose $-11x$ into $-14x$ and $+3x$.

$0 = 2x^2 - 14x + 3x - 21$

Group the terms, and factor.

$0 = (2x^2 - 14x) + (3x - 21)$
$0 = 2x(x - 7) + 3(x - 7)$
$0 = (2x + 3)(x - 7)$

Step 2

Set each factor equal to 0 and solve for x.

$2x + 3 = 0$ or $x - 7 = 0$
$2x + 3 = 0$
$\quad 2x = -3$
$\quad\quad x = -\dfrac{3}{2}$
$x - 7 = 0$
$\quad\quad x = 7$

The values of x that satisfy the given equation are $-\dfrac{3}{2}$ and 7.

Example

Solve the quadratic equation $0 = x^2 - 4x - 45$ by factoring.

Solution

Step 1

Factor the trinomial.

$0 = x^2 - 4x - 45$
$0 = (x - 9)(x + 5)$

Step 2

Set each factor equal to 0 and solve for x.

$0 = x - 9$ or $0 = x + 5$
$x = 9$ or $x = -5$

Example

Solve the quadratic equation $0 = x^2 + 4x - 21$ by factoring.

Solution

Step 1

Factor the trinomial.

$0 = x^2 + 4x - 21$
$0 = (x - 3)(x + 7)$

Step 2

Set each factor equal to 0 and solve for x.

$0 = x - 3$ or $0 = x + 7$
$x = 3$ or $x = -7$

20RF.2 Solve problems that involve quadratic equations.

FACTOR POLYNOMIALS USING A VARIETY OF FACTORING TECHNIQUES

Once a variety of factoring techniques have been learned, they can be used together to fully factor polynomial expressions requiring the use of more than one technique.

Most commonly, the identification of a greatest common factor (GCF) is the first step to fully factoring a polynomial.

Following the removal of the GCF, a number of factoring techniques may be required such as:

- Difference of Squares
- Grouping
- Decomposition
- Sum of Cubes
- Difference of Cubes

Example

Factor $6ax^2 - 24a$ completely.

Solution

Factor out the greatest common factor, $6a$.
$$6ax^2 - 24a = 6a(x^2 - 4)$$

Factor $x^2 - 4$ as a difference of squares.
$$\begin{aligned} 6ax^2 - 24a &= 6a(x^2 - 4) \\ &= 6a(x^2 - 2^2) \\ &= 6a(x + 2)(x - 2) \end{aligned}$$

Example

Factor $9a^2 + 39a - 30$ completely.

Solution

Factor out the greatest common factor, 3.
$$9a^2 + 39a - 30 = 3(3a^2 + 13a - 10)$$

Factor the trinomial.

To factor the trinomial $3a^2 + 13a - 10$ using the decomposition method, find two numbers with a product of $3 \times (-10) = -30$ and a sum of $+13$.

The numbers are $+15$ and -2.
$$\begin{aligned} &9a^2 + 39a - 30 \\ &= 3(3a^2 + 13a - 10) \\ &= 3(3a^2 + 15a - 2a - 10) \\ &= 3(3a(a + 5) - 2(a + 5)) \\ &= 3(3a - 2)(a + 5) \end{aligned}$$

As with all factoring, the factored form can be verified by multiplying the factors to get the original polynomial.
$$\begin{aligned} &3(3a - 2)(a + 5) \\ &= 3(3a^2 + 15a - 2a - 10) \\ &= 3(3a^2 + 13a - 10) \\ &= 9a^2 + 39a - 30 \end{aligned}$$

20RF.2 Solve problems that involve quadratic equations.

Solving Quadratic Equations Using the Quadratic Formula

The roots of a quadratic equation, $ax^2 + bx + c = 0$, in which $a \neq 0$, can be found using the **quadratic formula**, $x = \dfrac{-b \pm \sqrt{b^2 - 4ac}}{2a}$.

Example

Solve the equation $x^2 - 4x - 45 = 0$ using the quadratic formula.

Solution

Step 1
Identify the values of a, b, and c.
$a = 1 \quad b = -4 \quad c = -45$

Step 2
Substitute the values for a, b, and c into the quadratic formula, and solve for x.
$$x = \frac{-b \pm \sqrt{b^2 - 4ac}}{2a}$$
$$x = \frac{-(-4) \pm \sqrt{(-4)^2 - 4(1)(-45)}}{2(1)}$$
$$x = \frac{4 \pm \sqrt{16 + 180}}{2}$$
$$x = \frac{4 \pm \sqrt{196}}{2}$$
$$x = \frac{4 \pm 14}{2}$$

Therefore,
$$x = \frac{4 + 14}{2} = 9 \text{ or } x = \frac{4 - 14}{2} = -5.$$

Example

Determine the exact roots to the equation $x^2 - 8x + 5 = 0$ by applying the quadratic formula.

Solution

Step 1
Identify the values of a, b, and c.
$a = 1 \quad b = -8 \quad c = 5$

Step 2

Substitute the values for a, b and c into the quadratic formula, and solve for x.

$$x = \frac{-b \pm \sqrt{b^2 - 4ac}}{2a}$$

$$= \frac{-(-8) \pm \sqrt{(-8)^2 - 4(1)(5)}}{2(1)}$$

$$= \frac{8 \pm \sqrt{64 - 20}}{2}$$

$$= \frac{8 \pm \sqrt{44}}{2}$$

$$= \frac{8 \pm \sqrt{4 \times 11}}{2}$$

$$= \frac{8 \pm 2\sqrt{11}}{2}$$

$$= \frac{2(4 \pm \sqrt{11})}{2}$$

$$= 4 \pm \sqrt{11}$$

The roots of the given equation are $4 + \sqrt{11}$ and $4 - \sqrt{11}$.

Example

Solve the equation $\frac{3}{4}x^2 + 2x = 5$ using the quadratic formula.

Solution

Step 1

Rearrange the equation $\frac{3}{4}x^2 + 2x = 5$ to identify the values of a, b, and c.

In cases in which the values are rational, it is also helpful to multiply both sides of the equation by a multiple of the denominators to make the values integral.

$$\frac{3}{4}x^2 + 2x = 5$$

$$(4)\left(\frac{3}{4}x^2\right) + (4)(2x) = (4)(5)$$

$$3x^2 + 8x - 20 = 0$$

$$a = 3 \quad b = 8 \quad c = -20$$

Step 2

Substitute the values into the quadratic formula.

$$x = \frac{-b \pm \sqrt{b^2 - 4ac}}{2a}$$

$$x = \frac{-8 \pm \sqrt{8^2 - 4(3)(-20)}}{2(3)}$$

$$x = \frac{-8 \pm \sqrt{64 + 240}}{6}$$

$$x = \frac{-8 \pm \sqrt{304}}{6}$$

Step 3

Convert to a mixed radical.

$$x = \frac{-8 \pm \sqrt{(16)(19)}}{6}$$

$$x = \frac{-8 \pm 4\sqrt{19}}{6}$$

Divide each term in the numerator and denominator by 2.

$$x = \frac{-4 \pm 2\sqrt{19}}{3}$$

20RF.2 Solve problems that involve quadratic equations.

UNDERSTANDING THE DIFFERENCE AND CONNECTION BETWEEN ROOTS OF A QUADRATIC EQUATION AND FACTORS OF A QUADRATIC EXPRESSION

Quadratic expressions contain a monomial with a variable of degree two but no higher.

These expressions can be factored by dividing out the greatest common factor or by converting the expression into two binomials.

- The expression $3x^2 + 5x$ factors into $x(3x + 5)$.

- The expression $x^2 + 6x + 8$ factors into $(x + 2)(x + 4)$.

Quadratic equations differ from quadratic expressions in that they have an equal sign. A **quadratic equation** is any equation in the form $0 = ax^2 + bx + c$, in which a, b, and c are real numbers and $a \neq 0$. One method of solving a quadratic equation is to factor the equation, then set each factor equal to 0 and solve for the variable.

Example

With the equation $0 = x^2 + 6x + 8$, the expression $x^2 + 6x + 8$ factors into $(x + 2)(x + 4)$, leaving the equation $0 = (x + 2)(x + 4)$.

To solve the equation $0 = (x + 2)(x + 4)$, set the factors $(x + 2)$ and $(x + 4)$ to be equal to zero. If either of these factors is equal to zero, the value of the expression on the right-hand side of the equation will be equal to zero, as anything multiplied by zero is zero.

$0 = x + 2$
$-2 = x$
$0 = x + 4$
$-4 = x$

Therefore, the solutions, or roots, of the equation $0 = x^2 + 6x + 8$ are $x = -4$ and $x = -2$.

———————————————————

The solutions of a quadratic equation are also known as the roots of the equation. The roots of a quadratic equation can be found from the factors of the quadratic expression. Roots and factors are closely connected, but they are not the same thing.

20RF.2 Solve problems that involve quadratic equations.

MAKING CONNECTIONS BETWEEN THE ZEROS OF THE FACTORS OF A QUADRATIC FUNCTION AND THE x-INTERCEPTS OF ITS CORRESPONDING GRAPH

A quadratic function and its corresponding graph has these characteristics:

- The x-intercepts of a graph are located at the points where the graph touches or crosses the x-axis.
- The x-intercepts of the graph of a quadratic function can be used to determine the zeros of the quadratic function.
- In order to algebraically determine the x-intercepts of the graph from its defining function, substitute 0 for y, and then solve for x in the corresponding equation.

The graph of the function $y = (x + 3)(x - 1)$ is shown.

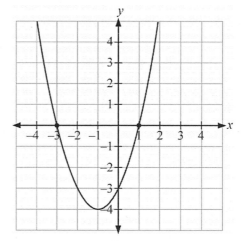

Since the graph of the function $y = (x + 3)(x - 1)$ crosses the x-axis at the points $(-3, 0)$ and $(1, 0)$, the x-intercepts are $x = -3$ and $x = 1$.

The x-intercepts of the graph of the quadratic function $y = (x + 3)(x - 1)$ can be determined algebraically by substituting 0 for y and solving for x in the corresponding quadratic equation.
$y = (x + 3)(x - 1)$
$0 = (x + 3)(x - 1)$

Apply the zero product property.

$$0 = x + 3 \quad \text{and} \quad 0 = x - 1$$
$$x = -3 \quad\quad\quad x = 1$$

Notice the connection between the x-intercepts of the graph of the quadratic function, $x = -3$ and $x = 1$, and the zeros of the factors of the quadratic function $y = (x + 3)(x - 1)$, namely $x = -3$ and $x = 1$. They are the very same.

In general, when a quadratic function is expressed in the factored form $y = a(x - r)(x - s)$, the x-intercepts of the graph and the zeros of the quadratic function are $x = r$ and $x = s$.

Because the solutions to quadratic equations are the zeros of corresponding quadratic functions, questions that require finding these zeros involve solving quadratic equations.

20RF.2 Solve problems that involve quadratic equations.

INTERPRETING THE NATURE OF THE ROOTS OF A QUADRATIC EQUATION USING A GRAPHICAL APPROACH

The **roots** of a quadratic equation are the values of the variable that satisfy the given quadratic equation. In other words, they are the solutions to the equation.

The nature of the roots of a quadratic equation can be shown graphically by determining if and where the graph of the corresponding function intersects the x-axis.

There are three possible scenarios:

1. Two real and distinct roots occur when the graph of the corresponding quadratic function intersects the x-axis at two distinct points.

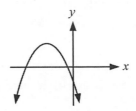

2. One real root (two equal solutions) occurs when the graph of the corresponding quadratic function touches the x-axis at one distinct point.

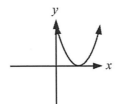

3. Non-real roots occur when the graph of the corresponding quadratic function does not touch the x-axis at any point.

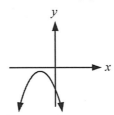

Non-real numbers, or imaginary numbers, are numbers that cannot be placed onto a number line. Examples of non-real roots are numbers such as $\sqrt{-5}$, $\sqrt{-16}$, and $\dfrac{6}{0}$.

Example

Using technology, you can graph the function $y = -3x^2 - 2x + 10$ to determine the nature of the roots.

Graphing the function $y = -3x^2 - 2x + 10$ gives this image.

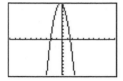

Since there are two distinct x-intercepts, this means there are two real and different roots.

20RF.2 Solve problems that involve quadratic equations.

DETERMINING THE x-INTERCEPTS OF A GRAPH GIVEN ITS QUADRATIC EQUATION IN THE FORM $y = ax^2 + bx + c$

The **x-intercepts** are where the parabola crosses the x-axis. Sometimes, x-intercepts are also referred to as **zeros**.

The x-intercepts of a quadratic relation of the form $y = ax^2 + bx + c$, $(a \neq 0)$ are the value (or values) of x that make the quadratic relation equal to zero. In other words, to find the x-intercepts, set y equal to 0 and solve for x.

$y = ax^2 + bx + c \Rightarrow 0 = ax^2 + bx + c$

The x-coordinates of each ordered pair where the parabola touches or intersects the x-axis are the x-intercepts, or zeros. For a quadratic function, there can be 0, 1, or 2 distinct real zeros.

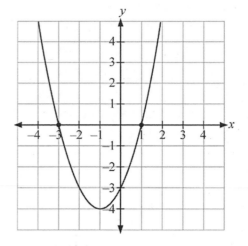

In the given graph, the x-intercepts are -3 and 1. The ordered pairs for the x-intercepts are $(-3, 0)$ and $(1, 0)$. Both y-values in the ordered pairs are 0.

Quadratic equations can be solved using factoring, the quadratic formula, or graphing.

Example

Solve the equation $0 = x^2 + 4x - 21$.

Solution

Method 1: Factoring
$0 = x^2 + 4x - 21$
$0 = (x - 3)(x + 7)$
$0 = (x - 3)$ or $0 = (x + 7)$
$x = 3$ or $x = -7$

Method 2: Using the quadratic formula

Substitute the values $a = 1$, $b = 4$, and $c = -21$, and then solve for x.

$x = \dfrac{-b \pm \sqrt{b^2 - 4ac}}{2a}$

$x = \dfrac{-(4) \pm \sqrt{(4)^2 - 4(1)(-21)}}{2(1)}$

$x = \dfrac{-4 \pm \sqrt{16 + 84}}{2}$

$x = \dfrac{-4 \pm \sqrt{100}}{2}$

$x = \dfrac{-4 \pm 10}{2}$

$$x = \frac{-4+10}{2} \text{ or } x = \frac{-4-10}{2}$$

$$x = \frac{6}{2} \text{ or } x = \frac{-14}{2}$$

$x = 3$ or $x = -7$

Method 3: Graphing

Enter the equation into the calculator by pressing the $\boxed{Y =}$ button. Then, access the CALCULATE menu by pressing $\boxed{2nd}$ $\boxed{Trace}$, and choose 2:Zero to determine the x-intercepts of the graph.

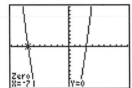 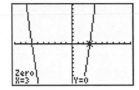

From the ZERO feature, the x-intercepts or zeros are $x = 3$ and $x = -7$.

Thus, the solution to the equation $0 = x^2 + 4x - 21$ is $x = 3$ or $x = -7$.

Method 1: Factoring

$0 = x^2 + 4x - 21$
$0 = (x - 3)(x + 7)$
$0 = (x - 3)$ or $0 = (x + 7)$
$x = 3$ or $x = -7$

Method 2: Using the quadratic formula

Substitute the values $a = 1$, $b = 4$, and $c = -21$, and then solve for x.

$$x = \frac{-b \pm \sqrt{b^2 - 4ac}}{2a}$$

$$x = \frac{-(4) \pm \sqrt{(4)^2 - 4(1)(-21)}}{2(1)}$$

$$x = \frac{-4 \pm \sqrt{16 + 84}}{2}$$

$$x = \frac{-4 \pm \sqrt{100}}{2}$$

$$x = \frac{-4 \pm 10}{2}$$

$$x = \frac{-4+10}{2} \text{ or } x = \frac{-4-10}{2}$$

$$x = \frac{6}{2} \text{ or } x = \frac{-14}{2}$$

$x = 3$ or $x = -7$

Method 3: Graphing

Enter the equation into the calculator by pressing the $\boxed{Y =}$ button. Then, access the CALCULATE menu by pressing $\boxed{2nd}$ $\boxed{Trace}$, and choose 2:Zero to determine the x-intercepts of the graph.

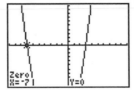 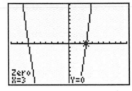

From the ZERO feature, the x-intercepts or zeros are $x = 3$ and $x = -7$.

Thus, the solution to the equation $0 = x^2 + 4x - 21$ is $x = 3$ or $x = -7$.

20RF.2 Solve problems that involve quadratic equations.

DETERMINING THE x-INTERCEPTS OF THE GRAPH OF A QUADRATIC FUNCTION GIVEN IN FACTORED FORM

The factored form of a quadratic function is $f(x) = a(x - r)(x - s)$, where r and s are the x-intercepts.

To determine the x-intercepts from factored form, set the equation equal to zero, and apply the zero product of multiplication. If the product of two factors is zero, at least one of the factors is equal to zero. Set each factor to zero, and solve for x.

Example

Determine the exact values of the *x*-intercepts on the graph of the function $y = (4x - 3)(x + 1)$.

Solution

Determine the *x*-intercepts.

Let $y = 0$.
$0 = (4x - 3)(x + 1)$

Use the original factored form. If the product of two factors is zero, at least one of the factors is equal to zero.

Then, $4x - 3 = 0$ or $x + 1 = 0$.
$4x - 3 = 0$
$\quad 4x = 3$
$\quad\quad x = \dfrac{3}{4}$
$x + 1 = 0$
$\quad x = -1$

Therefore, the *x*-intercepts are $\dfrac{3}{4}$ and -1.

20RF.2 Solve problems that involve quadratic equations.

DETERMINING THE *y*-INTERCEPT OF A QUADRATIC FUNCTION

The *y*-intercept of a quadratic function is located where the graph of the function crosses the *y*-axis.

Example

The function $y = x^2 - 2x - 3$ is represented by the given parabola.

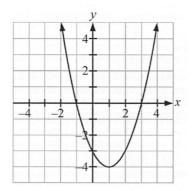

According to the graph, the parabola crosses the *y*-axis at -3, where *x* is equal to zero. The coordinates of the *y*-intercept are $(0, -3)$.

In general, the *y*-intercept of a quadratic function can be determined by substituting 0 for *x* and solving for *y*.

Example

Determine the *y*-intercept of the quadratic function $y = 2(x + 3)^2 - 7$.

Solution

To determine the *y*-intercept of $y = 2(x + 3)^2 - 7$, substitute 0 for *x* and solve for *y*.
$y = 2(x + 3)^2 - 7$
$y = 2(0 + 3)^2 - 7$
$y = 2(3)^2 - 7$
$y = 2(9) - 7$
$y = 18 - 7$
$y = 11$

The *y*-intercept is 11.

Even if a quadratic function is given in factored form, $y = a(x - r)(x - s)$, you can still substitute 0 for *x* and solve for *y* to find the *y*-intercept.
$y = a(x - r)(x - s)$
$y = a(0 - r)(0 - s)$
$y = a \times r \times s$

Example

Determine the *y*-intercept of the quadratic function $y = (2x - 3)(x + 5)$.

Solution

To determine the *y*-intercept of $y = (2x - 3)(x + 5)$, substitute 0 for *x* and solve for *y*.
$y = (2x - 3)(x + 5)$
$y = (2(0) - 3)(0 + 5)$
$y = (-3)(5)$
$y = -15$

The *y*-intercept is -15.

If a quadratic function is given in the general form $y = ax^2 + bx + c$, the y-intercept is equal to c.

$y = ax^2 + bx + c$
$y = a(0)^2 + b(0) + c$
$y = c$

Example

Determine the y-intercept of the quadratic function $y = x^2 + 4x - 5$.

Solution

When a quadratic function is in the general form $y = ax^2 + bx + c$, the y-intercept is equal to c.

The quadratic function $y = x^2 + 4x - 5$ is in the general form $y = ax^2 + bx + c$. Since $c = -5$, the y-intercept is -5.

20RF.2 Solve problems that involve quadratic equations.

COMPARING STRATEGIES FOR SOLVING QUADRATIC EQUATIONS

Quadratic equations in the form $ax^2 + bx + c = 0$ can be solved using factoring, the quadratic formula, and technology.

Each method of solving quadratic equations has its own benefits. Using the factoring method may take less time than using the quadratic formula at first. If the equation cannot be factored, or if the process of factoring is too complicated, then the quadratic formula may be an easier method for solving the quadratic equation. Graphing the equation using a calculator, and solving for the zeros is another possible method for solving if the equation is not factorable. Graphing calculators can also help verify solutions.

The following tips can help you solve a quadratic equation of the form $ax^2 + bx + c = 0$:

1. Attempt to solve the equation by factoring.
2. If the equation cannot be solved by factoring or is difficult to factor, use the quadratic formula.
3. Use a graphical procedure to solve the equation or verify your solution.
4. Simplify the roots (solution values), if necessary, and clearly state the solution(s) using "$x = .$"

1. Which of the following graphs correctly represents the graph of the quadratic function $f(x) = (x + 1)(x - 5)$?

A.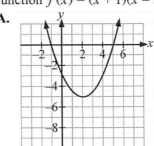

B.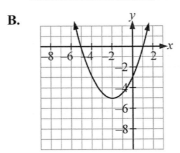

C.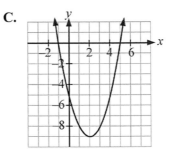

D.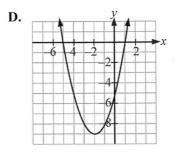

2. Which of the following graphs could be a sketch of the quadratic function
$y = -24x^2 + 1\ 000x - 3\ 250$?

A.

B.

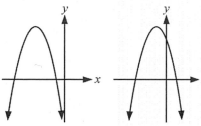

C.

D.

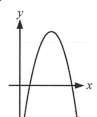
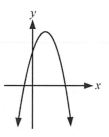

Use the following information to answer the next question.

The given graph of a quadratic function shows the coordinates of several points.

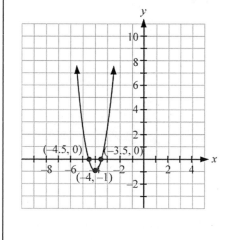

3. Which of the following points does **not** have its coordinates identified in the graph?

A. A zero

B. A vertex

C. A y-intercept

D. An x-intercept

4. Which of the following graphs represents the equation $y = x^2 + 3x + 2$?

A.

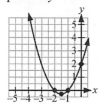

B.

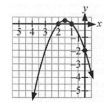

C.

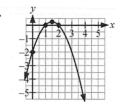

D.

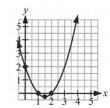

5. What is the y-coordinate of the vertex of the function $y = -(x + 4)(x + 1)$?

A. $\dfrac{9}{4}$

B. $\dfrac{3}{2}$

C. $-\dfrac{7}{4}$

D. $-\dfrac{5}{2}$

6. What is the equation of the axis of symmetry of the graph of the quadratic function $y = 2(x + 5)(x - 1)$?

A. $x = -3$

B. $x = -2$

C. $x = 2$

D. $x = 3$

Use the following information to answer the next question.

A small model rocket is launched from a second-story balcony deck. The path of the rocket is represented by the given graph.

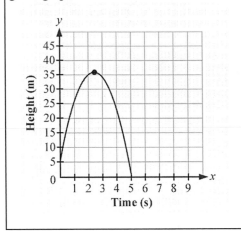

7. Once it is launched, how much time does the rocket take to strike the ground?

   A. 3 s   **B.** 4 s

   C. 5 s   **D.** 6 s

Use the following information to answer the next question.

The graph of the quadratic function $f(x)$ is shown.

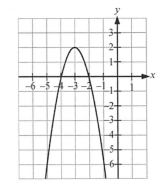

Numerical Response

8. If $(f(-3))^2 + k = 9$, the value of k is

_____.

9. What are the coordinates of the vertex of the function $y = -x^2 - 2x + 6$?

   A. $(-1, 7)$

   B. $(0, 6)$

   C. $(1, 5)$

   D. $(1.65, 0)$

10. One factor of $x^2 - 9x + 20$ is

   A. $(x - 10)$ **B.** $(x + 5)$

   C. $(x - 4)$ **D.** $(x + 2)$

Use the following information to answer the next question.

A math teacher asks his class to solve the quadratic equations $8x^2 - 6x + 7 = 2x^2 + 7x + 12$. The partial solution of each of two students is given below.

Tara

$$8x^2 - 6x + 7 = 2x^2 + 7x + 12$$
$$6x^2 - 13x - 5 = 0$$
$$6x^2 - 10x - 3x - 5 = 0$$
$$2x(3x - 5) - 1(3x - 5) = 0$$
$$(3x - 5)(2x - 1) = 0$$

Ruth

$$8x^2 - 6x + 7 = 2x^2 + 7x + 12$$
$$0 = -6x^2 + 13x + 5$$
$$x = \frac{-13 \pm \sqrt{(13)^2 - 4(-6)(5)}}{2(-6)}$$
$$x = \frac{-13 \pm \sqrt{169 + 120}}{-12}$$
$$x = \frac{-13 \pm \sqrt{289}}{-12}$$

11. Which of the following statements with respect to the partial solution of Tara and Ruth is true?

   A. Both partial solutions are correct.

   B. Both partial solutions are incorrect.

   C. Tara's partial solution is correct and Ruth's partial solution is incorrect.

   D. Tara's partial solution is incorrect and Ruth's partial solution is correct.

Use the following information to answer the next question.

> Two quadratic equations are given.
>
> I. $x^2 + x + 1 = 0$
>
> II. $x^2 + 5x + 3 = 0$

12. Which of the following statements **best** describes the roots of the given quadratic equations?

   A. Both equations have real roots.

   B. Both equations have non-real roots.

   C. Equation I has real roots, and equation II has non-real roots.

   D. Equation I has non-real roots, and equation II has real roots.

Numerical Response

13. The exact value of the y-intercept of the graph of $y = \dfrac{1}{3}(x - 3)^2 - 2$ is _____.

Written Response

14. Determine the real number solutions for $2y^2 + 11y = -15$ using the quadratic formula.

Numerical Response

15. The number of different real zeros of the quadratic function $y = (3x + 2)(x - 2)$ is _____.

16. The x-intercepts of the quadratic equation $y = 3x^2 - 27x - 210$ are

   A. $x = -5$ and $x = 14$

   B. $x = -7$ and $x = 12$

   C. $x = -9$ and $x = 3$

   D. $x = -10$ and $x = 17$

17. When using the decomposition method, the factored form of the trinomial $2x^2 + 5x - 3$ is

   A. $(x - 1)(x + 3)$

   B. $(2x + 1)(x - 3)$

   C. $(2x - 1)(x + 3)$

   D. $2(x - 1)(x + 3)$

ANSWERS AND SOLUTIONS
RELATIONS AND FUNCTIONS

1. C	6. B	11. D	16. A
2. C	7. C	12. D	17. C
3. C	8. 5	13. 1	
4. A	9. A	14. WR	
5. A	10. C	15. 2	

1. C

The x-intercepts of the quadratic function written in the factored form $f(x) = (x + 1)(x - 5)$ are found by setting each factor to zero.

$$x + 1 = 0 \qquad \text{and} \qquad x - 5 = 0$$
$$x = -1 \qquad\qquad\qquad x = 5$$

The equation of the axis of symmetry is located halfway between the x-intercepts, so it would be defined as

$$x = \frac{-1 + 5}{2} = \frac{4}{2} = 2$$

To find the vertex $(2, k)$, substitute the x-value into the function, and solve for k.

$$f(x) = (x + 1)(x - 5)$$
$$k = (2 + 1)(2 - 5)$$
$$k = (3)(-3)$$
$$k = -9$$

The vertex of the graph is $(2, -9)$. The graph with x-intercepts of -1 and 5 and with the correct vertex is given in choice C.

2. C

Use a graphing calculator to get the following graph of the function $y = -24x^2 + 1\ 000x - 3\ 250$.

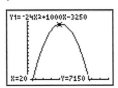

The graph is displayed using these window settings:
x:$[-10, 50, 5]$ y:$[-200, 8\ 500, 500]$

Therefore, this graph could be a sketch of the quadratic function $y = -24x^2 + 1\ 000x - 3\ 250$.

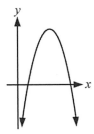

3. C

The x-intercepts are the locations where the graph intersects the x-axis. These are identified as $(-4.5, 0)$ and $(-3.5, 0)$.

The zeros are the same locations as the x-intercepts. These are also identified as $(-4.5, 0)$ and $(-3.5, 0)$.

The vertex is the location of the maximum or minimum point on the graph. This is identified as $(-4, -1)$.

The y-intercept is the location where the graph intersects the y-axis. This is not identified.

4. A

Step 1

Factor the equation $y = x^2 + 3x + 2$.

$$y = x^2 + 3x + 2$$
$$y = (x + 2)(x + 1)$$

Step 2

Find the x-intercepts by setting y to 0.

$y = (x + 2)(x + 1)$
$0 = (x + 2)(x + 1)$

Find the values of x that would allow the right side of the equation to also equal 0.

$0 = x + 2$
$-2 = x$
$0 = x + 1$
$-1 = x$

Since $x = -2$ and $x = -1$, the x-intercepts are $(-2, 0)$ and $(-1, 0)$.

Step 3

Find the y-intercept by setting x to 0.

$y = (x + 2)(x + 1)$
$y = (0 + 2)(0 + 1)$
$y = (2)(1)$
$y = 2$

The y-intercept is $(0, 2)$.

Step 4

Find the axis of symmetry by averaging the x-values of the x-intercepts.

The x-values of the x-intercepts are $x = -2$ and $x = -1$. The average, or midpoint, between the two points is $x = \dfrac{(-2) + (-1)}{2} = -\dfrac{3}{2}$. Therefore, the equation of the axis of symmetry is $x = -\dfrac{3}{2}$, or $x = -1.5$.

Step 5

Find the vertex.

Since the vertex occurs along the axis of symmetry, the x-value of the vertex will equal $-\dfrac{3}{2}$. Substitute this value for x, and solve for y to find the coordinates of the vertex.

$y = (x + 2)(x + 1)$
$y = \left(\left(-\dfrac{3}{2}\right) + 2\right)\left(\left(-\dfrac{3}{2}\right) + 1\right)$
$y = \left(-\dfrac{3}{2} + \dfrac{4}{2}\right)\left(-\dfrac{3}{2} + \dfrac{2}{2}\right)$
$y = \left(\dfrac{1}{2}\right)\left(-\dfrac{1}{2}\right)$
$y = -\dfrac{1}{4}$

The vertex is at point $\left(-\dfrac{3}{2}, -\dfrac{1}{4}\right)$, or $(-1.5, -0.25)$.

Step 6

Determine which of the given graphs correctly represents $y = x^2 + 3x + 2$.

The graph of the equation $y = x^2 + 3x + 2$ should have x-intercepts at $(-2, 0)$ and $(-1, 0)$, a y-intercept at $(0, 2)$, and a vertex at $(-1.5, -0.25)$. The correct graph of the equation is shown here.

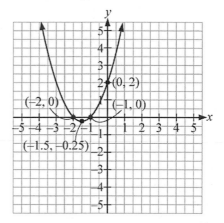

5. **A**

Step 1

Determine the x-intercepts.

Set the equation equal to 0, and apply the zero product property.

$y = -(x + 4)(x + 1)$
$0 = x + 4$
$-4 = x$
$0 = x + 1$
$-1 = x$

Step 2

Determine the midpoint of the x-intercepts.

$M = \left(\dfrac{x_1 + x_2}{2}, \dfrac{y_1 + y_2}{2}\right)$
$M = \left(\dfrac{(-4) + (-1)}{2}, \dfrac{0 + 0}{2}\right)$
$M = \left(\dfrac{-5}{2}, \dfrac{0}{2}\right)$
$M = \left(-\dfrac{5}{2}, 0\right)$

Step 3

Substitute the x-coordinate from the midpoint into the equation to solve for y.

$$y = -(x + 4)(x + 1)$$
$$y = -\left(-\frac{5}{2} + 4\right)\left(-\frac{5}{2} + 1\right)$$
$$y = -\left(-\frac{5}{2} + \frac{8}{2}\right)\left(-\frac{5}{2} + \frac{2}{2}\right)$$
$$y = -\left(\frac{3}{2}\right)\left(-\frac{3}{2}\right)$$
$$y = \frac{9}{4}$$

The coordinates of the vertex of the function $y = -(x + 4)(x + 1)$ are $\left(-\frac{5}{2}, \frac{9}{4}\right)$. The y-coordinate of the vertex is $\frac{9}{4}$.

6. B

Step 1

Determine the x-intercepts.

Set the equation equal to 0, and apply the zero product property.

$$0 = 2(x + 5)(x - 1)$$
$$0 = x + 5$$
$$-5 = x$$
$$0 = x - 1$$
$$1 = x$$

Step 2

Determine the midpoint of the x-intercepts.

$$M = \left(\frac{x_1 + x_2}{2}, \frac{y_1 + y_2}{2}\right)$$
$$M = \left(\frac{-5 + 1}{2}, \frac{0 + 0}{2}\right)$$
$$M = (-2, 0)$$

Since the x-coordinate of the axis of symmetry is -2, the equation of the axis of symmetry is $x = -2$.

7. C

The rocket will strike the ground where the parabola intersects the x-axis after it has reach the vertex. The parabola intersects the x-axis at 5 s, so it takes the rocket 5 s to strike the ground.

Thus, the time it takes the rocket to hit the ground is 5 seconds.

8. 5

Step 1

Determine the value of $f(-3)$.

Using the graph of the function, find the value of y when $x = -3$.

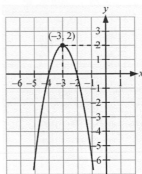

Therefore, $f(-3) = 2$.

Step 2

Determine the value of k.

$$(f(-3))^2 + k = 9$$
$$(2)^2 + k = 9$$
$$4 + k = 9$$
$$k = 9 - 4$$
$$k = 5$$

Therefore, the value of k is 5.

9. A

The solution can be found by using a TI-83 or similar calculator.

Step 1

Graph the equation.

Press $\boxed{Y =}$, and enter $-x^2 - 2x + 6$ in Y_1. Next, press $\boxed{\text{ZOOM}}$, and select 6:ZStandard.

The calculator should display the graph.

Step 2

Determine the coordinates of the vertex.

It can been seen from the graph that the vertex is a maximum. To determine the coordinates of the vertex, access the CALC menu by pressing 2nd TRACE , and select 4:maximum.

Move the cursor to the left of the vertex when asked for a left bound, and press ENTER . Move the cursor to the right of the vertex when asked for a right bound, and press ENTER twice.

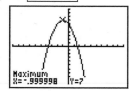

The coordinates of the vertex of the function $y = -x^2 - 2x + 6$ are $(-1, 7)$.

10. C

Step 1

Determine which two numbers have a sum of -9 and a product of $+20$.

$(-5) + (-4) = -5 - 4 = -9$ and $(-5) \times (-4) = +20$.

The two numbers are -5 and -4.

Step 2

Open two sets of brackets. Inside each set of brackets, write the same variable that was used in the given trinomial.

$(x\underline{\hspace{1cm}})(x\underline{\hspace{1cm}})$

Step 3

Place one of the numbers in the first set of brackets and the other number in the second set.

$(x - 5)(x - 4)$

One of the factors of $x^2 - 9x + 20$ is $(x - 4)$.

11. D

Step 1

To solve by factoring (Tara's Procedure), began by rearranging the equation

$8x^2 - 6x + 7 = 2x^2 + 7x + 12$ to $6x^2 - 13x - 5 = 0$.

Factor by decomposition by finding two numbers that have a product of -30 ($a \times c = 6 \times (-5)$) and a sum of -13 (b value). In this case these numbers are -15 and 2.

$6x^2 - 15x + 2x - 5 = 0$

Tara has made a mistake at this stage of her procedure.

Step 2

To solve by using the quadratic formula (Ruth's procedure) rearrange the equation

$8x^2 - 6x + 7 = 2x^2 + 7x + 12$ to

$0 = -6x^2 + 13x + 5$

$x = \dfrac{-b \pm \sqrt{b^2 - 4ac}}{2a}$

Substitute -6 for a, 13 for b, and 5 for c into the quadratic formula.

$x = \dfrac{-(13) \pm \sqrt{(13)^2 - 4(-6)(5)}}{2(-6)}$

$x = \dfrac{-13 \pm \sqrt{169 + 120}}{-12}$

$x = \dfrac{-13 \pm \sqrt{289}}{-12}$

Ruth's procedure is correct.

Step 2

Compare the two partial solutions.

Tara's partial solution has an error and Ruth's is correct.

Therefore, alternative D is correct.

12. D

Determine the nature of the roots of each equation by graphing the equation and checking if there are any x-intercepts.

Step 1

Graph equation I.

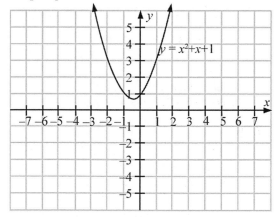

The graph has no x-intercepts, meaning equation I has non-real roots.

Step 2

Graph equation II.

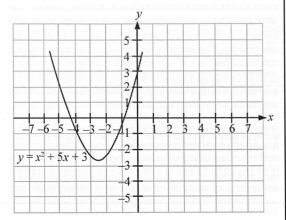

$$y = x^2 + 5x + 3$$

The graph has two distinct x-intercepts, meaning equation II has real roots.

Therefore, equation I has non-real roots, and equation II has real roots.

13. 1

To determine the y-intercept, let $x = 0$ in

$$y = \frac{1}{3}(x - 3)^2 - 2.$$

$$y = \frac{1}{3}(0 - 3)^2 - 2$$

$$= \frac{1}{3}(9) - 2$$

$$= 3 - 2$$

$$= 1$$

Therefore, the y-intercept is 1.

14. WR

Step 1

Write the equation in the general form,

$$ax^2 + bx + c = 0.$$

$$2y^2 + 11y = -15$$

$$2y^2 + 11y + 15 = 0$$

Step 2

Use the quadratic formula to solve the equation.

For a general quadratic equation, $ax^2 + bx + c = 0$, the value of x is given by the formula

$$x = \frac{-b \pm \sqrt{b^2 - 4ac}}{2a}.$$

Use the formula to determine the value of y.

$$y = \frac{-11 \pm \sqrt{11^2 - 4(2)(15)}}{2(2)}$$

$$y = \frac{-11 \pm \sqrt{121 - 120}}{4}$$

$$y = \frac{-11 \pm \sqrt{1}}{4}$$

$$y = \frac{-11 \pm 1}{4}$$

Therefore, $y = -\frac{5}{2}$ or $y = -3$.

15. 2

The given quadratic function has two unique factors, and each factor will yield one real zero.

Determine the zeros of the function

$$y = (3x + 2)(x - 2).$$

$$3x + 2 = 0$$

$$3x = -2$$

$$x = -\frac{2}{3}$$

$$x - 2 = 0$$

$$x = 2$$

Therefore, the function has two different real zeros.

16. A

Step 1

Factor out the greatest common factor from the trinomial.

$$y = 3x^2 - 27x - 210$$

$$y = 3(x^2 - 9x - 70)$$

Step 2

Factor the trinomial.

$$y = 3(x^2 - 9x - 70)$$

$$y = 3(x - 14)(x + 5)$$

Step 3

Set $y = 0$ and solve the equation by equating each factor to zero.

$$0 = 3(x - 14)(x + 5)$$

$$0 = x - 14$$

$$14 = x$$

$$0 = x + 5$$

$$-5 = x$$

The x-intercepts of $y = 3x^2 - 27x - 210$ occur at $x = -5$ and $x = 14$.

17. C

For the trinomial $2x^2 + 5x - 3$, the product of the coefficient of the x^2 term and the constant term is $2 \times (-3) = -6$. The middle term has a coefficient of 5.

Step 1

Find two integers that have a product of -6 and sum of 5.

The pairs of integers with a product of -6, along with their respective sums, are as shown.

Product	Sum
$1 \times (-6) = -6$	$1 + (-6) = -5$
$2 \times (-3) = -6$	$2 + (-3) = -1$
$3 \times (-2) = -6$	$3 + (-2) = 1$
$6 \times (-1) = -6$	$6 + (-1) = 5$

The two integers required are -1 and 6.

Step 2

Express $5x$ as $-x + 6x$, and then factor by grouping to obtain a common factor.

$$2x^2 + 5x - 3 = 2x^2 - x + 6x - 3$$
$$= x(2x - 1) + 3(2x - 1)$$
$$= (2x - 1)(x + 3)$$

The complete factorization of $2x^2 + 5x - 3$ is $(2x - 1)(x + 3)$.

UNIT TEST — RELATIONS AND FUNCTIONS

Use the following information to answer the next question.

Brad is attempting to sketch the graph of the quadratic function $f(x) = -2(x + 4)(x + 2)$. He makes the following four statements:

Statement I: The x-intercepts of the graph are -4 and -2.

Statement II: The equation of the axis of symmetry of the graph is $x = -3$.

Statement III: The vertex of the graph is $(-3, 8)$.

Statement IV: The graph opens downward.

1. Which of the statements is **incorrect**?

   A. I   **B.** II

   C. III   **D.** IV

Use the following information to answer the next question.

A graph of a quadratic function is given.

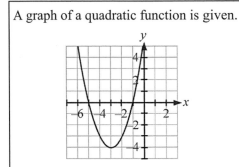

2. What are the coordinates of the x-intercepts?

   A. $(-5, 0)$ and $(-1, 0)$

   B. $(0, -5)$ and $(0, -1)$

   C. $(-3, -4)$ and $(0, 5)$

   D. $(5, 0)$ and $(1, 0)$

Use the following information to answer the next question.

The flight path of a flare fired from the top of a cliff to the ground can be described by the graph of the quadratic function $h(t) = -4.9t^2 + 29.4t + 352.8$, where $h(t)$ is the height, in metres, of the flare above the ground at a time, t, in seconds. Yosef wanted to use his graphing calculator to find the time, in seconds, when the flare hit the ground at $h(t) = 0$, namely the t-intercept.

3. The window Yosef used to display the whole flight of the flare to the ground ($h(t) = 0$) was ____*i*____, and the t-intercept was ____*ii*____.

   Which of the following rows correctly completes this statement?

   A.

i	*ii*
x:$[-10, 10, 1]$ y:$[-10, 10, 1]$	6.0 seconds

   B.

i	*ii*
x:$[-10, 20, 1]$ y:$[-10, 500, 1]$	6.0 seconds

   C.

i	*ii*
x:$[-10, 10, 1]$ y:$[-10, 500, 1]$	12.0 seconds

   D.

i	*ii*
x:$[-10, 20, 1]$ y:$[-10, 500, 1]$	12.0 seconds

4. What is the range of the graph of the quadratic function $y = 2(x + 11)(x - 7)$?

   A. $y \geq -162$ **B.** $y \leq -77$

   C. $y \leq -11$ **D.** $y \geq 7$

Use the following information to answer the next question.

The unit value of a particular stock, in Japanese yen (JPY), followed a quadratic pattern over a period of 20 consecutive days. Part of this trend is portrayed in the bar graph shown below.

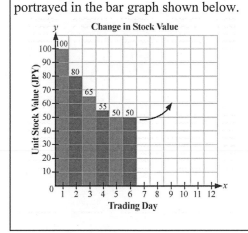

Numerical Response

5. Based on the trend, the stock would recover to its original value of 100 JPY on day _____.

6. What is the vertex of the function $y = 2(x - 3)(x - 7)$?

   A. (3, 7)   **B.** (5, −8)

   C. (−5, 8)   **D.** (−3, −7)

Use the following information to answer the next question.

The graph of the quadratic function $f(x)$ is shown.

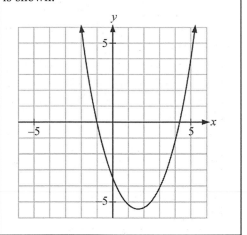

7. Which of the following statements about $f(x)$ is **true**?

   A. $f(0) = 0$ **B.** $f(0) = 4$

   C. $f(-1) = 0$ **D.** $f(-4) = 2$

8. The axis of symmetry on the graph of the function $y = (x - 1)(x - 2)$ is

   A. $x = \dfrac{3}{2}$ **B.** $x = \dfrac{1}{2}$

   C. $x = -\dfrac{1}{2}$ **D.** $x = -\dfrac{3}{2}$

9. What is the minimum value of the quadratic function $y = 3(x - 5)(x - 1)$?

   A. −12   **B.** −4

   C. 4   **D.** 12

Numerical Response

10. The value of the maximum of the quadratic function $y = -5(x + 8)(x - 2)$ is _____.

11. When the expression $x^2 + 3x - 40$ is factored, the result is

   A. $(x + 8)(x - 5)$

   B. $(x - 8)(x + 5)$

   C. $(x + 8)(x + 5)$

   D. $(x - 8)(x - 5)$

12. The solutions to the quadratic equation
$13 - x = 4x^2 + 3x - 35$ are

   A. $x = 3$, $x = -4$

   B. $x = 5$, $x = -3$

   C. $x = 7$, $x = -5$

   D. $x = 13$, $x = -7$

13. Which of the following trinomials is **not** factorable?

   A. $3x^2 + 22x + 7$

   B. $6x^2 + 23x + 7$

   C. $8x^2 + 30x + 7$

   D. $9x^2 + 21x + 7$

14. What are the coordinates of the x-intercepts of the quadratic function $y = x^2 + 13x + 36$?

   A. $(0, 9)$ and $(0, 4)$

   B. $(9, 0)$ and $(4, 0)$

   C. $(-9, 0)$ and $(-4, 0)$

   D. $(0, -9)$ and $(0, -4)$

Numerical Response

15. The exact value of the y-intercept on the graph of $y = (4x - 2)(3x - 1)$ is _____.

16. If the binomial $40z^4 - 135z$ can be factored as $az(bz - c)(dz^2 + ez + f)$, what is the value of $d + e + f$?

   A. 7   **B.** 8

   C. 19   **D.** 27

17. Which of the following graphs represents a quadratic equation that has two real and distinct roots?

A.

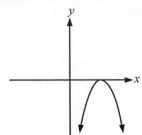

B.

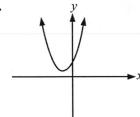

C.

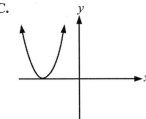

D.

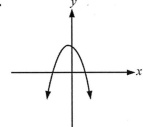

Use the following information to answer the next question.

Ozzie was asked by his teacher to solve the equation

$-2x^2 - 3x + 19 = -10x^2 - 25x + 5$ by factoring. Ozzie's partial solution to the equation is shown.

1. $-8x^2 + 22x + 14 = 0$
2. $-2(4x^2 - 11x - 7) = 0$
3. $-2(4x^2 - 4x - 7x - 7) = 0$
4. $-2((4x^2 - 4x) + (-7x - 7)) = 0$
5. $-2(4x(x - 1) - 7(x - 1)) = 0$

18. Which of the following statements about Ozzie's partial solution is **true**?

  A. Ozzie's partial solution is correct.

  B. Ozzie made his first error in step 1.

  C. Ozzie made his first error in step 3.

  D. Ozzie made his first error in step 5.

Numerical Response

19. The expression $36x^2 + 18x$ written in factored form is $Ax(Bx + C)$, where A, B, and C are whole numbers. The value of $A + B + C$ is _____.

ANSWERS AND SOLUTIONS — UNIT TEST

1. C	6. B	11. A	16. C
2. A	7. C	12. A	17. D
3. D	8. A	13. D	18. B
4. A	9. A	14. C	19. 21
5. 10	10. 125	15. 2	

1. C

For the quadratic function given in the factored form $f(x) = -2(x + 4)(x + 2)$, determine the following features of its graph:

- The x-intercepts are -4 and -2, since these values make each factor equal 0.

$$x + 4 = 0 \qquad \text{and} \qquad x + 2 = 0$$
$$x = -4 \qquad\qquad x = -2$$

- The equation of the axis of symmetry is located halfway between the x-intercepts:

$$x = h = \frac{r + s}{2} = \frac{-4 + (-2)}{2} = -3$$

- The graph of the function opens downward since the numerical coefficient $a < 0$.

- The vertex of the graph (h, k) can be found, since it lies on the axis of symmetry ($x = -3$). Substitute $x = -3$, and solve for k in the function.

$$f(x) = -2(x + 4)(x + 2)$$
$$k = -2(-3 + 4)(-3 + 2)$$
$$= -2(1)(-1)$$
$$= 2$$

The vertex is $(-3, 2)$.

In statement III, Brad incorrectly states that the vertex of the graph is $(-3, 8)$.

2. A

The x-intercepts are the points where the graph intersects the x-axis.

The coordinates of these points are $(-5, 0)$ and $(-1, 0)$.

3. D

Enter the function $h(t) = -4.9t^2 + 29.4t + 352.8$ into your $[Y_1 =]$ button on your graphing calculator. Then, press GRAPH and use WINDOW (ZOOM 6).

$$Y_1 = -4.9x^2 + 29.4x + 352.8$$

The graph only shows the negative x-intercept which does not apply to this question. Also, the top (maximum) of the graph is not visible. Therefore, the WINDOW needs to be made larger to the right (x_{max}) and moved up (y_{max}) a lot. The window that seems appropriate is given in alternatives B or D as:

$x:[-10, 20, 1]$
$y:[-10, 500, 1]$

When this WINDOW setting is used, the whole graph is shown with its maximum and the positive x-intercept, namely the point representing when the flare hits the ground. Then, carry out the 2nd TRACE ZERO feature to determine that this x-intercept is 12.0, as shown below:

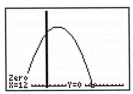

4. A

Step 1

Identify the x-intercepts.

In factored form, or $y = a(x - r)(x - s)$, the x-intercepts of the graph of the quadratic function are equal to the values of r and s.

Since the equation is in the factored form $y = 2(x + 11)(x - 7)$, the x-intercepts are -11 and 7.

Step 2

Find the coordinates of the vertex.

Use the formula $x = \dfrac{r + s}{2}$ to find the x-value.

Substitute -11 for r and 7 for s.

$$x = \frac{-11 + 7}{2}$$
$$x = \frac{-4}{2}$$
$$x = -2$$

Find the y-coordinate. Substitute -2 for x in the equation $y = 2(x + 11)(x - 7)$.

$$y = 2(-2 + 11)(-2 - 7)$$
$$y = 2(9)(-9)$$
$$y = -162$$

The coordinates of the vertex are $(-2, -162)$.

Step 3

Determine the range.

Since $a > 0$, the graph opens upward, and the minimum y-value is -162.

Therefore, the range of the function $y = 2(x + 11)(x - 7)$ is $y \geq -162$.

5. 10

A quadratic pattern is symmetrical in that it decreases and increases from its minimum point in equivalent steps. The drops on the left side of the minimum over the first 5 days are

$$\begin{array}{ccccc} {\scriptstyle -20} & {\scriptstyle -15} & {\scriptstyle -10} & {\scriptstyle -5} \\ 100 \to & 80 \to & 65 \to & 55 \to & 50. \end{array}$$ Therefore, the increases on the right side of the graph from day 6 onward will follow the same pattern of

$$\begin{array}{ccccc} {\scriptstyle +5} & {\scriptstyle +10} & {\scriptstyle +15} & {\scriptstyle +20} \\ 50 \to & 55 \to & 65 \to & 80 \to & 100. \end{array}$$

This increased pattern of the stock can be represented in the completed graph below.

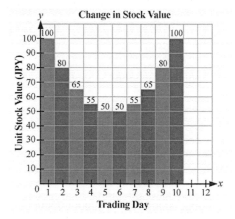

According to the completed pattern shown in the graph, the stock recovers to its original value of 100 JPY on day 10.

6. B

Step 1

Determine the x-intercepts.

Set the equation equal to 0, and apply the zero product property.

$$y = 2(x - 3)(x - 7)$$
$$0 = x - 3$$
$$3 = x$$
$$0 = x - 7$$
$$7 = x$$

Step 2

Determine the midpoint of the x-intercepts.

$$M = \left(\frac{x_1 + x_2}{2}, \frac{y_1 + y_2}{2} \right)$$
$$M = \left(\frac{3 + 7}{2}, \frac{0 + 0}{2} \right)$$
$$M = \left(\frac{10}{2}, \frac{0}{2} \right)$$
$$M = (5, 0)$$

Step 3

Substitute the x-coordinate from the midpoint into the equation to solve for y.

$$y = 2(x - 3)(x - 7)$$
$$y = 2(5 - 3)(5 - 7)$$
$$y = 2(2)(-2)$$
$$y = -8$$

The coordinates of the vertex of the function $y = 2(x - 3)(x - 7)$ are $(5, -8)$.

7. C

The function $f(x) = y$ means that the point (x, y) is part of the graph of $f(x)$.

The statements $f(0) = 0$, $f(0) = 4$, $f(-1) = 0$, and $f(-4) = 2$ correspond to the points $(0, 0)$, $(0, 4)$, $(-1, 0)$, and $(-4, 2)$. To evaluate the given statements, check to see if the corresponding points $(0, 0)$, $(0, 4)$, $(-1, 0)$, and $(-4, 2)$ are on the graph of $f(x)$.

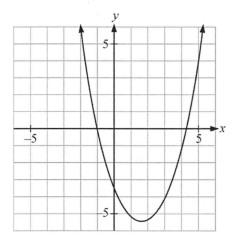

The only point on the the graph is $(-1, 0)$. Therefore, the statement $f(-1) = 0$ is true.

8. A

Step 1

Determine the x-intercepts.

Set the equation to 0, and apply the zero product property.

$0 = (x - 1)(x - 2)$
$0 = x - 1$
$1 = x$
$0 = x - 2$
$2 = x$

Step 2

Determine the midpoint of the x-intercepts.

$M = \left(\dfrac{x_1 + x_2}{2}, \dfrac{y_1 + y_2}{2} \right)$

$= \left(\dfrac{1 + 2}{2}, \dfrac{0 + 0}{2} \right)$

$= \left(\dfrac{3}{2}, 0 \right)$

Since the x-coordinate of the axis of symmetry is $\dfrac{3}{2}$, the equation for the axis of symmetry is $x = \dfrac{3}{2}$.

9. A

The quadratic function $y = 3(x - 5)(x - 1)$ is in the factored form $y = a(x - r)(x - s)$, where $a = 3$, $r = 5$, and $s = 1$.

Step 1

Determine the x-coordinate of the vertex.

The x-coordinate of the vertex is located halfway between the x-intercepts. Use the formula $x = \dfrac{r + s}{2}$ to calculate the x-coordinate.

Substitute 5 for r and 1 for s into the formula.

$x = \dfrac{r + s}{2}$

$x = \dfrac{(5) + (1)}{2}$

$x = \dfrac{6}{2}$

$x = 3$

The x-coordinate of the vertex is 3.

Step 2

Determine the value of the minimum.

The y-coordinate of the vertex is equal to the minimum value. Substitute the x-coordinate, 3, into the original equation, $y = 3(x - 5)(x - 1)$, to determine the value of y.

$y = 3(x - 5)(x - 1)$
$y = 3((3) - 5)((3) - 1)$
$y = 3(-2)(2)$
$y = -12$

The value of the minimum of the quadratic function is -12.

10. 125

The quadratic function $y = -5(x + 8)(x - 2)$ is in the factored form $y = a(x - r)(x - s)$, where $a = -5$, $r = -8$, and $s = 2$.

Step 1

Determine the x-coordinate of the vertex.

The x-coordinate of the vertex is located halfway between the x-intercepts. Use the formula $x = \dfrac{r + s}{2}$ to calculate the x-coordinate.

Substitute -8 for r and 2 for s into the formula.

$x = \dfrac{r + s}{2}$

$x = \dfrac{(-8) + (2)}{2}$

$x = \dfrac{-6}{2}$

$x = -3$

The x-coordinate of the vertex is -3.

Step 2

Determine the value of the maximum.

The y-coordinate of the vertex is equal to the maximum value. Substitute the x-coordinate, -3, into the original equation, $y = -5(x + 8)(x - 2)$, to determine the value of y.

$y = -5(x + 8)(x - 2)$
$y = -5((-3) + 8)((-3) - 2)$
$y = -5(5)(-5)$
$y = 125$

The value of the maximum of the quadratic function is 125.

11. A

Step 1

Determine which two numbers have a sum of $+3$ and a product of -40.

$+8 - 5 = +3$ and $+8 \times -5 = -40$

The two numbers are $+8$ and -5.

Step 2

Open two sets of brackets. Inside each set of brackets, write the same variable that was used in the given trinomial.

$(x\_)(x\_)$

Step 3

Place the two numbers inside each set of brackets.

$(x + 8)(x - 5)$

12. A

Step 1

Express the equation in the form $0 = ax^2 + bx + c$.

$$13 - x = 4x^2 + 3x - 35$$
$$13 = 4x^2 + 4x - 35$$
$$0 = 4x^2 + 4x - 48$$

Step 2

Factor the equation.

$$0 = 4x^2 + 4x - 48$$
$$0 = 4(x^2 + x - 12)$$
$$0 = 4(x - 3)(x + 4)$$

Step 3

Solve the equation by equating each binomial factor to zero.

$$0 = x + 4$$
$$-4 = x$$
$$0 = x - 3$$
$$3 = x$$

The solutions for $13 - x = 4x^2 + 3x - 35$ are $x = 3$ and $x = -4$.

13. D

Step 1

Factor $3x^2 + 22x + 7$ by decomposition.

$$3x^2 + 22x + 7$$
$$= 3x^2 + x + 21x + 7$$
$$= (3x^2 + x) + (21x + 7)$$
$$= x(3x + 1) + 7(3x + 1)$$
$$= (x + 7)(3x + 1)$$

Step 2

Factor $6x^2 + 23x + 7$ by decomposition.

$$6x^2 + 23x + 7$$
$$= 6x^2 + 2x + 21x + 7$$
$$= (6x^2 + 2x) + (21x + 7)$$
$$= 2x(3x + 1) + 7(3x + 1)$$
$$= (2x + 7)(3x + 1)$$

Step 3

Factor $8x^2 + 30x + 7$ by decomposition.

$$8x^2 + 30x + 7$$
$$= 8x^2 + 2x + 28x + 7$$
$$= (8x^2 + 2x) + (28x + 7)$$
$$= 2x(4x + 1) + 7(4x + 1)$$
$$= (2x + 7)(4x + 1)$$

Step 4

Factor the trinomial $9x^2 + 21x + 7$.
No two integers have a product of $9 \times 7 = 63$ and a sum of 21.

Therefore, $9x^2 + 21x + 7$ is a prime polynomial and cannot be factored.

14. C

Method 1

Find the x-intercepts by factoring and solving the equation $0 = x^2 + 13x + 36$.

$$0 = x^2 + 13x + 36$$
$$0 = (x + 9)(x + 4)$$
$$0 = x + 9$$
$$x = -9$$
$$0 = x + 4$$
$$x = -4$$

The x-intercepts are -9 and -4.

Method 2

Use the quadratic formula, $x = \dfrac{-b \pm \sqrt{b^2 - 4ac}}{2a}$, to find the x-intercepts.

$$x = \frac{-b \pm \sqrt{b^2 - 4ac}}{2a}$$
$$x = \frac{-(13) \pm \sqrt{(13)^2 - 4(1)(36)}}{2(1)}$$
$$x = \frac{-13 \pm \sqrt{169 - (144)}}{2}$$
$$x = \frac{-13 \pm \sqrt{25}}{2}$$
$$x = \frac{-13 \pm 5}{\square}$$
$$x = \frac{-13 + 5}{2} \text{ or } x = \frac{-13 - 5}{2}$$
$$x = \frac{-8}{2} \text{ or } x = \frac{-18}{2}$$
$$x = -4 \text{ or } x = -9$$

Both methods provide the same answer, so the x-intercepts of the function $y = x^2 + 13x + 36$ are -9 and -4.

The y-values of the x-intercepts are equal to 0. Therefore, the coordinates of the x-intercepts are $(-9, 0)$ and $(-4, 0)$.

15. 2

To determine the y-intercept, substitute 0 for x in $y = (4x - 2)(3x - 1)$ and solve for y.

$$y = (4x - 2)(3x - 1)$$
$$y = (4(0) - 2)(3(0) - 1)$$
$$y = (-2)(-1)$$
$$y = 2$$

Therefore, the y-intercept is 2.

16. C

Step 1

Remove the GCF$5z$ from $40z^4 - 135z$.

$$40z^4 - 135z = 5z(8z^3 - 27)$$

Step 2

Factor the binomial $8z^3 - 27$ as a difference of cubes by using the pattern

$a^3 - b^3 = (a - b)(a^2 + ab + b^2)$.

Determine the cube root of each term.

$$\sqrt[3]{8z^3} = 2z$$

$$\sqrt[3]{27} = 3$$

$$8z^3 - 27 = \left(\begin{matrix} (2z - 3) \\ \times\ ((2z)^2 + (2z)(3) + (3)^2) \end{matrix}\right)$$

$$8z^3 - 27 = \left(\begin{matrix} (2z - 3) \\ \times\ (4z^2 + 6z + 9) \end{matrix}\right)$$

$$5z(8z^3 - 27) = 5z(2z - 3)(4z^2 + 6z + 9)$$

Step 3

Determine the value of $d + e + f$ for

$az(bz - c)(dz^2 + ez + f)$.

Compare $dz^2 + ez + f$ to $4z^2 + 6z + 9$. It follows that $d = 4$, $e = 6$, and $f = 9$.

$$d + e + f = 4 + 6 + 9$$
$$= 19$$

17. D

A quadratic equation with two real and distinct roots has a corresponding graph with two distinct x-intercepts.

Only this graph intersects the x-axis at two distinct points.

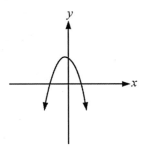

18. B

Ozzie's first error occurred in step 1:

$-2x^2 - 3x + 19 = -10x^2 - 25x + 5$ simplifies to $8x^2 + 22x + 14 = 0$. The steps Ozzie should have followed are given below.

Step 1

Factor 2 from the trinomial.

$2(4x^2 + 11x + 7) = 0$

Step 2

Decompose the middle term of the trinomial.

$2(4x^2 + 4x + 7x + 7) = 0$

Step 3

Group the terms into two pairs of two.

$2((4x^2 + 4x) + (7x + 7)) = 0$

Step 4

Remove the greatest common factor from each pair.

$2(4x(x + 1) + 7(x + 1)) = 0$

19. 21

The greatest common factor of 36 and 18 is 18, and the greatest common factor of x^2 and x is x.

Thus $36x^2 + 18x$ can be factored as follows:

$$36x^2 + 18x$$
$$= 18x(2x + 1)$$

The value of $A + B + C = 18 + 2 + 1 = 21$.

KEY Strategies for Success on Tests

KEY STRATEGIES FOR SUCCESS ON TESTS

This section is all about the skills and strategies you need to be successful on tests. It is designed for you to use together with your classroom learning and assignments.

FINDING OUT ABOUT THE TESTS

Here are some questions you may wish to discuss with your teacher to help you prepare for quizzes and tests:

- What will this test assess, or cover?

- How much time do I have to write the test?

- How important is this test to my final grade?

- Are there any materials provided for the test?

- What materials do I need to bring to write the test?

- What kind of questions are on the test? Will they be multiple choice? Short answer?

Having a good understanding of effective test-taking skills can help you do well on tests. Being familiar with different types of questions may also help you.

THINGS TO CONSIDER WHEN TAKING A TEST

It is normal to feel anxious before you write a test. You can manage this anxiety by using the following strategies:

- Think positive thoughts. Imagine yourself doing well on the test.

- Make a conscious effort to relax by taking several slow, deep, controlled breaths. Concentrate on the air going in and out of your body.

- Before you begin the test, ask questions if you are unsure of anything.

- Jot down key words or phrases from any instructions your teacher gives you.

- Look over the entire test to find out the number and kinds of questions on the test.

- Read each question closely, and reread if necessary.

- Pay close attention to key vocabulary words. Sometimes, these words are **bolded** or *italicized*, and they are usually important words in the question.

- If you are putting your answers on an answer sheet, mark your answers carefully. Always print clearly. If you wish to change an answer, erase the mark completely, and ensure that your final answer is darker than the one you have erased.

- Use highlighting to note directions, key words, and vocabulary that you find confusing or that are important to answering the question.

- Double-check to make sure you have answered everything before handing in your test.

- When taking tests, students often overlook the easy words. Failure to pay close attention to these words can result in an incorrect answer. One way to avoid this is to be aware of these words and to underline, circle, or highlight them while you are taking the test.

- Even though some words are easy to understand, they can change the meaning of the entire question, so it is important that you pay attention to them. Here are some examples.

all	always	most likely	probably	best	not
difference	usually	except	most	unlikely	likely

Example

1. Which of the following equations is incorrect?

   A. $3 + 2 = 5$

   B. $4 - 3 = 1$

   C. $5 \times 4 = 15$

   D. $6 \times 3 = 18$

HELPFUL STRATEGIES FOR ANSWERING MULTIPLE-CHOICE QUESTIONS

A multiple-choice question gives you some information and then asks you to select an answer from four choices. Each question has one correct answer. The other choices are distractors, which are incorrect.

The following strategies can help you when answering multiple-choice questions:

- Quickly skim through the entire test. Find out how many questions there are, and plan your time accordingly.

- Read and reread questions carefully. Underline key words, and try to think of an answer before looking at the choices.

- If there is a graphic, look at the graphic, read the question, and go back to the graphic. Then, you may want to underline the important information from the question.

- Carefully read the choices. Read the question first and then each choice that goes with it.

- When choosing an answer, try to eliminate those choices that are clearly wrong or do not make sense.

- Some questions may ask you to select the best answer. These questions will always include words like *best*, *most appropriate*, or *most likely*. All of the choices will be correct to some degree, but one of the choices will be better than the others in some way. Carefully read all four choices before choosing the answer you think is the best.

- If you do not know the answer, or if the question does not make sense to you, it is better to guess than to leave it blank.

- Do not spend too much time on any one question. Make a mark (*) beside a difficult question, and come back to it later. If you are leaving a question to come back to later, make sure you also leave the space on the answer sheet, if you are using one.

- Remember to go back to the difficult questions at the end of the test; sometimes, clues are given throughout the test that will provide you with answers.

- Note any negative words like *no* or *not*, and be sure your answer fits the question.

- Before changing an answer, be sure you have a very good reason to do so.

- Do not look for patterns on your answer sheet, if you are using one.

HELPFUL STRATEGIES FOR ANSWERING WRITTEN-RESPONSE QUESTIONS

A written response requires you to respond to a question or directive indicated by words such as *explain*, *predict*, *list*, *describe*, *show your work*, *solve*, or *calculate*. The following strategies can help you when answering written-response questions:

- Read and reread the question carefully.

- Recognize and pay close attention to directing words such as *explain*, *show your work*, and *describe*.

- Underline key words and phrases that indicate what is required in your answer, such as *explain*, *estimate*, *answer*, *calculate*, or *show your work*.

- Write down rough, point-form notes regarding the information you want to include in your answer.

- Think about what you want to say, and organize information and ideas in a coherent and concise manner within the time limit you have for the question.

- Be sure to answer every part of the question that is asked.

- Include as much information as you can when you are asked to explain your thinking.

- Include a picture or diagram if it will help to explain your thinking.

- Try to put your final answer to a problem in a complete sentence to be sure it is reasonable.

- Reread your response to ensure you have answered the question.

- Ask yourself if your answer makes sense.

- Ask yourself if your answer sounds right.

- Use appropriate subject vocabulary and terms in your response.

ABOUT MATHEMATICS TESTS

WHAT YOU NEED TO KNOW ABOUT MATHEMATICS TESTS

To do well on a mathematics test, you need to understand and apply your knowledge of mathematical concepts. Reading skills can also make a difference in how well you perform. Reading skills can help you follow instructions and find key words, as well as read graphs, diagrams, and tables. They can also help you solve mathematics problems.

Mathematics tests usually have two types of questions: questions that ask for understanding of mathematics ideas and questions that test how well you can solve mathematics problems.

HOW YOU CAN PREPARE FOR MATHEMATICS TESTS

The following strategies are particular to preparing for and writing mathematics tests:

- Know how to use your calculator, and, if it is allowed, use your own for the test.

- Note taking is a good way to review and study important information from your class notes and textbook.

- Sketch a picture of the problem, procedure, or term. Drawing is helpful for learning and remembering concepts.

- Check your answer to practice questions by working backward to the beginning. You can find the beginning by going step by step in reverse order.

- Use the following steps when answering questions with graphics (pictures, diagrams, tables, or graphs):

  1. Read the title of the graphic and any key words.

  2. Read the test question carefully to figure out what information you need to find in the graphic.

  3. Go back to the graphic to find the information you need.

  4. Decide which operation is needed.

- Always pay close attention when pressing the keys on your calculator. Repeat the procedure a second time to be sure you pressed the correct keys.

TEST PREPARATION COUNTDOWN

If you develop a plan for studying and test preparation, you will perform well on tests.

Here is a general plan to follow seven days before you write a test.

COUNTDOWN: 7 DAYS BEFORE THE TEST

1. Create your own personal test preparation plan.

2. Review the following information:

   – Areas to be included on the test

   – Types of test items

   – General and specific test tips

3. Start preparing for the test at least seven days before the test. Develop your test preparation plan,
   and set time aside to prepare and study.

COUNTDOWN: 6, 5, 4, 3, 2 DAYS BEFORE THE TEST

1. Review old homework assignments, quizzes, and tests.

2. Rework problems on quizzes and tests to make sure you still know how to solve them.

3. Correct any errors made on quizzes and tests.

4. Review key concepts, processes, formulas, and vocabulary.

5. Create practice test questions for yourself, and answer them. Work out many sample problems.

COUNTDOWN: THE NIGHT BEFORE THE TEST

1. Use the night before the test for final preparation, which includes reviewing and gathering materials needed for the test before going to bed.

2. Most importantly, get a good night's rest, and know you have done everything possible to do well on the test.

TEST DAY

1. Eat a healthy and nutritious breakfast.

2. Ensure you have all the necessary materials.

3. Think positive thoughts, such as "I can do this," "I am ready," and "I know I can do well."

4. Arrive at your school early, so you are not rushing, which can cause you anxiety and stress.

Summary of How to Be Successful during a Test

You may find some of the following strategies useful for writing a test:

- Take two or three deep breaths to help you relax.
- Read the directions carefully, and underline, circle, or highlight any important words.
- Look over the entire test to understand what you will need to do.
- Budget your time.
- Begin with an easy question or a question you know you can answer correctly rather than follow the numerical question order of the test.
- If you cannot remember how to answer a question, try repeating the deep breathing and physical relaxation activities. Then, move on to visualization and positive self-talk to get yourself going.
- When answering questions with graphics (pictures, diagrams, tables, or graphs), look at the question carefully, and use the following steps:

  1. Read the title of the graphic and any key words.
  2. Read the test question carefully to figure out what information you need to find in the graphic.
  3. Go back to the graphic to find the information you need.

- Write down anything you remember about the subject on the reverse side of your test paper. This activity sometimes helps to remind you that you do know something and are capable of writing the test.
- Look over your test when you have finished, and double-check your answers to be sure you did not forget anything.

PRACTICE TEST

1. What is the range of the graph of the quadratic function $y = -(x + 9)(x - 5)$?

   A. $y \leq 49$ **B.** $y \geq 49$

   C. $y \geq -9$ **D.** $y \leq -9$

Use the following information to answer the next question.

> Loly's teacher asks her to determine the coordinates of the vertex of the parabola defined by the equation
> $y = 2x^2 - 12x + 13$.
> Loly decides to use a graphical approach.

2. Loly will find that the coordinates of the vertex of the parabola defined by the given equation are

   A. $(2, -4)$ **B.** $(2, -5)$

   C. $(3, -4)$ **D.** $(3, -5)$

Use the following information to answer the next question.

> A football kicked during a football game followed a parabolic path. This path can be modelled by graphing the equation
> $h = -2t^2 + 11t - 3, t \geq 1$, where t is the number of seconds that have elapsed since the football was kicked and h is the height of the football above the ground in yards.

3. How long did it take the football to reach a height of 12 yards above the ground after it was kicked?

   A. 2.0 seconds   **B.** 2.5 seconds

   C. 3.0 seconds   **D.** 3.5 seconds

Use the following information to answer the next question.

> Rachel is asked to factor four different polynomials. The given table shows the four polynomials and the student's solutions.

	Polynomial	Student's Solution
I	$8x^3 + 4x^2$	$4x^2(2x + 1)$
II	$25a^2 - 4b^2c^2$	$(5a + 2bc)(5a - 2bc)$
III	$2x^2 - 18y^2$	$2(x + 3y)(x - 3y)$
IV	$4a^3 - a$	$a(2a - 1)^2$

4. Which polynomial did Rachel factor **incorrectly**?

   A. Polynomial I   **B.** Polynomial II

   C. Polynomial III   **D.** Polynomial IV

Use the following information to answer the next question.

> For the quadratic expression
> $y = x^2 - 2x - 15$, a student factored the equation to obtain $y = (x + 3)(x - 5)$.

5. The factored form that the student used leads to the determination of the

   A. vertex of the graph of a parabola

   B. minimum value of a parabola

   C. x-intercepts of a parabola

   D. y-intercept of a parabola

Use the following information to answer the next question.

The graph of a quadratic expression is given below.

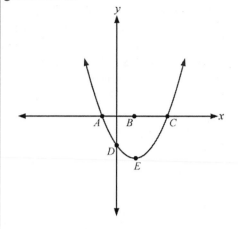

6. The points that will help solve for the factors of the quadratic expression are

   A. *A* and *D*   **B.** *A* and *C*

   C. *B* and *E*   **D.** *A*, *B*, and *C*

Use the following information to answer the next question.

The results of a college entrance exam were normally distributed with a mean of 280 and a standard deviation of 50. A decision was made to adjust the students' original marks. The results were translated to a normal distribution with a mean of 60 and a standard deviation of *k*.

7. If a particular student with an original mark of 370 obtains an adjusted mark of 87, then the value of *k* is

   A. 10   **B.** 12

   C. 15   **D.** 16

Use the following information to answer the next question.

In July, the average temperature in Vanderhoof, BC, varies with a normal distribution. During this month, the mean temperature is 28.7°C with a standard deviation of 5.9°C.

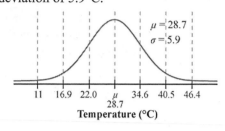

8. Which of the following temperatures has the highest probability of occurring in Vanderhoof in July?

   A. 22.8°C   **B.** 28.7°C

   C. 34.6°C   **D.** 40.5°C

Use the following information to answer the next question.

The length of time required to complete a school's scholarship exam is normally distributed with a mean of 60 minutes and a standard deviation of 17.5 minutes.

9. If 90% of the students completed the examination in the time allowed, then the time allowed for the examination was

   A. 78 min   **B.** 80 min

   C. 82 min   **D.** 84 min

Use the following information to answer the next question.

Statistics taken on a random sample of ticket buyers for a concert revealed that the amount of time they waited in line to purchase their tickets was normally distributed with a mean of 160 min and a standard deviation of 10 min.

Numerical Response

10. To the nearest tenth, the percentage of people who stood in line between 150 and 180 min is _____.

Use the following information to answer the next question.

A polling company does a survey during an election and reports 52% support for a particular candidate, with a 4.9% margin of error at a 95% confidence level. A newspaper commissions the company to do a second poll but asks that the margin of error be cut in half, even though the confidence level should stay the same.

11. If the polling company surveyed 400 people in the first survey, approximately how many should they survey the second time?

  A. 200   **B.** 800

  C. 1 200   **D.** 1 600

Use the following information to answer the next question.

A cereal manufacturing company surveyed 1 000 college students, representing a normally distributed population. The results of the survey showed that 65% of the students surveyed ate cereal for breakfast on a regular basis.

12. What is the 95% confidence interval for the estimated population proportion?

  A. 0.35 ± 0.0296

  B. 0.35 ± 0.0248

  C. 0.65 ± 0.0296

  D. 0.65 ± 0.0248

Use the following information to answer the next question.

A national chain of fitness centres randomly surveyed 250 members to determine how many members were happy with the overall availability of the equipment during the day. The survey found that 100 members were happy with the availability of the equipment. The proportion of the population who are happy with the availability of the equipment was estimated to be 0.4.

Numerical Response

13. To the nearest hundredth, what is the margin of error at a 95% confidence level for the estimated population proportion? _____

Use the following information to answer the next question.

Pipe A can fill a tank in 45 hours, and pipe B can fill the tank in 36 hours.

14. If both pipes are opened, how long does it take to fill the tank?

  A. 9 hours   **B.** 20 hours

  C. 36 hours   **D.** 45 hours

Use the following information to answer the next question.

The given table shows the rate of change of some entity with respect to time for a particular situation.

Time	1	4	8	10
Rate of change with respect to time	2	16	256	1 024

15. Which of the following situations would **most likely** create the data in the given table?

A. A farmer recording population numbers when breeding rabbits

B. A passenger recording speeds as a vehicle accelerates to highway speeds

C. A pilot recording the air temperature as an airplane descends from 37 000 ft

D. A student recording the temperature on a thermometer when it is placed in a pot of boiling water

Use the following information to answer the next question.

Betty bought 43 L of gasoline for $40.64.

Numerical Response

16. The unit rate that Betty paid for the gasoline was $_____/L.

Use the following information to answer the next question.

A sphere with a radius *r* has a volume of 212 cm³.

17. After a scale factor of 2.5 has been applied to this sphere, what is the radius of the sphere rounded to the nearest hundredth of a centimetre?

A. 8.34 cm   **B.** 8.87 cm

C. 9.25 cm   **D.** 9.63 cm

Use the following information to answer the next question.

On the grid below, $\triangle ABC$ is transformed to $\triangle A'B'C'$.

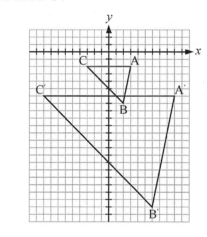

18. In comparison to $\triangle ABC$, $\triangle A'B'C'$ has been increased in size by a factor of

A. $\frac{1}{4}$ **B.** $\frac{1}{3}$

C. 3   **D.** 4

Use the following information to answer the next question.

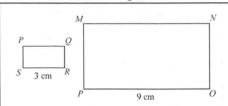

A scale drawing is given where rectangle *PQRS* is the original diagram and rectangle *MNOP* is the image diagram.

Numerical Response

19. What is the scale factor of the given diagram? _____

Use the following information to answer the next question.

Two types of cylindrical fence posts are available at a lumber yard. One type of fence post has a diameter of 9 cm and a height of 3 m. The second type of fence post has the same height as the first but twice the volume.

20. The diameter of the second type of fence post, to the nearest tenth, is

A. 12.7 cm   **B.** 14.0 cm

C. 16.8 cm   **D.** 18.0 cm

Use the following information to answer the next question.

Vickie has a sketch of an irregular polygon with an area, A_1, of 260 cm^2, and she wants to apply a scale factor of 2.2 to it.

21. Rounded to the nearest whole number, what is the area, A_2, of the new irregular polygon?

A. 572 cm^2 **B.** 834 cm^2

C. 1 258 cm^2 **D.** 1 646 cm^2

Use the following information to answer the next question.

A trapezoid with an area, A_1, of 21 m^2 has a scale factor of 0.82 applied to it.

Numerical Response

22. Rounded to the nearest tenth, the area, A_2, of the new trapezoid is _____ m^2.

Use the following information to answer the next question.

Two triangles are given.

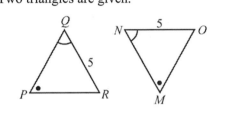

23. Which set of conditions for congruency proves these triangles are congruent?

A. RHL   **B.** SSS

C. SAS   **D.** AAS

Use the following information to answer the next question.

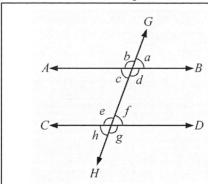

Lines *AB* and *CD* are parallel, and *GH* is a transversal.

24. Which of the following pairs of angles are same-side interior angles?

 A. ∠*b* and ∠*c*

 B. ∠*c* and ∠*e*

 C. ∠*d* and ∠*h*

 D. ∠*e* and ∠*g*

Use the following information to answer the next question.

Triangle *RST* is given.

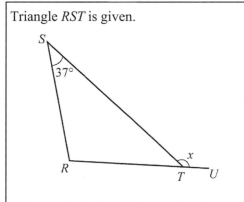

25. Which of the following measures is **not** a possible measure for ∠*x*?

 A. 28°   **B.** 76°

 C. 134°   **D.** 171°

26. If the sum of the interior angles of a polygon is 3 240°, then the polygon has

 A. 14 sides   **B.** 16 sides

 C. 18 sides   **D.** 20 sides

Use the following information to answer the next question.

A diagram is given with certain angles marked.

27. To the nearest degree, what is the value of angle *X*? _____ °

Use the following information to answer the next question.

To display a valuable trophy, the staff at a hockey arena roped off a triangular area and installed a security camera.
The security camera was installed so that it rotated continually between the two longest ropes through the angle θ, as shown in the given diagram.

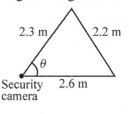

28. The measure of angle θ, rounded to the nearest degree, is

 A. 53°   **B.** 57°

 C. 64°   **D.** 70°

Use the following information to answer the next question.

From the top of a 115 m fire tower, Sue observes smoke in two different locations. She dispatches Gaetan and Bryan to investigate. When Gaetan arrives at the scene of the first smoke sighting, he uses his measuring tools to calculate that he is 334 m from the base of the fire tower and that the angle of elevation from where he is standing to the top of the tower is 19°. When Bryan arrives at the scene of the second smoke sighting, he uses his measuring tools to calculate that the angle of elevation from where he is standing to the top of the fire tower is 16°.

After Gaetan and Bryan have radioed their information to Sue, she estimates that the angle from Gaetan to the base of the fire tower to Bryan is 110°, as shown in the diagram.

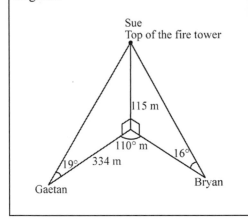

29. What is the distance between Gaetan and Bryan correct to the nearest metre?
    A. 346 m   B. 391 m
    C. 584 m   D. 603 m

Use the following information to answer the next question.

At 4:00 P.M., the distance between the tip of the minute hand and the tip of the hour hand on a clock is 20 cm.

30. If the length of the minute hand is 15 cm, then the approximate length of the hour hand is
    A. 5.00 cm   B. 7.71 cm
    C. 13.23 cm   D. 15.00 cm

Use the following information to answer the next question.

From a particular point, Jennifer determined that the angle of elevation to the top of her school was 18°. When she walked 12.5 m closer to the school, she determined that the angle of elevation to the top of the school was 29°, as illustrated in the diagram.

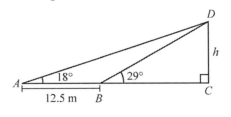

Numerical Response

31. Correct to the nearest metre, the height of the school, h, is _____ m.

Use the following information to answer the next question.

In the diagram shown, $\angle BAC \cong \angle EAD$ and $AC \cong AD$.

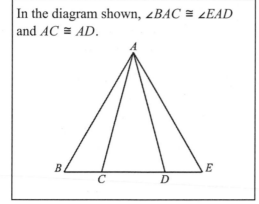

32. Which of the following congruency statements **cannot** be proven?

   A. $\angle CAD \cong \angle BAC + \angle EAD$

   B. $\angle ACD \cong \angle ADC$

   C. $\angle B \cong \angle E$

   D. $AB \cong AE$

Use the following information to answer the next question.

Leonard studies the given pattern.
  $3 \times 5 = 15$
  $7 \times 11 = 77$
 $15 \times 21 = 315$
 $17 \times 25 = 425$
He then makes the conjecture that multiplying any two odd numbers together will result in an odd number.

33. If Leonard wanted to show by using deductive reasoning that his conjecture is true in every case, which of the following formulas would help him?

   A. $2(mn + m + n)$, where $m, n \in I$

   B. $4(2mn + m + n)$, where $m, n \in I$

   C. $2mn + m + n + 1$, where $m, n \in I$

   D. $2(2mn + m + n) + 1$, where $m, n \in I$

Use the following information to answer the next question.

At a recreation centre, 38 people said they used the swimming pool, 28 said they used the fitness room, and 16 said they used both the swimming pool and fitness room. In total, 50 people were surveyed.

34. Which of the following Venn diagrams illustrates this information?

  A.   Fitness   Swimming
           room   pool

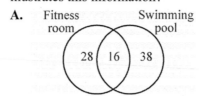

  B.   Fitness   Swimming
           room   pool

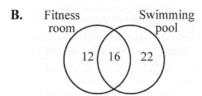

  C.   Fitness   Swimming
           room   pool

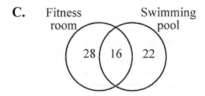

  D.   Fitness   Swimming
           room   pool

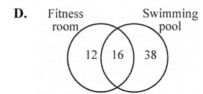

Use the following information to answer the next question.

Barry and Mark are each asked to rationalize the denominator of the radical expression $\dfrac{14\sqrt{5} + 10\sqrt{2}}{\sqrt{24}}$. Each boy's partial solution is shown below.

Barry

$$\frac{14\sqrt{5} + 10\sqrt{2}}{\sqrt{24}} = \frac{14\sqrt{5} + 10\sqrt{2}}{2\sqrt{6}}$$

$$= \frac{7\sqrt{5} + 5\sqrt{2}}{\sqrt{6}}$$

$$= \frac{7\sqrt{5} + 5\sqrt{2}}{\sqrt{6}} \times \frac{\sqrt{6}}{\sqrt{6}}$$

$$= \frac{7\sqrt{30} + 5\sqrt{12}}{6}$$

$$= \frac{7\sqrt{30} + 5\sqrt{4}\sqrt{3}}{6}$$

Mark

$$\frac{14\sqrt{5} + 10\sqrt{2}}{\sqrt{24}} = \frac{14\sqrt{5} + 10\sqrt{2}}{\sqrt{24}} \times \frac{\sqrt{24}}{\sqrt{24}}$$

$$= \frac{14\sqrt{120} + 10\sqrt{48}}{24}$$

$$= \frac{14\sqrt{4}\sqrt{30} + 10\sqrt{16}\sqrt{3}}{24}$$

35. Which of the following statements about Barry's and Mark's partial solutions is **true**?

A. Both Barry and Mark have a correct partial solution.

B. Both Barry and Mark have an incorrect partial solution.

C. Barry has a correct partial solution, and Mark has an incorrect partial solution.

D. Barry has an incorrect partial solution, and Mark has a correct partial solution.

Use the following information to answer the next question.

The approximate speed of a car prior to a collision can be determined using the formula $s = \sqrt{169d}$, in which d is the length of the skid marks, in metres, after the brakes were applied, and s is the speed of the car, in kilometres per hour, prior to the brakes being applied.

36. If the skid marks were 8 m long, what is the speed of the car, s, in simplest radical form?

A. $13\sqrt{2}$ km/h

B. $25\sqrt{5}$ km/h

C. $26\sqrt{2}$ km/h

D. $52\sqrt{2}$ km/h

Use the following information to answer the next question.

When $24\sqrt{35}$ is divided by $6\sqrt{7}$, the quotient is of the form $a\sqrt{b}$, where a and b represent whole numbers and the remainder is zero.

Numerical Response

37. The numerical value of the sum of a and b is _____.

Use the following information to answer the next question.

Mark's attempt at solving the radical equation $\sqrt{x} + \sqrt{x - 12} = 6$ by using an algebraic process is shown.

1. $\sqrt{x - 12} = 6 - \sqrt{x}$
2. $(\sqrt{x - 12})^2 = (6 - \sqrt{x})^2$
3. $x - 12 = 36 - 12\sqrt{x} + x$
4. $-48 = -12\sqrt{x}$
5. $4 = \sqrt{x}$
6. $2 = x$

38. Mark made his first error in step

A. 3   B. 4

C. 5   D. 6

Juanita and Tatima are each asked to determine the solution to the equation $\sqrt{x+19} - \sqrt{x+3} = 2$. The partial solution of each student is shown.

Juanita's partial solution:
$$\sqrt{x+19} - \sqrt{x+3} = 2$$
$$\sqrt{x+19} = 2 + \sqrt{x+3}$$
$$x + 19 = x + 7 + 4\sqrt{x+3}$$
$$12 = 4\sqrt{x+3}$$
$$3 = \sqrt{x+3}$$

Tatima's partial solution:
$$\sqrt{x+19} - \sqrt{x+3} = 2$$
$$\sqrt{x+19} = 2 + \sqrt{x+3}$$

She graphs $y_1 = \sqrt{x+19}$ and $y_2 = 2 + \sqrt{x+3}$ and determines the x-intercepts of each graph.

39. Which of the following statements with respect to the partial solutions of Juanita and Tatima is **true**?

  A. Both partial solutions are correct.

  B. Both partial solutions are incorrect.

  C. Juanita's partial solution is correct, and Tatima's partial solution is incorrect.

  D. Juanita's partial solution is incorrect, and Tatima's partial solution is correct.

A blank 3-by-3 grid needs to be filled using the following set of 9 tiles.

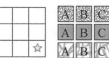

Clues are given to help determine which tile goes in which square. Clues can indicate a letter but not the background pattern, a background pattern but not the letter, or both the background pattern and the letter. The clues are given in the orientation in which they appear in the puzzle.

40. Which of the following tiles appears in the starred square?

  A.   **B.** 🄲

  C. A   **D.** C

ANSWERS AND SOLUTIONS — PRACTICE TEST

1. A	9. C	17. C	25. A	33. D
2. D	10. 81.5	18. C	26. D	34. B
3. B	11. D	19. 3	27. 65	35. A
4. D	12. C	20. A	28. A	36. C
5. C	13. 0.06	21. C	29. D	37. 9
6. B	14. B	22. 14.1	30. B	38. D
7. C	15. A	23. D	31. 10	39. C
8. B	16. 0.95	24. B	32. A	40. B

1. A

Step 1

Identify the x-intercepts.

The quadratic function is in the form
$y = a(x - r)(x - s)$, so the x-intercepts are equal to the values of r and s.

For the function $y = -(x + 9)(x - 5)$,
the x-intercepts are -9 and 5.

Step 2

Find the coordinates of the vertex.

Use the formula $x = \dfrac{r + s}{2}$ to find the x-value.

Substitute -9 for r and 5 for s.

$$x = \frac{-9 + 5}{2}$$
$$= \frac{-4}{2}$$
$$= -2$$

Find the y-value of the vertex. Substitute -2 for x into the original equation $y = -(x + 9)(x - 5)$.

$$y = -(-2 + 9)(-2 - 5)$$
$$= -(7)(-7)$$
$$= 49$$

The coordinates of the vertex are $(-2, 49)$.

Step 3

Determine the range.

Since $a = -1$, the graph of the quadratic function opens downward and the minimum y-value is the y-coordinate of the vertex (49).

Therefore, the range of the quadratic function is $y \leq 49$.

2. D

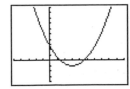

Use an appropriate window setting on a graphing calculator, and graph $y = 2x^2 - 12x + 13$ as shown.

Since the resulting parabola opens upward, it has a minimum y-value.

The coordinates of the vertex can be determined by correctly using the $\boxed{\text{TRACE}}$ key on a graphing calculator or by entering the following sequence of key strokes:

$\boxed{\text{2nd}} \rightarrow \boxed{\text{TRACE}} \rightarrow \boxed{3} \mapsto$ move cursor to the left

of the vertex $\rightarrow \boxed{\text{ENTER}} \mapsto$ move cursor to the right

of the vertex $\rightarrow \boxed{\text{ENTER}} \rightarrow \boxed{\text{ENTER}}$

The resulting coordinates of the vertex are $(3, -5)$.

3. B

Use the TI-83 Plus graphing calculator to plot the line $y = 12$ and the parabola $y = -2x^2 + 11x - 3$. Then use the INTERSECTION feature to find the intersection points of the two graphs.

The first intersection point is: $(2.5, 12)$

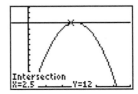

The second intersection point is: $(3, 12)$

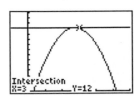

The first value of x is closest to the moment of the kick, so the first value of x is the time taken for the ball to reach a height of 12 m. Therefore, the least number of seconds it took the football to reach a height of 12 yards above the ground is 2.5 seconds.

4. D

Step 1

Factor polynomial I by removing the greatest common factor of $4x^2$ from each term.

$8x^3 + 4x^2 = 4x^2(2x + 1)$

Polynomial I was factored correctly by Rachel.

Step 2

Factor polynomial II as a difference of squares:

$a^2 - b^2 = (a + b)(a - b)$.

$25a^2 - 4b^2c^2$

$= \left(\begin{array}{l} \left(\sqrt{25a^2}\right) + \left(\sqrt{4b^2c^2}\right) \\ \times \ \left(\sqrt{25a^2}\right) - \left(\sqrt{4b^2c^2}\right) \end{array} \right)$

$= (5a + 2bc)(5a - 2bc)$

Polynomial II was factored correctly by Rachel.

Step 3

Factor polynomial III by removing the greatest common factor of 2 from each term and factoring the result as a difference of squares.

$2x^2 - 18y^2$

$= 2(x^2 - 9y^2)$

$= 2(\sqrt{x^2} + \sqrt{9y^2}) \times (\sqrt{x^2} - \sqrt{9y^2})$

$= 2(x + 3y)(x - 3y)$

Polynomial III was factored correctly by Rachel.

Step 4

Factor polynomial IV by removing the greatest common factor of a and factoring the result as a difference of squares.

$4a^3 - a$

$= a(4a^2 - 1)$

$= a(\sqrt{4a^2} + \sqrt{1}) \times (\sqrt{4a^2} - \sqrt{1})$

$= a(2a + 1)(2a - 1)$

Polynomial IV was not factored correctly by Rachel.

5. C

Recall that when a quadratic equation is expressed in the factored form $y = a(x - m)(x - n)$, the x-intercepts of the graph of the quadratic function will occur at $x = m$ and $x = n$.

6. B

Recall that when a quadratic equation is expressed in the factored form $y = a(x - m)(x - n)$, the x-intercepts of the graph of the quadratic function will occur at $x = m$ and $x = n$. Therefore, the x-intercepts will help solve for the factors of the quadratic expression. The x-intercepts occur at points A and C.

7. C

Step 1

Determine the z-score for the student's original mark.

Substitute the student's mark of 370, the mean of 280, and the standard deviation of 50 for x, μ, and σ, respectively, into the z-score formula, and simplify.

$z = \dfrac{x - \mu}{\sigma}$

$= \dfrac{370 - 280}{50}$

$= \dfrac{90}{50}$

$= 1.8$

When the marks are translated to a new normal distribution with a mean of 60 and a standard deviation of k, the z-score of each adjusted mark remains unchanged.

Therefore, the z-score for the adjusted mark of 87 is 1.8.

Step 2

Determine the standard deviation k.

Substitute 87, 60, 1.8, and k for x, μ, z, and σ in the z-score formula.

$z = \dfrac{x - \mu}{\sigma}$

$1.8 = \dfrac{87 - 60}{k}$

Simplify.

$1.8k = 87 - 60$

$k = \dfrac{87 - 60}{1.8}$

$= 15$

Thus, the value of k is 15.

8. B

One of the characteristics of normally distributed data sets is that most of the data are located close to the mean. Therefore, of the given temperatures, 28.7°C is most likely to occur.

9. C

In this problem, the value of 90% corresponds to an area of 0.90 under the normal curve to the left of the time allowed.

Step 1

Use a calculator or a z-score table to determine the z-score corresponding to an area of 0.9.

According to the calculator, the value is $z = \text{invNorm}(0.90, 0, 1) = 1.281\ 551\ 567$.

When using the z-score table, the closest area of 0.8997 corresponds to a z-score of $z = 1.28$. Therefore, the z-score is 1.28.

Step 2

Determine the number of minutes allowed for the exam.

Use the z-score formula by substituting 1.28 for z, 60 for μ, and 17.5 for σ.

$$z = \frac{x - \mu}{\sigma}$$

$$1.28 = \frac{x - 60}{17.5}$$

Step 3

Solve for x, the number of minutes allotted for the exam.

$x - 60 = (1.28)(17.5)$

$x - 60 = 22.4$

$x = 82.4$

Rounded to the nearest minute, the time allotted for the examination was 82 min.

10. **81.5**

Step 1

Sketch the standard normal curve that represents the given data.

The mean of the data is given as 160 min, and the standard deviation is 10 min.

Label the centre with the data mean, and label the values that are ±1, ±2, and ±3 standard deviations from the mean.

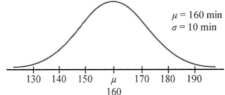

μ = 160 min
σ = 10 min

130 140 150 μ 170 180 190
              160
Time ticket buyers waiting in line (min)

Step 2

Shade the area between the two boundaries given.

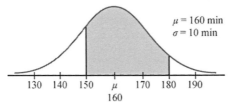

μ = 160 min
σ = 10 min

130 140 150 μ 170 180 190
              160
Time ticket buyers waiting in line (min)

Step 3

By adding the percentages representing each shaded standard deviation region, determine the probability represented by the shaded area.

The percentages of each shaded standard deviation region are 34%, 34%, and 13.5%.

34% + 34% + 13.5% = 81.5%

Therefore, 81.5% of people waited between 150 and 180 min.

11. **D**

The margin of error can be calculated using the formula $ME = z_{\frac{\alpha}{2}}\sqrt{\dfrac{\bar{p}(1 - \bar{p})}{n}}$.

Step 1

Determine the equation that represents the new margin of error, ME_2.

Let n_2 represent the number of people in the new survey.

$$ME = z_{\frac{\alpha}{2}}\sqrt{\frac{\bar{p}(1 - \bar{p})}{n}}$$

$$ME_2 = z_{\frac{\alpha}{2}}\sqrt{\frac{0.52(1 - 0.52)}{n_2}}$$

Step 2

Set up an equation to solve for the number of people in the new survey.

The new margin of error is equal to half the old margin of error ME_1.

$$ME_2 = \frac{1}{2}ME_1$$

$$z_{\frac{\alpha}{2}}\sqrt{\frac{0.52(1 - 0.52)}{n_2}} = \left(\frac{1}{2}\right)z_{\frac{\alpha}{2}}\sqrt{\frac{0.52(1 - 0.52)}{n_1}}$$

$$z_{\frac{\alpha}{2}}\sqrt{\frac{0.52(1 - 0.52)}{n_2}} = \left(\frac{1}{2}\right)z_{\frac{\alpha}{2}}\sqrt{\frac{0.52(1 - 0.52)}{400}}$$

Step 3

Divide both sides by $z_{\frac{\alpha}{2}}$.

$$\sqrt{\frac{0.52(1 - 0.52)}{n_2}} = \left(\frac{1}{2}\right)\sqrt{\frac{0.52(1 - 0.52)}{400}}$$

Step 4

Square both sides.

$$\frac{0.52(1 - 0.52)}{n_2} = \left(\frac{1}{4}\right)\frac{0.52(1 - 0.52)}{400}$$

Step 5

Simplify.

$$\frac{1}{n_2} = \left(\frac{1}{4}\right)\frac{1}{400}$$

$$\frac{1}{n_2} = \frac{1}{1\,600}$$

$$n_2 = 1\,600$$

Therefore, the company needs to survey approximately 1 600 people. (Note that the question asks for an approximation because the support rate of 52 % might not be exactly repeated in the second survey.)

12. C

The estimated population proportion, which is the sample proportion, $\bar{p}$, is 65%, or 0.65. To determine the confidence interval, first calculate the margin of error and then the confidence interval.

Step 1

Determine the margin of error, ME.

Apply the formula $ME = z_{\frac{\alpha}{2}}\sqrt{\dfrac{\bar{p}(1-\bar{p})}{n}}$.

At a 95% confidence level, the value of $z_{\frac{\alpha}{2}}$ is 1.96.

Substitute 1 000 for n, 0.65 for $\bar{p}$, and 1.96 for $z_{\frac{\alpha}{2}}$

in the formula $ME = z_{\frac{\alpha}{2}}\sqrt{\dfrac{\bar{p}(1-\bar{p})}{n}}$.

$ME = 1.96 \times \sqrt{\dfrac{(0.65)(1-0.65)}{1\ 000}}$

$ME = 1.96 \times \sqrt{\dfrac{0.2275}{1\ 000}}$

$ME \approx 0.029\ 56$

Step 2

Determine the confidence interval.

The confidence interval for a sample proportion is of

the form $\bar{p} \pm z_{\frac{\alpha}{2}}\sqrt{\dfrac{\bar{p}(1-\bar{p})}{n}}$. Therefore, the

confidence interval is 0.65 ± 0.0296, or $65 \pm 2.96\%$.

13. 0.06

To find the margin of error for the estimated proportion of the population, use the formula

$ME = z_{\frac{\alpha}{2}}\sqrt{\dfrac{\bar{p}(1-\bar{p})}{n}}$, where $\bar{p}$ is the proportion of

the sample, n is the sample size, α is the level of

significance, and $z_{\frac{\alpha}{2}}$ is the z-value of the area of $\dfrac{\alpha}{2}$

in the upper tail of the standard normal distribution curve.

Step 1

Determine the value of $\dfrac{\alpha}{2}$.

At a 95% confidence interval, the confidence coefficient is 0.95 and the level of significance, α, is equal to $1 - 0.95 = 0.05$. Therefore, the value of

$\dfrac{\alpha}{2}$ is equal to $\dfrac{0.05}{2} = 0.025$.

Step 2

Determine the value of $z_{\frac{\alpha}{2}}$.

From the z-score table, the z-value of the area of 0.025 in the upper tail of the standard normal distribution curve is 1.96 ($1 - 0.025 = 0.975$, which is the area to the left of the z-value found on the z-score table).

Step 3

Determine the margin of error for the estimated population proportion, $\bar{p}$.

Substitute 250 for n, 0.4 for $\bar{p}$, and 1.96 for $z_{\frac{\alpha}{2}}$ into

the formula $ME = z_{\frac{\alpha}{2}}\sqrt{\dfrac{\bar{p}(1-\bar{p})}{n}}$.

$ME = z_{\frac{\alpha}{2}}\sqrt{\dfrac{\bar{p}(1-\bar{p})}{n}}$

$ME = 1.96 \times \sqrt{\dfrac{(0.4)(1-0.4)}{250}}$

$ME = 1.96 \times \sqrt{\dfrac{0.24}{250}}$

$ME \approx 0.0607$

At a 95% confidence level, the margin of error for the estimated population proportion, to the nearest hundredth, is 0.06.

14. B

The portion of the tank filled by pipe A after 1 hour is $\dfrac{1}{45}$.

The portion of the tank filled by pipe B in 1 hour is $\dfrac{1}{36}$.

The portion of the tank filled by both pipes in 1 hour is as follows:

$\dfrac{1}{45} + \dfrac{1}{36} = \dfrac{4}{180} + \dfrac{5}{180}$

$= \dfrac{9}{180}$

$= \dfrac{1}{20}$

Since $\dfrac{1}{20}$ of the tank is filled after one hour, the total number of hours to fill the tank is the reciprocal.

$\dfrac{20}{1} = 20$ hours

Therefore, the tank will be full in 20 hours if both pipes are opened.

15. A

The population of rabbits breeding over time is the only given situation that increases exponentially. This would mean that the rate of change increases rapidly, as illustrated in the given table.

16. 0.95

Step 1
Write the rate.

The rate is $\dfrac{\$40.64}{43\text{ L}}$.

Step 2
Calculate the unit rate.
Divide the first term ($\$40.64$) by the second term ($43$ L).
$40.64 \div 43 = 0.945\,116\,27$

The unit rate that Betty paid was $\$0.95\,/\,\text{L}$ or $\dfrac{\$0.95}{\text{L}}$.

17. C

Step 1
Apply the scale factor to the volume of the sphere. Substitute 212 for V_{sphere} and 2.5 for the scale factor in the equation $V_2 = V_{sphere} \times \text{scale factor}^3$.

$V_2 = V_{sphere} \times \text{scale factor}^3$
$\quad = 212 \times (2.5)^3$
$\quad = 212 \times 15.625$
$\quad = 3\ 312.5\text{ cm}^3$

Step 2
Determine the radius of the expanded sphere.

$V_2 = \dfrac{4\pi r^3}{3}$

$3\ 312.5 = \dfrac{4(3.14)r^3}{3}$

$r^3 = \dfrac{(3\ 312.5)(3)}{(4)(3.14)}$

$\quad = \dfrac{9\ 937.5}{12.56}$

$\quad = 791.2022$

Solve for r.

$r = \sqrt[3]{791.2022}$
$\quad = 9.2490$
$\quad \approx 9.25\text{ cm}$

18. C

The base and height of $\triangle ABC$ are 6 and 5 units, respectively. The base and height of $\triangle A'B'C'$ are 18 and 15 units, respectively. To determine how much $\triangle A'B'C'$ has increased in size by, compare the base and height of each triangle.

The ratio of the base of the enlarged triangle to the original triangle is $\dfrac{18}{6} = 3$, while the ratio of the height of the enlarged triangle to the original triangle is $\dfrac{15}{5} = 3$. Thus, $\triangle A'B'C'$ is three times larger than $\triangle ABC$.

19. 3

Step 1
Pick one known length in the image diagram.
$PO = 9$ cm

Step 2
Find the corresponding length in the original diagram.
$SR = 3$ cm

Step 3
Use the scale factor formula to determine the scale factor.

$\text{scale factor} = \dfrac{\text{image length}}{\text{original length}}$

$\quad = \dfrac{PO}{SR}$

$\quad = \dfrac{9\text{ cm}}{3\text{ cm}}$

$\quad = 3$

The diagram shows a reduction with a scale factor of 3.

20. A

Step 1
Determine the volume in terms of π for the first type of fence post by applying the formula for the volume of a cylinder.
The diameter of the first type of fence post is 9 cm; therefore, the radius is $9 \div 2 = 4.5$ cm. Substitute 4.5 for r and 3 m $= 300$ cm for the height, h, and then solve for V.

$V = \pi r^2 h$
$V = \pi \times 4.5^2 \times 300$
$V = \pi \times 20.25 \times 300$
$V = 6\ 075\pi\text{ cm}^3$

Step 2
Determine the volume of the second type of fence post in terms of π.
Since the volume of the second type of fence post is twice the volume of the first type, it follows that the volume of the second type is
$6\ 075\pi \times 2 = 12\ 150\pi\text{ cm}^3$.

Step 3

Determine the radius of the second type of fence post by applying the formula for the volume of a cylinder. Substitute 12 150π for V and 300 for h, and then solve for r.

$$V = \pi r^2 h$$
$$12\ 150\pi = \pi r^2(300)$$
$$12\ 150\pi = 300\pi r^2$$
$$\frac{12\ 150\pi}{300\pi} = r^2$$
$$40.5 = r^2$$
$$\sqrt{40.5} = r$$
$$6.36 \approx r$$

The radius of the second type of fence post is approximately 6.36 cm.

Step 4

Determine the diameter of the second type of fence post.

Since the diameter is twice the length of the radius, it follows that the diameter of the second type of fence post is approximately 6.36 cm $\times$ 2 $\approx$ 12.7 cm.

21. C

As the scenario requires applying the scale factor to an area, the scale factor should be squared, so use the formula $A_2 = A_1 \times (\text{scale factor})^2$.

Substitute 260 for A_1 and 2.2 for the scale factor.

$$A_2 = A_1 \times (\text{scale factor})^2$$
$$A_2 = 260 \times (2.2)^2$$
$$A_2 = 260 \times 4.84$$
$$A_2 = 1\ 258.4$$
$$A_2 \approx 1\ 258\ \text{cm}^2$$

Rounded to the nearest whole number, Vickie's new irregular polygon will have an area of 1 258 cm^2.

22. 14.1

Use the formula $A_2 = A_1 \times (\text{scale factor})^2$.

Substitute 21 for A_1 and 0.82 for the scale factor.

$$A_2 = A_1 \times (\text{scale factor})^2$$
$$= 21 \times (0.82)^2$$
$$= 21 \times 0.6724$$
$$= 14.1204$$
$$\approx 14.1\ \text{m}^2$$

Rounded to the nearest tenth, the new trapezoid will have an area of 14.1 m^2.

23. D

Step 1

Identify which sides or angles are identified.

$$\angle P = \angle M$$
$$\angle Q = \angle N$$
$$QR = NO = 5$$

Since the sides QR and NO are not between the given angles, they are non-included sides.

Step 2

Identify the condition that will prove congruency.

Since the triangles are not right-angle triangles, the right-angle-hypotenuse-leg (RHL) condition does not apply.

Since only one side length of each triangle is given, the side-side-side (SSS) condition does not apply.

Since only one side length of each triangle is given, the side-angle-side (SAS) condition does not apply.

Since the two angles and the non-included side are identical, the condition that verifies congruency is angle-angle-side (AAS).

24. B

Step 1

Identify the interior angles.

Interior angles are angles found inside two parallel lines.

There are four interior angles in the diagram: $\angle c$, $\angle d$, $\angle e$, and $\angle f$.

Step 2

Identify the pairs of same-side interior angles.

Same-side angles are angles that are on the same side of a transversal.

- $\angle c$ and $\angle e$ are two interior angles that are on the same side of the transversal GH.
- $\angle d$ and $\angle f$ are two interior angles that are on the same side of the transversal GH.

25. A

The exterior angle theorem states that an exterior angle of a triangle is equal to the sum of the remote (opposite) interior angles, so $\angle x = \angle R + \angle S$.
From this, you can conclude that the exterior angle is greater than both opposite interior angles, so $\angle x > \angle R$ and $\angle x > \angle S$. In the diagram, $\angle R$ is not given, so you can use the value of $\angle S$.
$$\angle x > \angle S$$
$$\angle x > 37°$$
Of the given alternatives, the only value that is not possible for $\angle x$ is 28° since it is the only value that is less than 37°.

26. D

Use the formula for the sum of the measures of the interior angles of a polygon to determine the number of sides.

The sum of the measures of the interior angles of a polygon of n sides is equal to $(n-2)180°$.

Therefore, $(n-2)180° = 3\ 240°$.

Solve for n.
$$n - 2 = 18$$
$$n = 20$$

Therefore, the polygon has 20 sides.

27. 65

Step 1

Determine the measure of $\angle EBC$.

Apply the supplementary angles property for cyclic quadrilaterals, which states that the opposite angles in a cyclic quadrilateral are supplementary.
$$\angle EBC + \angle EDC = 180°$$
$$\angle EBC + 85° = 180°$$
$$\angle EBC = 180° - 85°$$
$$\angle EBC = 95°$$

Step 2

Determine the measure of $\angle EBA$.

Angles on a straight line have a sum of 180°.
$$\angle EBA + \angle EBC = 180°$$
$$\angle EBA + 95° = 180°$$
$$\angle EBA = 180° - 95°$$
$$\angle EBA = 85°$$

Step 3

Determine the measure of $\angle X$.

The $\angle X$ is an interior angle in $\triangle AEB$. The sum of the interior angles of a triangle is 180°.
$$\angle X + \angle EBA + \angle BAE = 180°$$
$$\angle X + 85° + 30° = 180°$$
$$\angle X + 115° = 180°$$
$$\angle X = 180° - 115°$$
$$\angle X = 65°$$

The value of angle X is 65°.

28. A

Substitute the known values into the cosine formula, and solve for θ:

$$\cos A = \frac{b^2 + c^2 - a^2}{2bc}$$
$$\cos \theta = \frac{2.3^2 + 2.6^2 - 2.2^2}{2(2.3)(2.6)}$$
$$\cos \theta = \frac{7.21}{11.96}$$
$$\theta = \cos^{-1}\left(\frac{7.21}{11.96}\right)$$
$$\theta \approx 52.926°$$

Rounded to the nearest degree, the measure of θ is 53°.

29. D

Step 1

Label the diagram as shown:

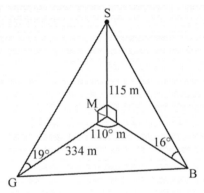

Step 2

Apply the tangent ratio to determine the length of BM.

$$\tan 16° = \frac{115}{BM}$$
$$BM = \frac{115}{\tan 16°}$$
$$BM = 401 \text{ m}$$

Step 3

Apply the cosine law to determine the length of GB.
$$a^2 = b^2 + c^2 - 2bc\cos A$$
$$GB^2 = (334)^2 + (401)^2 - 2(334)(401)\cos 110°$$
$$GB^2 = 111\ 556 + 160\ 801 - 91\ 616$$
$$GB^2 = 363\ 973$$
$$\sqrt{GB^2} = \sqrt{363\ 973}$$
$$GB = 603.30 \text{ m}$$

Rounded to the nearest metre, Gaetan and Bryan are 603 m apart.

30. B

Step 1

Draw and label a diagram that represents the situation.

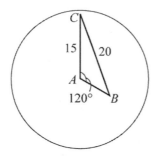

Step 2

Find the measures of angles B and C.

Since two sides and an angle opposite to one of the sides are given, apply the law of sines.

$$\frac{a}{\sin A} = \frac{b}{\sin B}$$

$$\frac{20}{\sin 120°} = \frac{15}{\sin B}$$

$$\frac{\sin 120°}{20} \times 15 = \sin B$$

$$\sin^{-1}\left(\frac{\sin 120°}{20} \times 15\right) = B$$

$$40.5° \approx B$$

The sum of all the interior angles in a triangle is 180°.

$$\angle C \approx 180° - (120° + 40.5°)$$
$$\approx 19.5°$$

Step 3

Use the law of sines to determine the side length AB.

$$\frac{a}{\sin A} = \frac{c}{\sin C}$$

$$\frac{20}{\sin 120°} \approx \frac{AB}{\sin 19.5°}$$

$$\frac{20}{\sin 120°} \times \sin 19.5° \approx AB$$

$$7.71 \approx AB$$

The approximate length of the hour hand is 7.71 cm.

31. 10

Step 1

Determine the length of side BD by applying the sine law.

In $\triangle ABD$, observe that $\angle ABD = 180° - 29° = 151°$. Thus, the measure of $\angle ADB$ is $180° - 151° - 18° = 11°$.

$$\frac{BD}{\sin \angle A} = \frac{AB}{\sin \angle ADB}$$

Substitute 18° for $\angle A$, 12.5 for AB, and 11° for $\angle ADB$.

$$\frac{BD}{\sin 18°} = \frac{12.5}{\sin 11°}$$

$$BD \times \sin 11° = 12.5 \times \sin 18°$$

$$BD = \frac{12.5 \times \sin 18°}{\sin 11°}$$

$$BD \approx 20.24 \text{ m}$$

Step 2

Solve for h in right triangle BCD.

Substitute 29° for $\angle DBC$, h for DC, and 20.24 for BD.

$$\sin \angle DBC = \frac{DC}{BD}$$

$$\sin 29° = \frac{h}{20.24}$$

$$h = 20.24 \times \sin 29°$$

$$h \approx 9.81 \text{ m}$$

The height of the school, to the nearest metre, is 10 m.

32. A

Since $AC \cong AD$, $\triangle ACD$ is an isosceles triangle. If two sides of a triangles are congruent, the angles opposite the congruent side are congruent. Therefore, $\angle ACD \cong \angle ADC$. The following two-column proof can illustrate that $\triangle ACB \cong \triangle ADE$.

Statements	Reasons
$\angle BAC \cong \angle EAD$	Given
$AC \cong AD$	Given
$\angle ACD \cong \angle ADC$	Isosceles triangle theorem
$\angle ACD + \angle ACB \cong 180°$	Form a straight angle
$\angle ADC + \angle EDA \cong 180°$	Form a straight angle
$\angle ADC + \angle ACB \cong 180°$	Substitution
$\angle ADC + \angle EDA \cong \angle ADC + \angle ACB$	Substitution
$\angle EDA \cong \angle ACB$	Subtract common angle $(\angle ADC)$
$\triangle ACB \cong \triangle ADE$	ASA

Since $\triangle ACB \cong \triangle ADE$, it follows that $\angle B \cong \angle E$ and $AB \cong AE$. This is because corresponding parts of congruent triangles are congruent. The congruency statement that cannot be proven is that $\angle CAD \cong \angle BAC + \angle EAD$.

33. **D**

Use deductive reasoning to show that Leonard's conjecture is true.

Let $2m + 1$ and $2n + 1$ represent any two odd numbers, where $m, n \in I$.

Determine the equation for multiplying any two odd numbers together.
$(2m + 1) \times (2n + 1)$
$= 4mn + 2m + 2n + 1$
$= 2(2mn + m + n) + 1$

Since any number multiplied by 2 is even, it follows that $2(2mn + m + n)$ is even. Whenever 1 is added to an even number, it becomes odd. Therefore, $2(2mn + m + n) + 1$ is odd.

Thus, the expression $2(2mn + m + n) + 1$, where $m, n \in I$, will help Leonard prove his conjecture.

34. **B**

Step 1

Determine the number of people surveyed who used both the swimming pool and the fitness room.
Since 16 people used both the swimming pool and the fitness room, the number 16 should be located in the overlapping region of the two circles.

Step 2

Determine the number of people surveyed who only used the fitness room.
$28 - 16 = 12$
The number 12 should be placed inside the circle that represents the fitness room.

Step 3

Determine the number of people surveyed who only used the swimming pool.
$38 - 16 = 22$
The number 22 should be placed inside the circle that represents the swimming pool.

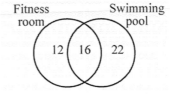

35. **A**

The correct solution for the rationalization of the expression $\dfrac{14\sqrt{5} + 10\sqrt{2}}{\sqrt{24}}$ is $\dfrac{7\sqrt{30} + 10\sqrt{3}}{6}$. To check if Barry's or Mark's partial solutions are correct, continue simplifying their expressions to see if they result in the correct solution.

Step 1

Continue Mark's partial solution as follows:
$$\frac{14\sqrt{4}\sqrt{30} + 10\sqrt{16}\sqrt{3}}{24} = \frac{(14)(2)\sqrt{30} + (10)(4)\sqrt{3}}{24}$$
$$= \frac{28\sqrt{30} + 40\sqrt{3}}{24}$$
$$= \frac{(4)(7)\sqrt{30} + (4)(10)\sqrt{3}}{(6)(4)}$$
$$= \frac{7\sqrt{30} + 10\sqrt{3}}{6}$$

Step 2

Continue the partial solution of Barry's as follows:
$$\frac{7\sqrt{30} + 5\sqrt{4}\sqrt{3}}{6} = \frac{7\sqrt{30} + (5)(2)\sqrt{3}}{6}$$
$$= \frac{7\sqrt{30} + 10\sqrt{3}}{6}$$

Mark's partial solution is equal to Barry's partial solution, and both are equal to the correct rationalization of the denominator for the equation $\dfrac{14\sqrt{5} + 10\sqrt{2}}{\sqrt{24}}$. Therefore, both of the boys have a correct partial solution.

36. C

Determine the speed of the car, s, in simplified radical form.

Step 1

Substitute 8 for d in the formula $s = \sqrt{169d}$.

$$s = \sqrt{169d}$$
$$= \sqrt{169 \times 8}$$

Step 2

Factor 8 into two factors, in which one factor is the greatest perfect square.

Since the factors of 8 are 1, 2, 4, and 8, in which 4 is the largest perfect square, the expression can be simplified as follows:

$$s = \sqrt{169 \times 8}$$
$$= \sqrt{169 \times 4 \times 2}$$

Step 3

Use the multiplication property of radicals, $\sqrt[n]{xy} = \sqrt[n]{x} \times \sqrt[n]{y}$, to rewrite the radical.

$$s = \sqrt{169 \times 4 \times 2}$$
$$= \sqrt{169} \times \sqrt{4} \times \sqrt{2}$$

Step 4

Evaluate the radicals that are square roots of perfect squares, and simplify.

$$s = \sqrt{169} \times \sqrt{4} \times \sqrt{2}$$
$$= 13 \times 2 \times \sqrt{2}$$
$$= 26\sqrt{2}$$

In simplest radical form, the speed of the car, s, is $26\sqrt{2}$ km/h.

37. 9

Step 1

Divide $24\sqrt{35}$ by $6\sqrt{7}$.

In general, $a\sqrt{x} \div b\sqrt{y} = (a \div b)\sqrt{x \div y}$.

Therefore, $24\sqrt{35} \div 6\sqrt{7} = (24 \div 6)\sqrt{35 \div 7} = 4\sqrt{5}$.

Step 2

Identify the values of a and b.

From the given information, $24\sqrt{35} \div 6\sqrt{7} = a\sqrt{b}$.
Step 1 showed that $24\sqrt{35} \div 6\sqrt{7} = 4\sqrt{5}$, so $a\sqrt{b} = 4\sqrt{5}$.

Thus, $a = 4$ and $b = 5$.

Step 3

Determine the sum of a and b.
$$a + b = 4 + 5 = 9$$

38. D

Mark did not make any errors in steps 1 through 5. However, in step 6, he took the square root of 4 instead of squaring 4. The correct solution to the equation is $x = 16$.

39. C

Step 1

Analyze Juanita's partial solution.

Juanita isolated one radical, squared both sides to eliminate it, and simplified the equation on both sides. Her partial solution is correct, but a couple of steps were left out, which may cause some confusion. The missing steps are included in the following partial solution.

$$\sqrt{x + 19} - \sqrt{x + 3} = 2$$
$$\sqrt{x + 19} = 2 + \sqrt{x + 3}$$
$$x + 19 = (2 + \sqrt{x + 3})^2$$
$$x + 19 = 4 + 4\sqrt{x + 3} + x + 3$$
$$x + 19 = x + 7 + 4\sqrt{x + 3}$$
$$12 = 4\sqrt{x + 3}$$
$$3 = \sqrt{x + 3}$$

Step 2

Analyze Tatima's partial solution.

Tatima's solution was correct until she decided to find the x-intercepts of each graph. To find the solution, she would need to identify the x-coordinates of the points of intersection of the two graphs.

40. B

Step 1

Fill in the blank grid with the patterns and letters from the first clue.

Step 2

Add the patterns and letters from the second clue.

Step 3

Determine which tile goes into the starred square. According to the second clue, the tile in the starred square has speckles. There is already a speckled tile with the letter A in the top left square and a speckled tile with a letter B in the middle square. This means that the only speckled tile remaining is the speckled C.

Therefore, the only tile that can go into the starred square is the speckled C tile:

NOTES

NOTES

254

NOTES

NOTES

NOTES

NOTES

BOOK ORDERING INFORMATION

SENIOR HIGH SCHOOL TITLES

Castle Rock Research offers the following resources to support Alberta students. You can order any of these materials online at:

www.castlerockresearch.com/store

SOLARO.com - Study Online		The KEY		SNAP	Prob Solved	Class Notes
$29.95 ea.*		$29.95 ea.*		$29.95 ea.*	$19.95 ea.*	$19.95 ea.*
Biology 30	Mathematics 30-1	Biology 30	Mathematics 30-1	Biology 20	Biology 20	Biology 20
Biology 20	Mathematics 30-2	Biology 20	Mathematics 30-2	Chemistry 30	Chemistry 30	Chemistry 30
Chemistry 30	Mathematics 30-3	Chemistry 30	Mathematics 30-3	Chemistry 20	Chemistry 20	Chemistry 20
Chemistry 20	Mathematics 20-1	Chemistry 20	Mathematics 20-1	Mathematics 30-1	Mathematics 30-1	Mathematics 30-1
Physics 30	Mathematics 20-2	English 30-1	Mathematics 20-2	Mathematics 30-2	Mathematics 30-2	Mathematics 30-2
Physics 20	Mathematics 20-3	English 30-2	Mathematics 20-3	Mathematics 31	Mathematics 31	Mathematics 31
Science 30	Mathematics 20-4	English 20-1	Mathematics 20-4	Mathematics 20-1	Mathematics 20-1	Mathematics 20-1
Science 20	Mathematics 10 C	English 10-1	Mathematics 10 C	Mathematics 10 C	Mathematics 10 C	Mathematics 10 C
Science 10	Mathematics 10-3	Physics 30	Mathematics 10-3	Physics 30	Physics 30	Physics 30
English 30-1	Mathematics 10-4	Physics 20	Mathematics 10-4	Physics 20	Physics 20	Physics 20
English 30-2	Social Studies 30-1	Science 30	Social Studies 30-1	Science 10	Science 10	Science 10
English 20-1	Social Studies 30-2	Science 20	Social Studies 30-2			
English 20-2	Social Studies 20-1	Science 10	Social Studies 20-1			
English 10-1	Social Studies 10-1		Social Studies 10-1			
English 10-2						

Prices do not include taxes or shipping.

Study online using **SOLARO,** with access to multiple courses available by either a monthly or an annual subscription.

The KEY Study Guide is specifically designed to assist students in preparing for unit tests, final exams, and provincial examinations.

The **Student Notes and Problems (SNAP) Workbook** contains complete explanations of curriculum concepts, examples, and exercise questions.

The **Problem Solved** contains exercise questions and complete solutions.

The **Class Notes** contains complete explanations of curriculum concepts.

If you would like to order Castle Rock resources for your school, please visit our school ordering page:

www.castlerockresearch.com/school-orders/